POWER ELECTRONICS

PWS-KENT SERIES IN ENGINEERING

POWER ELECTRONICS

MARVIN J. FISHER

Washington University
St. Louis, Missouri

PWS-KENT PUBLISHING COMPANY

Boston

PWS–KENT
Publishing Company

Sponsoring Editor: Jonathan Plant
Assistant Editor: Mary Thomas
Editorial Assistant: Heidi Greenman
Production Editor: Chris Crochetière
Manufacturing Coordinator: Peter D. Leatherwood
Interior Designer: Nancy Blodget
Cover Designer: Designworks
Typesetter: Syntax International, PTE., LTD.
Text and Cover Printer: The Maple-Vail Book Manufacturing Group

PWS-KENT Publishing Company is a division of Wadsworth, Inc.

Printed in the United States of America.
1 2 3 4 5 6 7 8 9 − 95 94 93 92 91

Library of Congress Cataloging-in-Publication Data

Fisher, Marvin J.
    Power electronics/Marvin J. Fisher.
       p.   cm.
    Includes index.
    ISBN 0-534-92360-7
    1. Power electronics.   2. Semiconductor switches.   I. Title.
TK7881. 15.F57   1991
621.31'7—dc20
                                    90-46873
                                      CIP

PREFACE

The objective of this textbook is to introduce the reader to the subject of power electronics, presenting the basic processes of efficient energy conversion by electronic means through the use of power semiconductor switches. The energy conversion process is one whereby some aspect of an electrical source is changed. One example of this change is the process of altering a DC source voltage from one value to another. The use of a semiconductor switch, which may closely approach an ideal switch, enables this process to be done in a highly efficient manner.

The methods of such energy conversion are presented in a manner that is largely independent of the actual switch used. It is only in the case of certain circuits that the discussion must be performed with respect to a specific switch. For example, in the case of the phase-controlled rectifier, the switching action almost always is performed using the silicon-controlled rectifier (SCR).

The discussion in this textbook is suitable for seniors in electrical engineering. To understand the processes of power electronics, the student needs a good knowledge of the basic topics that usually are provided by sophomore- and junior-level courses. Among these are circuit analysis, including second-order transients and piecewise linear methods. In addition, a basic knowledge of electronic devices, such as PN-junction diodes and bipolar junction transistors, and their analysis in electronic circuits is required.

The material of the book is more than can be covered in a single three semester-hour course. The instructor of such a course can select those topics and chapters that are most appropriate when considering the students' needs. This selection depends on the prerequisites required for the course. For those students who have extensive semiconductor background, Chapters 2, 3, and 4 may be omitted and most of the remainder can be covered in a three semester-hour course. The topics in Appendix A can be omitted for those who have adequate preparation in piecewise linear transient circuit analysis.

The early chapters discuss the major semiconductor devices that are used as switches. Models are presented that can be used for circuit analysis in subsequent chapters. Basic idealized models are provided as well as extensions to represent some of the devices' major nonideal characteristics. This enables the use of a particular model that depends on the need for accuracy in representing the semiconductor in the circuit.

Material on the design aspects of power electronics is included in response to the requirement of accrediting bodies in recent years for such emphasis in the electrical engineering curriculum. Design is addressed in the main text, in examples, and in the problems. Additional areas of design coverage include the effects of inductor resistance, the effect of nonideal transformer coupling, and the determination of snubber component values to limit switching device stresses. Another design topic relates to thermal considerations and the calculation of resulting semiconductor junction temperature.

This textbook developed from informal class notes that evolved from twenty years of teaching the subject at Washington University using the limited textbook resources then available. Certain specialized books that covered a limited topic were available, no general, broad coverage books with the viewpoint of a textbook were to be found.

I wish to acknowledge the assistance provided by the School of Engineering and Applied Science of Washington University. Individuals who were helpful were Dean of Engineering James M. McKelvey, and the Chairman of Electrical Engineering, Professor Barry E. Spielman. Also important were the comments and suggestions of the reviewers of the manuscript.

Frederick Brockhurst	Rose-Hulman Institute of Technology
Adly A. Girgis	Clemson University
Thomas G. Habetler	Georgia Institute of Technology
Daniel Hart	Valparaiso University
Mark Nelms	Auburn University
William Portnoy	Texas Tech University
A.G. Potter	Iowa State University
William Sayle	Georgia Institute of Technology
S. Yuvarajan	North Dakota State University

Finally, this book would not have been completed without the able help of my wife, Janet. She provided the word processing and proofreading skills that were so very necessary for the successful completion of the writing.

Marvin J. Fisher

C O N T E N T S

6   AC–AC PHASE CONTROL   256

7   DC–DC CONVERTERS   290

8 INVERTERS

CHAPTER · 1

Introduction

1.1

POWER ELECTRONICS

The term *power electronics* covers a wide range of electronic circuits in which the objective is to control the transfer of electrical power from a source to a load. This control may take many different forms; for example, it may be only the amount of power from source to load. Frequently, however, it requires changing the nature of the electrical power delivered to the load as compared to the nature of the power from the source. An example is changing the frequency of an AC source to another frequency as required by the load.

In all of these changes or controls of power transfer from source to load, the efficiency of the process is important. If the power to be transferred is large and if it is done inefficiently, then large losses occur. The economic value of these losses becomes appreciable; furthermore, these losses must be removed from the equipment to prevent overheating.

Such control is almost always done by using *switching* techniques: Some electronic device is used as a switch in either an open or closed state. With an ideal switch, the control can be done in such a manner that prevents loss. Of course, no real element performs as this ideal switch, but there are a number of devices close enough to the ideal device to be useful: Examples are power bipolar junction transistors (BJT), metal-oxide semiconductor field-effect transistors (MOSFET), silicon-controlled rectifiers (SCR), bidirectional gate-controlled thyristors (TRIAC), and gate turnoff SCRs (GTO). Because of the requirement for high efficiency, linear operation of electronic devices seldom is used in the power stages of such equipment.

The power-electronics era marks its beginning from the introduction of the SCR (thyristor) in 1957. Although other controllable devices such as the mercury arc rectifier certainly had been available for many years, such devices were large, often required auxiliary equipment, and were not efficient in low and moderate voltage circuits. The introduction of the SCR thus marked the beginning of a period in which power control shifted largely from rotating machines and static magnetic amplifiers to electronic devices. During this early period, progress was slowed by reliability problems, but after the early 1960s the SCR began to be used in many more applications. Since that time, the other switching devices cited above have been developed, so that one now must choose the most suitable device for a given application.

1.2
TYPES OF CONTROL

Several general conversion arrangements are used in the majority of power-electronic applications.

AC–DC: In this case, the AC line-voltage source is converted by rectification to a unidirectional source, which later may be filtered to approximate a DC source. The output DC voltage can be made variable by using a controlled rectifier, in which case one application would be as a source to drive a DC motor in a variable-speed mode.

DC–DC: A DC voltage of one value is converted to another DC voltage, either larger or smaller. An application for such a system, usually called a *switching power converter*, could be conversion of the output of solar cells on a spacecraft to another voltage value in order to power various spacecraft systems.

DC–AC: A DC source is switched to provide an alternating voltage to a load. The output of such an inverter—not a sinusoid but instead a rectangular or perhaps stepped waveform—is suitable for driving an AC motor in a variable-speed mode by changing the output frequency.

AC–AC: In this case an AC output of variable frequency is synthesized by using appropriate segments of the input to achieve the desired output waveform. The input usually is a three-phase source, and the output generally is a frequency lower than the input. Such systems, although theoretically attractive, have not yet been widely used commercially because of the complex control needed to make them function properly.

AC–AC: The AC input is switched on and off periodically once in each half-cycle to produce a phase-controlled alternating output of the same fundamental frequency as the input. The output voltage is reduced when compared to the input's. Such a device thus controls the power transferred from source to load. An example is the control of incandescent lamp intensity in residential lighting.

AC–DC–AC: Further arrangements are possible by combining two of the preceding methods. Commercial frequency AC power often is rectified first to produce an intermediate DC stage. The power from the DC intermediate stage then is inverted to provide a variable-frequency AC output, which then is used to drive an AC motor in a variable-speed mode.

1.3
EFFICIENCY CONSIDERATIONS

The efficiency of a switching control, as compared to that of a linear control, is illustrated by the following example. A DC source of 100 volts (V) is available to supply 100 watts (W) to a 20-ohm (Ω) load. This can be done in two possible ways as shown in Figures 1.1 and 1.2. In the linear control of Figure 1.1, the value of R must be 24.7 Ω to provide a current of 2.24 amperes (A) and 100 W to the 20-Ω load. The power to the load is 100 W, but 124 W is lost in R in

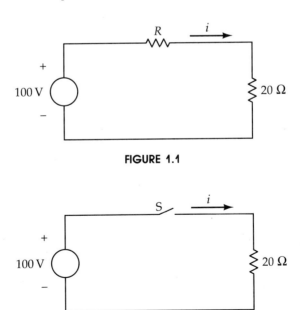

FIGURE 1.1

FIGURE 1.2

the process of controlling the power to the load. The efficiency of energy transfer from source to load is 45% with 124 W lost in the process.

In contrast, the ideal switch S in Figure 1.2 is arranged so as to be periodically open and closed. With the switch closed, the load power is 500 W, and with the switch open the load power is zero, all as shown in Figure 1.3. If the switch is closed 20% of the time, then the average load power is 20% of 500 W, or 100 W as desired. There are no losses, so the entire source energy is delivered to the load. Of course, there are no ideal switches, but if the ideal switch is approximated by a BJT, the result would be quite close to the ideal circuit operation.

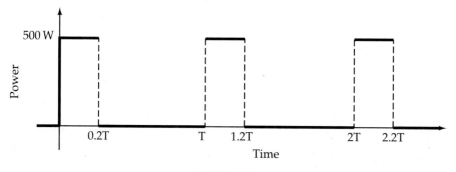

FIGURE 1.3

The major loss at a moderate switching frequency results from the transistor's collector-to-emitter saturation voltage. If this were 2 V, then the conducting switch loss would be approximately 10 W. This occurs 20% of the time and results in an average power loss of 2 W. Thus, for 98 W to the load, 100 W would need to be supplied from the source, yielding an efficiency of 98% in controlling the transfer of the power from source to load. This is an idealization, of course, because there are other, although generally smaller, losses in other parts of the switching cycle, and there also would need to be some power supplied to the control circuits. It does illustrate, however, the high efficiency that can be achieved.

We might ask, of course, whether the load power pulsating between 0 and 500 W is a suitable replacement for a constant value of 100 W. This depends upon the particular load, and in many cases some filtering may be needed to make the load power acceptable. The necessity for filtering suggests that we use as high a switching frequency as possible. Present chopper designs that use switching frequencies above 20 kilohertz (kHz) are common, and designs above 500 kHz now are being developed.

Another way to look at the example is by noting that a DC value of 44.7 V applied to the load is required to provide the desired value of 100 W.

A low-pass filter inserted between the switch and the load would provide a relatively constant voltage to the load. Such an arrangement is shown in Figure 1.4. The fraction of the period that switch S is closed now must be 44.7%. The circuit shown is a simplified version of a DC–DC converter like those we will examine in Chapter 7.

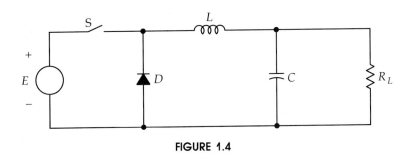

FIGURE 1.4

Where applicable, power-control efficiency is dramatically improved by switching techniques as opposed to linear control. Efficiency of transformation and control higher than 90% is quite often achievable; much lower numbers are seen with linear control.

1.4
SWITCHING DEVICE RATINGS

Appreciable amounts of power can be controlled by power semiconductor devices. Table 1.1 shows the order of magnitude of voltage and current that can be switched by some commercially available devices. Both maximum voltage and maximum current capability generally are not available simultaneously in a given device.

TABLE 1.1

Device Type	Device	Maximum Blocking Voltage (V)	Maximum Current (A)
Rectifier	Standard Recovery	4000	7000
	Fast Recovery	2400	1500
Transistor	BJT	1500	500
	MOSFET	1000	180
Thyristor	SCR	4000	5000
	GTO	4000	500
	TRIAC	1200	300

1.5

USE OF POWER SEMICONDUCTORS

The following information provides some idea of the size and importance of power electronics. Essentially, all variable-speed industrial motor drives use some form of power-electronics system. For many years SCRs dominated; they were used as phase-controlled rectifiers to supply a variable voltage to a DC motor to obtain variable-speed operation. In the last few years, AC–DC–AC inverters that supply variable frequency to AC motors have begun to take over a large fraction of this market.

Many of the DC power supplies used for general electronic equipment are of the switching type, with a DC-switching power supply following rectification of the AC source that powers the equipment. Other applications include the light dimmer switch used in residential construction and the variable-speed control used in portable power tools. In the very high power range, commercial AC power is rectified to provide long-distance transmission as direct current. At the receiving end of the transmission line, a DC–AC converter operates at 60 Hz to provide energy to the AC system. Such an arrangement provides both economic and operational advantages to an electric utility company. Such power-electronics systems thus are found in a wide range of consumer and industrial equipment.

1.6

METHODS OF ANALYSIS

The method of analysis we will use models a semiconductor device with a piecewise linear model. A new model is used whenever the semiconductor operation crosses into a new region represented by another model. In the simplest of models, there are two states: The semiconductor is either conducting or nonconducting. Refinements to this model can be added whenever the need exists. Such second-order models sometimes are necessary, for example, to represent semiconductor losses.

Most applications of semiconductors in power electronics can be modeled quite well by this first-order technique. The major circuit-operating mode is determined by using a very simple model of an idealized switching element. If necessary, refinements are added to the analysis to account for the actual non-ideal device. An example is in a resonant circuit analysis in which lossless LC inductor-capacitor (LC) analysis is used. Losses in a switching element or resistance in an inductor are accounted for only if there is significant effect. Because the intent is to produce an efficient power-conversion process, losses should not be a major component of circuit operation.

Wherever possible, the intent is to make the circuit analysis independent of the particular device used as the switch. In certain cases, this is not possible, such as in AC–DC conversion where an SCR is the only viable switching element. In other situations, such as a DC–DC converter, more than one switching element might be used. The design choice from among an SCR, a BJT, or MOSFET would depend on the power level, the desired switching frequency, and the efficiency required.

In Chapters 2, 3, and 4, the various semiconductor switches will be considered. They are modeled, and some operating requirements are analyzed. In the remaining chapters, the various types of power control are analyzed and design methods are presented.

CHAPTER · 2

> ## *Power Diodes*

In this chapter we consider some of the major characteristics of power-rectifying diodes. These diodes usually are PN-junction devices, although Schottky barrier diodes are used in certain applications. Basic models for the diode, including dynamic behavior, are of greatest interest and are considered in the following sections.

2.1

PN-JUNCTION DIODES

The most common power-rectifying element is the PN-junction diode, a single junction mounted in a package suitable for conducting significant current. Such devices have relatively little voltage across the element in forward operation. In reverse operation, such devices conduct only a very small current when subjected to a reverse voltage.

PN-junction diodes are capable of a rapid transition from conducting to blocking states. Basic devices are manufactured by processes that produce diodes with switching times of only a few microseconds. Such devices are suitable for rectifying relatively low frequency voltages such as 60-Hz power sources. In contrast to such relatively slow devices, other techniques can produce PN-junction diodes that are capable of switching from a conducting to nonconducting state in tens of nanoseconds. Such fast-recovery rectifiers are suitable for use in a circuit operating with rapidly changing current and voltage. A fast-recovery rectifier costs more than a slower device and thus should be used only where necessary.

Static Circuit Models

The circuit model used to represent a PN-junction diode can be as simple as an idealized rectifying element, such as that shown in the graph in Figure 2.1(a). In many cases, this may be sufficiently accurate, but in others more exact modeling is necessary. Parts (a), (b), and (c) of Figure 2.1 depict three possible piecewise linear graphs that can be used and thus increasingly more complex models.

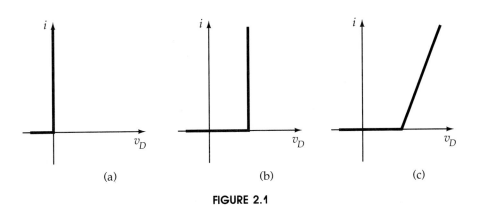

(a)   (b)   (c)

FIGURE 2.1

Circuit models with the characteristics shown in Figure 2.1 are given in Figure 2.2. The diode symbol in each part of the figure is an ideal element; in parts (b) and (c) they are modified by the addition of ideal circuit elements. If the diode is represented by one of the models in Figure 2.2, then the circuit analysis can be accomplished using piecewise linear-circuit analysis.

An examination of the voltage–current characteristic of the PN-junction diode provides information that allows us to fit one of the three idealized models to the actual characteristic. Depending upon the current range and the circuit

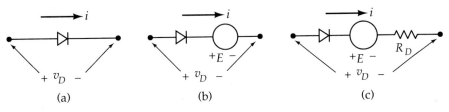

(a)   (b)   (c)

FIGURE 2.2

voltage, the model with the fewest elements that can accurately predict circuit performance is used. As an illustration, the simple circuit in Figure 2.3 can be used. The diode symbol shown represents the actual nonideal device. If the model in Figure 2.1(a) is used, wherein v_D is identically set to zero, the current is found to be

$$I = \frac{V}{R}. \tag{2.1}$$

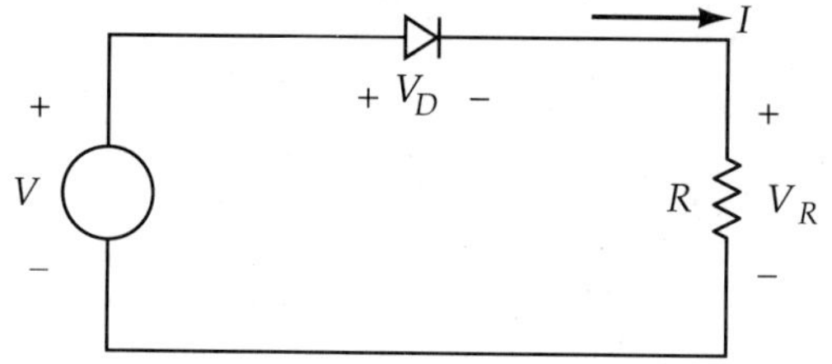

FIGURE 2.3

For a value of $V = 100$ V, the value of V_D of approximately 1 V may frequently be neglected. If, however, V has a value of 2 V, this neglect of V_D generally will produce an unacceptable error. In this situation, the model in either Figure 2.2(b) or (c) must be selected. In those cases of large current value, the model shown in (c) may need to be selected to predict an accurate value of current.

Generally, the reverse current in PN-junction diodes is negligible, but in certain circuit arrangements, especially at high temperature, the reverse current may not be negligible. This situation can be approximated with a resistor added in parallel with the model to permit such reverse current. As a linear element, the resistor value can only approximate at best the actual reverse current over the entire range of reverse voltage. The value should be selected so that the reverse current is correct at the most critical condition.

In addition to the static models presented thus far, certain dynamic effects may need to be included. One is the junction capacitance, which represents charge in the depletion zone of the reverse-biased PN junction. This capacitance is nonlinear and depends on device reverse voltage. In many cases, the capacitance value is small enough to be neglected especially when considering other capacitors that may be present.

EXAMPLE 2.1

The circuit in Figure 2.3 uses a 1N5402 rectifier in a circuit with $V = 100$ V and $R = 11$ Ω. Find the resulting current.

Solution   If the model of Figure 2.1(a) is used,

$$I = \frac{100}{11} = 9.1 \text{ A.}$$

If the model of Figure 2.1(b) is used, the value of V_D is required. The datasheet for this rectifier gives typical and maximum values of 1.0 and 1.2 V, respectively, at $25°$ C for a current of 9.4 A. If the typical value is used,

$$I = \frac{100 - 1.0}{11} = 9 \text{ A.}$$

If the maximum value is used,

$$I = \frac{100 - 1.2}{11} = 8.98 \text{ A.}$$

Replotting the data for a typical 1N5402 (from Appendix B) on linear graph coordinates enables a model of $E = 0.86$ V and $R_D = 0.0135$ Ω to be determined. Using these values, I can be obtained.

$$I = \frac{V - E}{R + R_D} = \frac{100 - 0.86}{11 + 0.0135} = 9.00 \text{ A.}$$

In this particular example, the addition of R_D has little effect.   ∎

E X A M P L E   2 . 2

The voltage source in Example 2.1 is changed to -200 V. The datasheet value of reverse current at a reverse voltage of 200 V for this device is a maximum value of 500 microamperes (μA) at $T_J = 150°$ C. Find:

(a) a circuit model representing operation with reverse voltage

(b) the circuit current

(c) the value of V_R.

Solution

(a) Considering the worst case of 500 μA, the reverse current can be represented by a resistor of $200/500 = 0.4$ megohms (MΩ) in parallel with the rest of the model. The circuit becomes that shown in Figure 2.4.

(b) The reverse current value then is calculated to be

$$I = \frac{-200}{11 + 0.4 \times 10^6} = -500 \times 10^{-6} \text{ A.}$$

(c) The value of V_R is calculated using the value of I:

$$V_R = (11)(I) = -0.0055 \text{ V.}$$

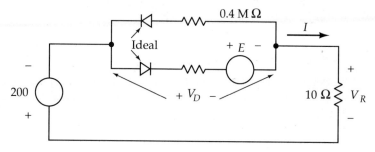

FIGURE 2.4

V_R is negligible in comparison to the -200-V value of the source voltage. Almost all of the source voltage appears as reverse voltage across the rectifier device. The reverse current is quite small compared to the forward current calculated in Example 2.1; for most purposes, it may be neglected. ∎

E X A M P L E 2 . 3

The circuit in Figure 2.3 has a voltage source of 5 V, a resistor of 0.2 Ω, and a diode of type 1N3879. The characteristic curve of a 1N3879 (typical at 150° C) is shown in Figure 2.5. Find the current using each of the three models in Figure 2.2.

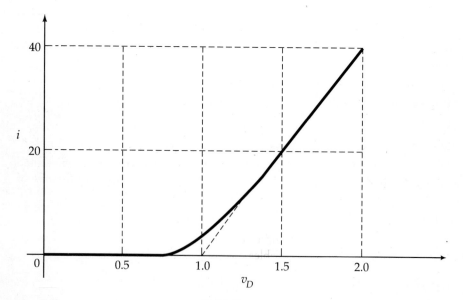

FIGURE 2.5

Solution

(a) Ideal diode with diode voltage equal to zero:

$$I = \frac{5.0}{0.2} = 25 \text{ A}.$$

(b) Using an ideal diode with voltage source of 1.0 V in series:

$$I = \frac{5.0 - 1.0}{0.2} = 20.0 \text{ A}.$$

(c) The reciprocal of the slope of the characteristic in Figure 2.5 is determined to be 0.0263 Ω. Use a model of an ideal diode in series with 1.00 V and a resistor of 0.0263 Ω:

$$I = \frac{5.0 - 1.0}{0.2 + 0.0263} = 17.67 \text{ A}.$$

The three parts of this example clearly show the effect of using the various models on the predicted current. For such a low source voltage, the first model obviously is inaccurate in determining the circuit current. The effort needed to use the third model may not be necessary. With the added resistance element, this model would be needed only for larger values of diode current. ∎

Turnoff Recovery

Diode turnoff with subsequent reverse-bias voltage requires a negative device current to charge the PN junction to a value that corresponds to the reverse voltage. Only after such charging does the reverse current become the small value of steady-state reverse current as specified on the datasheet. This reverse recovery current may have significant effects on total circuit performance.

A graph of diode current versus time during the recovery interval is shown in Figure 2.6. In this graph, circuit action and element values determine the rate at which device current is reduced from its original value to zero. After current zero, the external circuit still determines the current's rate of change. During this time, the voltage across the diode is essentially zero; this value can be used to model circuit behavior. Because the diode is as yet unable to support reverse voltage, the slope of current versus time does not change as the current becomes negative. Only after the junction region has sufficient charge supplied can the junction begin to support reverse voltage and cause reduction in reverse current to the steady-state value.

The peak reverse current and the recovered charge (shown by the shaded area) are functions of several variables, including initial current, temperature, and current rate of change during the turnoff process in addition to the characteristics of the particular device. Depending upon the design of the PN device, the rate of change of reverse current after the peak can be either quite abrupt or relatively

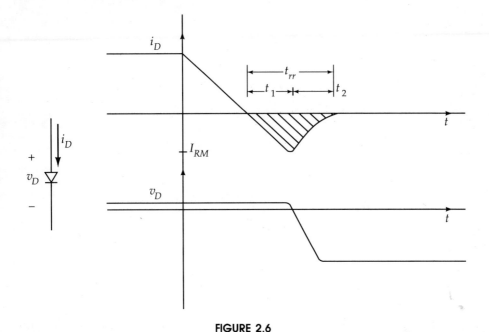

FIGURE 2.6

slow. This effect generally is negligible for 60-Hz rectifier operation. The rate of current reduction as the source voltage reverses is so small that the rectifier recovers almost as fast as the changes occur. As reverse voltage is applied to the circuit, reverse current will be needed to charge the junction, but the value generally is small when compared to normal rectifier current. Such devices, which are meant for low-frequency operation, generally are not characterized for this effect.

The values of reverse current and reverse recovery time can be determined for certain fast-recovery rectifiers. Using the graph in Figure 2.6, the following equations can be written:

$$Q_{rr} = 0.5 I_{RM} t_{rr} \tag{2.2}$$

$$I_{RM} = \left(\frac{d i_D}{dt} \right) t_1 \tag{2.3}$$

$$t_{rr} = \frac{2 Q_{rr}}{(d i_D / dt)(t_1)}. \tag{2.4}$$

In the preceding equations, Q_{rr} is the recovered charge shown in the shaded area in Figure 2.6, I_{RM} is the peak reverse current, t_{rr} is the reverse recovery time, and times t_1 and t_2 are subdivisions of t_{rr}. The above equations can be used to find t_{rr} and I_{RM}. In the first of two limiting cases, t_2 is negligible compared to t_{rr} and corresponds to an abrupt recovery; in the second case, t_2 is equal to one-half of t_{rr}, which corresponds to a very soft recovery. In the first case, $t_2 = 0$ and $t_1 = t_{rr}$, the equations become

$$t_{rr} = \left(\frac{2Q_{rr}}{di_D/dt}\right)^{0.5} \tag{2.5}$$

$$I_{RM} = \left[2Q_{rr}\left(\frac{di_D}{dt}\right)\right]^{0.5}. \tag{2.6}$$

In the second case, $t_1 = t_2 = \dfrac{t_{rr}}{2}$, the equations become

$$t_{rr} = \left(\frac{4Q_{rr}}{di_D/dt}\right)^{0.5} \tag{2.7}$$

$$I_{RM} = \left[Q_{rr}\left(\frac{di_D}{dt}\right)\right]^{0.5}. \tag{2.8}$$

These two solutions provide limiting cases for the actual situation, which probably lies somewhere between the two cases. The values of Q_{rr} are strongly circuit dependent; they are available from the datasheets for certain fast-recovery rectifiers.

EXAMPLE 2.4

A 1N3879 diode operates with an initial current of 20 A at a junction temperature of 100° C. The diode recovers blocking capability in a circuit in which the current is reversed at a rate of 20 amperes/microsecond (A/μs). Find t_{rr} and I_{RM}.

Solution   From the datasheet for this device, the typical Q_{rr} value for these conditions is 0.22 microcoulomb (μC). Using the case in which t_2 is negligible, the solution becomes:

$$t_{rr} = \left[\frac{(2)(0.22 \times 10^{-6})}{20 \times 10^6}\right]^{0.5}$$

$$t_{rr} = 148 \times 10^{-9} \text{ s}$$

$$I_{RM} = [(2)(0.22 \times 10^{-6})(20 \times 10^6)]^{0.5} = 2.97 \text{ A}.$$

If the calculations are repeated using the second set of assumptions, then

$$t_{rr} = 210 \times 10^{-9} \text{ s}$$

$$I_{RM} = 2.10 \text{ A}. \qquad \blacksquare$$

The change from peak reverse current can have a significant circuit effect, especially if t_2 is small compared to t_1. A circuit that illustrates the effect is shown in Figure 2.7. In this circuit, switch S closes with initial conditions of $i_1 = 0$ and $i_3 = I$. After the switch is closed, v_X remains at essentially zero value as i_1 increases and i_3 decreases. When $i_1 = I$, i_3 is 0 and the diode begins its reverse recovery. The value of v_X remains at zero and i_1 continues to increase until the peak reverse value of i_3 occurs.

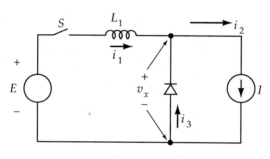

FIGURE 2.7

If diode reverse current is abruptly reduced to zero, the rate of change of i_3 and hence i_1 is large. The value of v_X will be large and diode failure may occur. The calculations of Example 2.5 illustrate the size of the numbers involved.

E X A M P L E   2 . 5

In the circuit in Figure 2.7, the t_2 portion of the recovery is quite small but nonzero. Find the reverse voltage across the diode as recovery occurs. Neglect any effect of junction capacitance. $E = 200$ V, $L = 30$ μH, $I_{RM} = 3$ A, and $t_2 = 50$ ns.

Solution

$$i_1 + i_3 = i_2$$

Because i_2 is constant;

$$\left(\frac{di_1}{dt}\right) + \left(\frac{di_3}{dt}\right) = 0$$

and

$$\frac{di_3}{dt} = \frac{I_{RM}}{t_2} = \frac{3}{50 \times 10^{-9}} = 60 \times 10^6 \text{ A/s.}$$

Therefore,

$$\frac{di_1}{dt} = -60 \times 10^6 \ \text{A/s}$$

$$v_X = E - L\left(\frac{di_1}{dt}\right)$$

$$v_X = 200 - (30 \times 10^{-6})(-60 \times 10^6) = 2000 \ \text{V}.$$

It is evident that appreciable reverse voltage can be developed by a rapid decrease of the reverse diode current.   ■

The following are solutions to the problem illustrated by Example 2.5:

(a) a slower recovery diode

(b) a snubber circuit in parallel with the diode

(c) a clamping device such as a zener diode in parallel with the diode

(d) some combination of the above.

One reason a fast-recovery diode is used is to limit the peak current that the switch must conduct upon turn on. This current is the value of i_2 plus diode reverse-recovery current. If the diode reverse current is large, then additional stress is placed on the switch. A fast-recovery diode helps this problem although it may introduce the problem demonstrated in Example 2.5. A snubber placed in parallel with the diode can reduce the voltage level without adding significantly to the switch peak current requirement. Figure 2.8 shows the modified circuit.

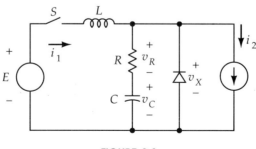

FIGURE 2.8

E X A M P L E 2 . 6

Design a snubber circuit to limit the reverse voltage on the diode in a circuit as in Figure 2.7. The peak diode reverse-recovery current is 5 A; the load current, i_2, is 20 A. Assume an abrupt diode recovery with $t_2 = 0$, $L = 25\ \mu$H, and $E = 200$ V. Find values of R and C to limit diode reverse voltage to 250 V and peak switch current to 26 A. Assume that the load current does not change during the interval of interest.

Solution   There are two variables in the problem and two constraints to be met so that R and C can be determined uniquely. No explicit design equations are available, however. Still, a reasonable estimate can be made and an analysis performed to determine whether suitable results are obtained. An iteration of the process can be performed to converge on a solution if it exists.

An equation for switch current (without damping) can be written using the equations of Appendix A:

$$i_1 = 20 + 5 \cos \omega t + 200 \left(\frac{C}{L}\right)^{0.5} \sin \omega t.$$

Peak switch current is limited to 26 A. An initial choice of capacitor value can be made by choosing a relatively arbitrary value for the sine term. A choice of 7-A peak current for this term in combination with the other terms produces an undamped peak value of $i_1 = 28.6$ A. With damping, the peak value will be less than 28.6 A:

$$200 \left(\frac{C}{L}\right)^{0.5} = 7\ \text{A}.$$

The combination of the above term with the cosine term, the DC term, and the actual damping that exists may make the current meet the peak requirement. With the given value of inductance, the capacitance in microfarads is found:

$$C = 0.03\ \mu\text{F}.$$

Using these values, the capacitor voltage without attenuation is given by

$$v_C = 200(1 - \cos \omega t) + 5 \left(\frac{L}{C}\right)^{0.5} \sin \omega t$$

$$v_C = 200 - 246 \cos (\omega t + 0.624).$$

Momentarily neglecting the voltage across the resistor, the 246-V value must decay to less than 50 V at the peak of the cosine term in order that v_C have a maximum no greater than 250 V:

$$\omega = \left(\frac{1}{LC}\right)^{0.5} = 1.155 \times 10^6\ \text{rad/s}.$$

The peak occurs when $(\omega t + 0.624) = \pi$;

$$t = 2.18 \times 10^{-6} \text{ s}$$

$$e^{-\alpha t} = \frac{50}{246} = 0.203$$

$$\alpha = 731,000 = \frac{R}{2L}$$

and

$$R = 36.6 \ \Omega.$$

We thus should use an initial design for which $C = 0.03 \ \mu F$ and $R = 37 \ \Omega$. An exact solution using these values is

$$i_1 = 20 + 7.043 \, e^{-\alpha t} \cos{(\omega_d t - 0.7814)}$$

$$v_X = 200 - 203.3 \, e^{-\alpha t} \cos{(\omega_d t + 1.398)},$$

where

$\alpha = 660,000/\text{s}$

$\omega_d = 947,490 \text{ rad/s}.$

Maximum i_1 occurs at $0.1826 \ \mu s$ and is 25.12 A.

Maximum v_X occurs at $1.2 \ \mu s$ and is 275.7 V.

These results do not meet the peak voltage requirement, so a second iteration is necessary. A larger capacitor would delay voltage buildup until the circuit damping can reduce capacitor voltage. A capacitor value of $0.05 \ \mu F$ yields maximum values of $i_1 = 25.2$ A at $0.3 \ \mu s$ and $v_X = 251.6$ V at $1.5 \ \mu s$. These values essentially meet the requirements. ∎

Forward Recovery

There is a time-varying effect that occurs at the turn on of the PN-junction diode; it may be described as a forward-recovery process. The full area of the PN junction does not conduct immediately as the diode turns on and the current is initially conducted in a restricted part of the junction. Although not explicitly shown in Figure 2.9, there must be a small parasitic circuit inductance that forces an initial zero current value. As conduction spreads to the full area, current density is decreased and the voltage between the diode terminals decreases. Figure 2.9 shows this effect for a typical device.

The effect shown in Figure 2.9 occurs on a time scale of a few microseconds. There is an increased power loss for this time interval as compared to the power after the turn-on period. The effect is important only for short conduction intervals that are periodic at a relatively high repetition frequency. The

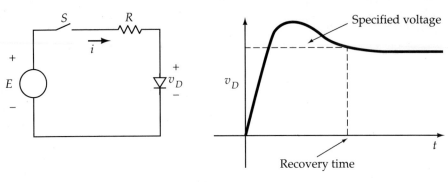

FIGURE 2.9

effect is negligible in those diodes used in 60-Hz rectifiers. It also is negligible in those circuit arrangements in which the diode current builds up slowly as a result of circuit inductance.

EXAMPLE 2.7

A 1N3879 rectifier is used in a circuit in which the forward current is 50 A periodically for 5% of a 25-μs period. The junction temperature is 25° C.

(a) What is the forward-recovery time?

(b) Estimate the increase in diode loss caused by this effect.

Solution

(a) The typical time from the 1N3879 datasheet for recovery to 1.1 V can be read as 0.85 μs.

(b) Because there are no data on the speed of the current rise time, and further-more no datasheet information on the size of the rectifier voltage prior to recovery, the question cannot be answered quantitatively. Because the forward recovery time is significant compared to the conduction time of 1.25 μs, the conduction losses will be larger than the steady-state losses. ∎

2.2

SCHOTTKY BARRIER DIODES

Schottky barrier diodes are constructed without the usual PN junction; as a result, they do not exhibit effects related to minority charge carriers. In par-ticular, there is no charge storage and no reverse-recovery time as in the case of the PN-junction diode. In the reverse direction, only a nonlinear capacitor need be used to represent the device's dynamic behavior.

One reason for using the Schottky diode is the relatively low conduction voltage that exists during forward current conduction. The tradeoff for the lower forward voltage is a larger reverse leakage current than would be usual for a PN-junction diode. The particular barrier metal used has an effect on the forward voltage as well as on the related leakage current. Barriers made of chromium produce the lowest forward voltage and the highest reverse current. Devices made of tungsten produce a greater forward voltage and a lower reverse current. Molybdenum and platinum produce intermediate results.

Schottky diodes are used in low-voltage rectifier circuits to improve the efficiency of the rectification process. Their relatively low reverse breakdown voltage is acceptable in such low-voltage applications.

Static Circuit Models

The static circuit models that can be used are identical in form to those for the PN-junction diode. The difference is in the values for the elements in the model. The forward voltage is smaller and results in lower conduction losses. The reverse leakage is larger than for corresponding PN-junction diodes.

E X A M P L E   2 . 8

A 1N5828 rectifier is used in a circuit to rectify a 20-V peak square wave alternating source. The static characteristic is shown in Figure 2.10. The load is a 1-Ω resistor, and the value of T_J is 100° C. Find:

(a) a suitable piecewise linear model for the rectifier

(b) the load current

(c) the rectifier losses assuming low-frequency operation.

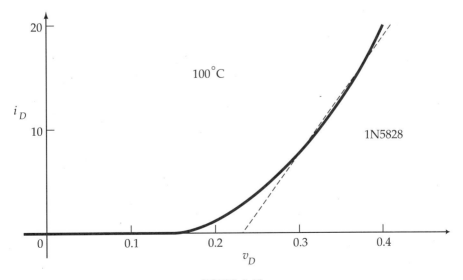

FIGURE 2.10

Solution

(a) From the graph in Figure 2.10, we can see that the slope of the piecewise linear graph corresponds to 0.008 Ω. Because this is relatively small compared to the 1-Ω load resistance value, a model consisting of an ideal diode in series with a 0.24-V source is good for predicting forward conduction current. The reverse current for this device at $100°$ C with 20-V reverse voltage is 30 milliamperes (mA). In general, this current cannot be represented by a resistor value because the leakage current is highly nonlinear. In this case, the reverse voltage is constant and the effect can be represented by a resistor with a value of 20 V/0.030 A, or 667 Ω. The model is shown in the circuit in Figure 2.11.

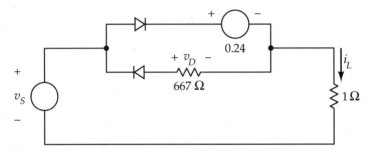

FIGURE 2.11

(b) During the positive portion of the source voltage,

$$i_L = \frac{20 - 0.24}{1} = 19.76 \text{ A.}$$

(c) Neglect of the 0.008-Ω value in a more complete model leads to substantial error in rectifier losses. For this part of the example, modify the circuit with the addition of the 0.008-Ω resistor. In forward conduction,

$$i_L = \frac{20 - 0.24}{1 + 0.008} = 19.60 \text{ A}$$

$$v_D = 0.24 + (19.60)(0.008) = 0.376 \text{ V}$$

$$P = (v_D)(i_L) = (0.376)(19.60) = 7.78 \text{ W.}$$

During reverse operation,

$$i_L = \frac{-20}{667 + 1} = -0.030 \text{ A}$$

$$v_D = (667)(i_L) = -19.97 \text{ V}$$

$$P = (v_D)(i_L) = (-19.97)(-0.030) = 0.60 \text{ W.}$$

Each of the above states (forward and reverse) occurs 50% of the time, so the diode power (P) is the average of the two values:

$$P_{avg} = \tfrac{1}{2}(7.78 + 0.60) = 4.19 \text{ W}. \qquad \blacksquare$$

Dynamic Performance

The one addition to the static model required to represent dynamic performance is a capacitor in parallel with the model. The value of this capacitor is a nonlinear function of reverse voltage. Most of the variation occurs for very small reverse voltage. Therefore, a constant value can be used with reasonable accuracy if the reverse voltage is relatively large. The following example illustrates this modeling process.

EXAMPLE 2.9

A 1N5828 diode is used in the circuit in Figure 2.12. From the datasheet in Appendix B, it is evident that a single capacitor value cannot represent the full reverse-bias range of the device. A single value, however, can provide a useful approximate model for the device. Accordingly, we select $C = 800$ picofarads (pF); $L_1 = 10 \ \mu\text{H}$, $L_2 = 10 \ \text{mH}$, and $i_2(0) = 20$ A.

(a) How long after the switch is closed does the diode current reach zero? For this part, a suitable value for diode forward voltage is zero.

(b) Find the peak diode reverse voltage.

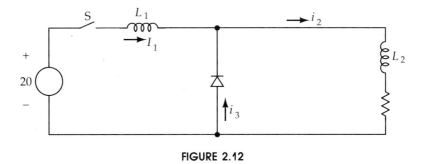

FIGURE 2.12

Solution

(a) The equations for the circuit during this interval are

$$10 \times 10^{-6}\left(\frac{di_1}{dt}\right) + 0 = 20$$

$$i_1(0) = 0, \qquad i_3(0) = i_2(0) = 20 \text{ A}$$

and

$$\frac{di_1}{dt} = 2 \times 10^6 \text{ A/s.}$$

During the initial interval, i_2 does not change appreciably because of the large value of L_2:

$$i_1 + i_3 = i_2 = 20 \text{ A}$$

$$\frac{di_3}{dt} = -\frac{di_1}{dt} = -2 \times 10^6 \text{ A/s.}$$

Therefore

$$i_3 = 20 - 2 \times 10^6 \, t$$

and i_3 becomes zero at $t = 10 \times 10^{-6}$ s. Thereafter, $i_3 = 0$ as far as the diode part is concerned. The element is modeled for part (b) by the capacitance value of 800 pF.

(b) Because L_2 is so large, the circuit may be modeled as shown in Figure 2.13.

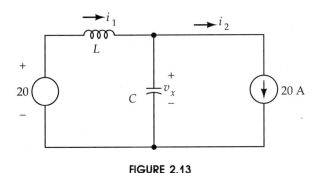

FIGURE 2.13

This is a basic LC-resonant circuit with a straightforward solution. The current i_2 actually is not determined by a current source, but is valid here for the short time of interest. A solution of the circuit yields

$$i_1 = 20 + 0.179 \sin \omega t$$

$$v_X = 20(1 - \cos \omega t)$$

where

$$\omega = 11.18 \times 10^6 \text{ rad/s}$$

and a new time origin has been selected; it begins at the end of the period for part (a).

As modeled, there is no damping present although there will be some in the actual circuit. The rate of decay is likely to be low enough that the peak value of v_X will be close to 40 V. The reverse-biased diode represented by the capacitor thus is subjected to a reverse voltage of nearly double the source voltage. A snubber circuit as shown in Example 2.10 can reduce this reverse voltage. ∎

EXAMPLE 2.10

The circuit in Example 2.9 has an added snubber that consists of a capacitor of 0.01 μF in series with a resistor of 30 Ω as shown in Figure 2.14. Repeat the solution of the previous example.

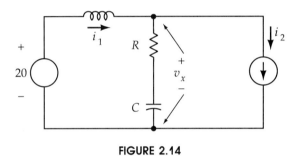

FIGURE 2.14

Solution

(a) Because the forward-biased diode is represented by zero voltage, there is no change for this part of the solution. This condition does, however, set the initial capacitor voltage at zero.

(b) The diode capacitance of 800 pF is so small in comparison to the snubber capacitor that it can be neglected. Figure 2.14 represents the circuit to be solved. A standard solution of this circuit yields

$$v_X = 20 - 22.72\, e^{-\alpha t} \cos(\omega_d t + 0.494)$$

$$i_1 = 20 + 0.718\, e^{-\alpha t} \sin(\omega_d t + 0.494)$$

where

$$\alpha = 1.5 \times 10^6 \text{ Np/s}$$
$$\omega_d = 2.784 \times 10^6 \text{ rad/s.}$$

The peak value of v_X is 26.27 V at $t = 775$ nanoseconds. This value represents a marked reduction in the reverse voltage across the diode. Other values of snubber components may yield an even lower value of reverse voltage.   ■

2.3

APPLICATION REQUIREMENTS

Series Connection

For very high voltage applications, the reverse-voltage capability of a single diode may not be adequate. A series connection of two or more elements sometimes is required. In such a case, the reverse voltage may not be shared equally between the elements in series, and one element can have excessive voltage applied. The graph in Figure 2.15 shows the static reverse current–voltage characteristic of two different diodes. Because the elements are in series, they must have the same reverse leakage current, although they obviously have two different values of reverse voltage. This may cause Diode 1 to exceed its reverse-voltage capability.

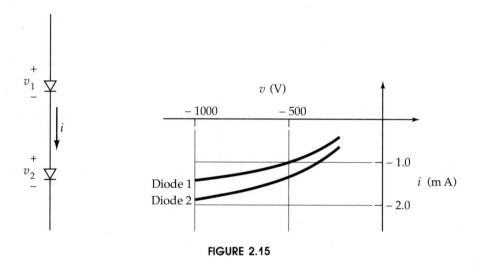

FIGURE 2.15

This problem can be solved by connecting voltage-sharing resistors in parallel with each diode. For these resistors to be effective, they must conduct a current several times larger than the diodes' leakage current. The obvious drawback of this solution is the power dissipated in the two resistors during reverse-bias operation. An example provides further understanding of the numbers involved.

EXAMPLE 2.11

Two diodes are connected in series as shown in Figure 2.16 with voltage-sharing resistors. The diodes have the characteristics shown in Figure 2.15. Find:

(a) The value of R such that neither diode has a reverse voltage greater than 55% of the total of 1600 V;

(b) The total reverse current and power;

(c) The reverse voltage for each diode, if voltage-sharing resistors are not used.

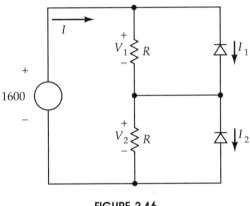

FIGURE 2.16

Solution

(a) The circuit diagram of Figure 2.16 shows an arrangement with two equal resistors to enforce sharing of reverse voltage. One diode supports 880 V, whereas the second supports only 720 V.

   From the graph in Figure 2.15, values of the two reverse currents can be found at $V_1 = 880$ V and $V_2 = 720$ V:

$$I_1 = 0.0012 \text{ A} \quad \text{and} \quad I_2 = 0.0015 \text{ A}.$$

Circuit equations for I give the following result:

$$I = \left(\frac{V_1}{R}\right) + I_1 = \left(\frac{V_2}{R}\right) + I_2.$$

Solving for R yields

$$R = 533{,}000 \ \Omega.$$

(b) The total current is found to be

$$I = \left(\frac{880}{R}\right) + I_1 = 0.00285 \text{ A}.$$

The total power is $P = (1600)(I) = 4.56$ W. The total current and reverse power losses are increased by this technique.

(c) From the graph in Figure 2.15, an iterative technique can supply an answer. For $I = -1.25$ mA, values of $V_1 = -1300$ V and $V_2 = -400$ V can be read from the graph. These correspond to a total reverse voltage of 1700 V, which is larger than the actual value. The resolution of the graph does not permit additional iterations, but the reverse voltage for Diode 1 must be approximately three times the value for Diode 2.   ∎

Hey cannot (handwritten margin note)

A related problem also exists in the dynamic sharing of voltage. As the reverse voltage changes rapidly, the change is initially distributed in inverse relation to the reverse-biased junction capacitance of the two elements. If these are unequal, dynamic sharing will be unequal. Additional capacitance placed in parallel with each of the diodes as shown in Figure 2.17 can reduce the inequality to an acceptable value. The capacitance required for an effective solution is one that is several times as large as the reverse-biased junction capacitance. Because voltage sharing is important only at high voltage, the appropriate junction capacitance to use in such a design is that corresponding to large reverse voltage.

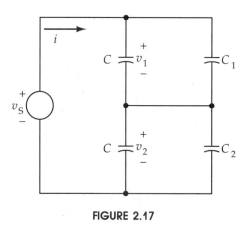

FIGURE 2.17

EXAMPLE 2.12

In the preceding example, the two diodes must support a reverse voltage that increases at a rate of 200 V/μs. Diode 1 has a junction capacitance of 200 pF, and Diode 2 has a junction capacitance of 250 pF. Select suitable capacitances to place in parallel with the diodes to force dynamic sharing of the reverse voltages within 10% of each other.

Solution   Diode 1 experiences greater voltage than Diode 2 because its capacitance is smaller. In Figure 2.17, junction capacitors are paralleled by capacitors of value C. Each section must have the same total current as shown in the following equation:

$$i = (C_1 + C)\left(\frac{dv_1}{dt}\right) = (C_2 + C)\left(\frac{dv_2}{dt}\right).$$

To meet the stated requirement of dynamic sharing,

$$\frac{dv_1}{dt} = 1.1\left(\frac{dv_2}{dt}\right).$$

Solution of the two equations yields

$$C = 300 \text{ pF}.$$

Note:

(a) At the time the total voltage is 1600 V, the value of v_1 is 838 V and v_2 is 762 V.

(b) If static voltage-sharing resistors are present as in Example 2.11, their effect is minor in enforcing dynamic sharing. The value of i in this problem is 52 mA as compared to 3 mA in Example 2.11.   ■

The added resistors or capacitors described in the two preceding examples are not desirable because they increase both circuit costs and losses. Another approach is to reduce the need for these elements by matching the diodes in their reverse characteristics. This must be done over the operating temperature range as well as at room temperature.

Parallel Connection

For very large current requirements, two or more diodes sometimes are used in parallel. The problem here is an unequal current sharing as a result of differing forward-conduction characteristics. The graph and circuit shown in Figure 2.18 help to illustrate the problem. For a given voltage applied to the two diodes, a different value of current exists in each device. A resistor of value R connected in series with each diode can help to establish values of I_1 and I_2 that are nearly equal. An example illustrates these ideas.

E X A M P L E   2 . 1 3

The two diodes shown in Figure 2.18 conduct a total of 100 A. Neither diode must conduct more than 55 A. Find:

(a) the value of two equal resistors to be inserted in series with each diode to produce this condition

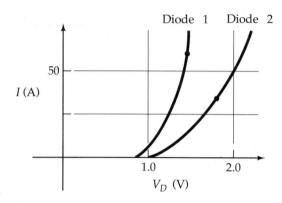 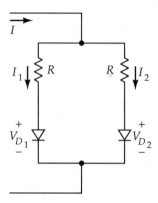

FIGURE 2.18

(b) the resistor losses

(c) the total voltage across the combination.

Solution

(a) From the graph in Figure 2.18, we can use values of $I_1 = 55$ A and $I_2 = 45$ A, and values of V_{D_1} and V_{D_2} can be found:

$$V_{D_1} = 1.5 \text{ V} \quad \text{and} \quad V_{D_2} = 1.8 \text{ V}$$

$$V = RI_1 + V_{D_1} = RI_2 + V_{D_2}$$

$$(R)(55) + 1.5 = (R)(45) + 1.8$$

$$R = 0.03 \ \Omega.$$

(b) The power in each of these resistors can be calculated:

$$P_{R_1} = (55)^2(0.03) = 90.75 \text{ W}$$

$$P_{R_2} = (45)^2(0.03) = 60.75 \text{ W}.$$

(c) The total voltage across the combination is

$$V = RI_1 + V_{D_1} = 1.65 + 1.5 = 3.15 \text{ V}.$$

The penalty for using the current-sharing resistors is an increased voltage across the combination and the loss of 151.5 W in the two resistors. Unless it is absolutely necessary to use the parallel arrangement, it is certainly better to use one device with an adequate current rating. ∎

A dynamic current-sharing means involves using a 1:1 transformer connected as in Figure 2.19. If the transformer is assumed to be ideal, the values of the two currents i_1 and i_2 must be equal. In a practical case, the transformer

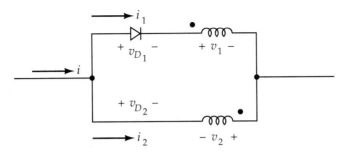

FIGURE 2.19

is not ideal and requires a magnetizing current. Values of i_1 and i_2 are not quite equal unless the diodes are identical. The transformer also must be designed so that it does not saturate under the existing conditions of unbalance. This method is suitable only for a pulse-type operating condition, but with such an application the losses associated with series resistors are eliminated. The trade-off is the additional cost and weight of the magnetic structure versus the losses of series resistors as the means of forcing current sharing.

A model of the arrangement in Figure 2.19 is shown in the circuit of Figure 2.20 for a nonideal transformer. It is assumed that the two windings are so

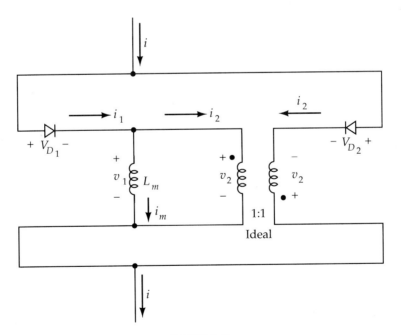

FIGURE 2.20

tightly coupled that leakage inductance may be neglected. Winding resistance also is neglected. The transformer equivalent circuit reduces to a magnetizing inductance plus an ideal $1:1$ transformer as required by the connection shown in Figure 2.19. The circuit in Figure 2.20 also includes the two diodes that share the total current.

The transformer operates with a unidirectional magnetic flux. To reset the magnetic core after each current pulse, the core must have an air gap incorporated in its structure.

The following equations can be written for this circuit:

$$v_{D_1} + v_1 = v_{D_2} - v_2 \tag{2.9}$$

$$v_1 = v_2 \tag{2.10}$$

$$i_m = i_1 - i_2 \tag{2.11}$$

$$v_1 = L_m\left(\frac{di_m}{dt}\right). \tag{2.12}$$

A solution of the preceding equations yields the following results:

$$v_1 = 0.5(v_{D_2} - v_{D_1}) \tag{2.13}$$

$$L_m = \frac{0.5(v_{D_2} - v_{D_1})(\Delta t)}{\Delta(i_1 - i_2)} \tag{2.14}$$

where Δt is the interval of diode conduction and $\Delta(i_1 - i_2)$ is the permitted difference between i_1 and i_2 at the end of the conduction interval.

EXAMPLE 2.14

Two diodes are connected in parallel in the circuit in Figure 2.19. The total current is 200 A with a conduction interval of 4 ms. The two diodes have a 0.2-V difference in conduction voltage. The current difference between the two diodes at the end of the conduction interval must not exceed 8 A. Find:

(a) the magnetizing inductance of the two coupled inductors

(b) the voltage across the transformer terminals during operation.

Solution

(a) From Equation 2.14,

$$L_m = \frac{(0.5)(0.2)(0.004)}{8} = 0.000050 \text{ H}.$$

(b) From Equation 2.13,

$$v_1 = 0.5(0.2) = 0.1 \text{ V}. \qquad \blacksquare$$

2.4

PROBLEMS

2.1 Find piecewise linear models for a 1N5402 rectifier diode valid in the range of 0 to 5 A. Do this for each of the three parts in Figure 2.2.

2.2 (a) Repeat Problem 2.1 for a current range of 0 to 20 A.

(b) Compare the values with those obtained for Problem 2.1.

2.3 A diode with a piecewise linear model of $E = 1.0$ V and $R = 0.05 \, \Omega$ is used in the circuit of Figure 2.3 with $V = 100$ V and $R_L = 10 \, \Omega$. Find the resulting current using each of the three models in Figure 2.2.

2.4 Repeat Problem 2.3 with $V = 4$ V.

2.5 In the circuit in Figure 2.3, the diode is a 1N3879 and the source is a sinusoid of 40-V peak value of frequency 1000 Hz. For a load resistance of 2.4 Ω, find the following:

(a) peak forward load current

(b) peak reverse current

(c) the graph of current versus time.

2.6 Repeat Problem 2.5 for a source voltage of 4-V peak value.

2.7 A diode of type 1N3883 is used in the circuit in Figure 2.3 at $T_J = 125°$ C. $V = -400$ V and $R_L = 75 \, \Omega$. Find the values of V_R for both typical and worst-case conditions.

2.8 A 1N3879 rectifier diode is used in the circuit in Figure 2.3 with $R_L = 10 \, \Omega$. The source voltage has a 100-Hz alternating rectangular waveform with peak value of 45 V. Find the average power loss in the diode.

2.9 A 1N3883 rectifier diode is used in the circuit in Figure 2.7. Initial current is 10 A with $E = 300$ V and $L = 20 \, \mu$H. Switch S is closed at $t = 0$. Assume $t_2 = 0$. Find:

(a) peak rectifier reverse current

(b) peak switch current.

2.10 Repeat Problem 2.9 assuming $t_2 = \dfrac{t_{rr}}{2}$.

2.11 A 1N3883 rectifier diode is used in the circuit in Figure 2.7. Assume t_2 is small, with a nonzero value of 0.1 μs. $L_1 = 15 \, \mu$H, $E = 200$ V, and $I = 15$ A. Use data from Appendix B for the diode at $100°$ C.

(a) Find I_{RM}.

(b) Assuming that i_3 changes linearly with time from its peak at the beginning of recovery to zero value, find the reverse diode voltage during recovery. Neglect diode capacitance.

(c) A snubber of $R = 50 \ \Omega$ and $C = 0.04 \ \mu F$ is added. Find the peak reverse voltage.

2.12   In a circuit like that in Figure 2.8, $E = 300$ V, $L_1 = 20 \ \mu H$, $i_2 = 30$ A, and the diode is a 1N3883. Design a snubber circuit to limit the peak diode recovery voltage to 400 V with peak switch current of 40 A.

2.13   Repeat Problem 2.11 with $E = 150$ V, $I = 20$ A, and $L_1 = 10 \ \mu H$. For part (c), use $C = 0.05 \ \mu F$ and $R = 75 \ \Omega$.

2.14   In the circuit in Figure 2.9, the switch is closed for 10 μs and then opened for 15 μs in a periodic manner. If the diode is a 1N3883, $R = 7.5 \ \Omega$, and $E = 300$ V, find the diode's forward-recovery time. Is this significant in comparison to the diode conduction time?

2.15   A low-frequency alternating square-wave voltage source of 35-V peak value is rectified by a 1N5828 with a load resistance of 3.5 Ω. $T_J = 100° $C. Find the rectifier power loss.

2.16   A Schottky diode (1N5828) is used in the circuit in Figure 2.12. $L_1 = 30 \ \mu H$, $L_2 = 100$ mH, $E = 25$ V, and $i_2 = 15$ A. The switch S is closed at $t = 0$. Find the peak diode reverse voltage.

2.17   Design a snubber circuit for Problem 2.16 that limits the peak diode reverse voltage to 40 V.

2.18   Two diodes having the characteristics shown in Figure 2.15 are connected in series. The total reverse voltage is 2000 V. Find:

(a) the reverse voltage for each diode

(b) the resistance value connected in parallel with each diode to limit reverse voltage on either diode to 1100 V.

(c) power lost in the voltage-sharing resistors.

2.19   Two diodes in series are subjected to a reverse voltage that increases at the rate of 100 V/μs. The diodes have junction capacitances of 500 pF and 700 pF.

Find the value of two equal capacitors to be placed in parallel with the diodes so that the reverse voltage of Diode 1 is not more than 10% greater than that of Diode 2.

2.20   Two diodes having the characteristics shown in Figure 2.18 are in parallel and conduct a forward current of 100 A. Find:

(a) the current in each diode

(b) the voltage across the combination.

2.21 **(a)** In Problem 2.20, find current-sharing resistors such that one diode does not conduct more than 60% of the current.

(b) What is the additional power loss compared to that found in Problem 2.20?

2.22 The two diodes shown in Figure 2.19 differ in voltage by 0.15 V, with 100 A in each diode. For a total current of 200 A, design coupled inductors such as those in Figure 2.19 so that the two currents do not differ by more than 3 A. The duration of conduction is 100 μs.

CHAPTER · 3

Thyristors

The *thyristor* is a multilayer semiconductor with several layers of alternating P- and N-type silicon. These regenerative devices can switch between conducting and nonconducting states. There are several members of the thyristor family, each characterized in part by which semiconductor layer is accessible by connection to an external terminal. Only a few of the more commonly used members of the family are discussed in this chapter.

3.1

SILICON-CONTROLLED RECTIFIER

The silicon-controlled rectifier (SCR) is widely used as a switching device, especially in higher voltage and higher current situations. The SCR has characteristics similar to a normal rectifier when it conducts in the forward direction. This forward current occurs only after the device has been gated into conduction by an input gate current at a third or control terminal. In a manner similar to that of the rectifier diode, the SCR also blocks current in the reverse direction.

The gate current required to initiate conduction need exist for only a short period of time. Thereafter, the device remains latched into a conducting state and gate current is no longer required. The SCR continues conduction until the device is reverse biased by either a reversal of the source voltage or an external circuit change such as to cause SCR turnoff. Another little used turnoff means is to reduce the current to less than some small value by either reducing source voltage or increasing load resistance. The minimum current level, below which such turnoff occurs, is called the "holding current."

Turn-On Requirements

The SCR has a four-layer PNPN semiconductor structure such as that shown in Figure 3.1(a), with junctions labeled J_1, J_2, and J_3. Figure 3.1(b) shows the circuit symbol of the SCR, with A and K terminals corresponding to the anode and cathode terminals of a two-terminal rectifier. A third terminal, the gate, provides control of the device. A model that is useful in predicting the latching nature of the SCR is shown in Figure 3.2. This model is evident upon dividing the middle PN regions in Figure 3.1(a) along the dotted line.

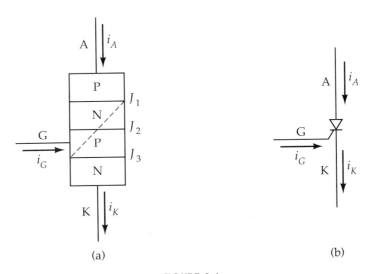

(a) (b)

FIGURE 3.1

A relatively simple model illustrates the two states, OFF and ON, that are possible for the SCR. From this model, it also is possible to understand the conditions necessary to turn on the SCR. The equations for the two collector currents are:

$$I_{C_1} = \alpha_1 I_{E_1} + I_{CBO_1} = \alpha_1 I_A + I_{CBO_1} \tag{3.1}$$

$$I_{C_2} = \alpha_2 I_{E_2} + I_{CBO_2} = \alpha_2 I_K + I_{CBO_2} \tag{3.2}$$

where I_{CBO_1} and I_{CBO_2} are the respective collector leakage currents of each transistor with open emitter.

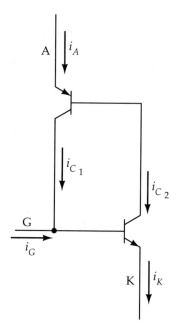

FIGURE 3.2

Two circuit relations that must be satisfied are given in Equations 3.3 and 3.4:

$$I_A = I_{C_1} + I_{C_2} \tag{3.3}$$

$$I_K = I_A + I_G. \tag{3.4}$$

Combining Equations 3.1 through 3.4 yields Equation 3.7 for I_A:

$$I_A = \alpha_1 I_A + I_{CBO_1} + \alpha_2 I_K + I_{CBO_2} \tag{3.5}$$

$$I_A = \alpha_1 I_A + I_{CBO_1} + \alpha_2 (I_A + I_G) + I_{CBO_2} \tag{3.6}$$

$$I_A = \frac{(\alpha_2)(I_G) + I_{CBO_1} + I_{CBO_2}}{1 - (\alpha_1 + \alpha_2)}. \tag{3.7}$$

With the SCR in the OFF state, leakage currents are small and the values of α_1 and α_2 are likewise small. Recombination in the transistor base regions thus is significant, and little collector current is produced by carriers injected into the base region. The denominator of the equation for I_A therefore is not much less than unity and the anode current is not large. The result is that the SCR remains in the OFF state.

To put the SCR into the conduction state, the device currents must be increased. If this happens, α_1 and α_2 increase; if their sum becomes unity, the

SCR turns on and remains latched in the ON state. Five methods can be used to increase the anode OFF-state current to a level that causes turn on:

(a) increase gate current, I_G

(b) increase device junction temperature, T_J

(c) increase anode to cathode voltage, V_{AK}

(d) increase the rate of change of anode to cathode voltage, dv_{AK}/dt

(e) inject energy into the junctions, principally by optical means.

The usual SCR is in an opaque package that is not affected by radiant energy. There are, however, low-level signal devices—light-activated SCRs (LASCRs)—but these are not considered here.

Of the other methods of turn on, only the first—using gate current—generally is used to intentionally turn on the device. The other three can be avoided by proper design. Proper cooling will limit the junction temperature so that turn on does not occur. Selection of the proper SCR ensures that rated anode-to-cathode voltage is not exceeded.

Limitation of dv_{AK}/dt generally is done by a snubber circuit. We will consider this in the section "Rapid Changes of SCR Voltage" (p. 67).

If the SCR current is increased by any of the described methods, then both α_1 and α_2 increase. As this process continues, the sum of α_1 and α_2 tends toward unity and the denominator of the equation for I_A becomes zero. I_A thus increases and the device turns on with an anode current that has no limit, at least by this model. Figure 3.3 shows how some of these effects relate to anode current.

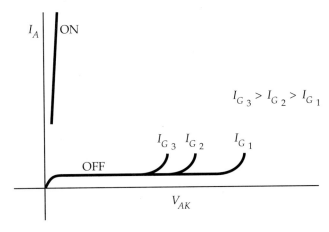

FIGURE 3.3

Of course, there must be a limit imposed by the external circuit. With an increase of anode current, the available voltage for V_{AK} is reduced, and ultimately the model no longer holds. With a very small value of V_{AK}, the two transistors of the model are in saturation, and the values of α_1 and α_2 are no longer useful in predicting the anode current.

ON-State Voltage

In the ON state, both transistors are in saturation, and all three junctions thus are forward-biased. This is similar to the case of saturation in a BJT wherein both junctions are forward-biased. There is a voltage, between anode and cathode, that is the combination of three forward-biased junctions, two of whose voltages are of opposite polarity. The net result is a voltage approximately equal to one junction voltage.

The value actually is larger than simply one junction voltage—for two reasons. The two forward-biased junctions of opposite polarity do not have equal voltage values and thus do not completely cancel each other. A second cause is the bulk semiconductor resistance of the P- or N-type material between terminals and junctions. Because of the above effects, the value of V_{AK} varies with anode current, and the value is best determined from the manufacturer's datasheets. Depending on anode current and temperature, V_{AK} values range from approximately 0.8 V to 3.0 V in the conducting state.

In modeling the SCR in the ON state for circuit calculations, the same models that were used for the PN-junction diode apply. In many cases, the very simple model of zero for V_{AK} is satisfactory because the device is used in circuits for which the source voltage is large when compared to V_{AK}.

Gate Current Requirements

To turn on the SCR, gate current is required. A very simple circuit that will do this is shown in Figure 3.4. If the load line of the gate circuit voltage source and resistance is superimposed on the nonlinear gate-cathode characteristic of the device, then conditions for turn on can be determined as seen in Figure 3.5.

The actual values of I_G and V_{GK} required to trigger the SCR vary widely and thus are unknown for an individual device. What is known is that the triggering conditions will not exceed some value stated on the datasheet. In Figure 3.5, the dashed rectangular area contains all possible triggering points. Curve 3 represents the typical nonlinear relation of gate current and voltage. Thus, if E_G and R_G produce a load line that falls outside the rectangle (as does Curve 1 in the figure), the SCR definitely will turn on, because the intersection of the load line and SCR characteristic occurs at a current greater than the turn-on gate current. If the load line crosses the rectangle (as does Curve 2), then the result is uncertain. Certain more sensitive devices will be gated on, but other

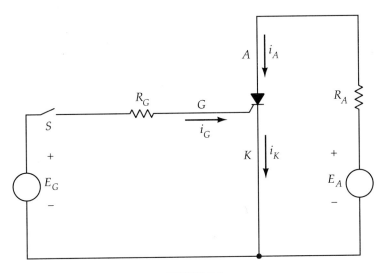

FIGURE 3.4

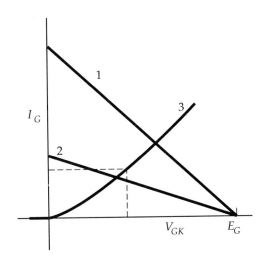

FIGURE 3.5

less sensitive devices will not have enough gate current to turn on. From a design point of view, Curve 2 is unacceptable; the design must ensure that all devices turn on when required.

The preceding analysis, however, is only partly sufficient. If the SCR is provided with only minimum current to cause turn on, anode current increases slowly, and turn-on losses may be increased unnecessarily. It is usual practice to provide a gate current that is two or more times larger than the minimum required value. A further increase in gate current is necessary if the device must operate at a low temperature, such as at $-40°$ C. This low temperature causes another $2:1$ increase in required gate current.

EXAMPLE 3.1

An SCR datasheet specifies a maximum gate current of 30 mA and a maximum V_{GK} of 2.5 V for turn on at 25° C. A 12-V source is available for turn on. Design a static trigger circuit that provides a gate current that is twice as large as necessary at $-40°$ C. The datasheet further specifies a $2:1$ increase in gate current requirements at $-40°$ C. Average gate power is limited to 0.5 W. V_{GK} at $-40°$ C is 1.2 V maximum at 120 mA.

Solution Because this is a design problem, there is no unique solution. At $-40°$ C, all possible turn-on points lie inside a rectangle (such as that in Figure 3.5). The upper right-hand corner of the rectangle has coordinates of 120 mA and 1.2 V if the $2:1$ overdrive is included. A load line such as in Curve 1—with an intercept at $E_G = 12$ and intersecting the corner of the rectangle—is one possible solution. The resistance value is found by the following equations:

$$v_{GK} = 12 - Ri_G$$

or

$$R = \frac{12 - v_{GK}}{i_G}$$

with

$$i_G = 0.120 \text{ A} \quad \text{and} \quad v_{GK} = 1.2 \text{ V}$$
$$R = 90 \text{ } \Omega.$$

Any value of R less than 90 Ω provides sufficient gate current for turn on. At the corner of the rectangle, gate power is determined to be

$$P_G = v_{GK}i_G$$
$$= (1.20)(0.120) = 0.144 \text{ W}.$$

This is less than the 0.5-W limit. A decreased value of R will increase this power, so R should not be made arbitrarily small. ∎

The previous discussion does not provide any model to describe the duration of gate current needed to cause SCR turn on. The turn-on process is not instantaneous and, depending on SCR size, a gate current lasting for an interval of perhaps 1 to 10 μs is required.

To provide the required gate current, the circuit shown in Figure 3.4 is only marginally useful. One frequently used arrangement charges a capacitor slowly over a period of time and then rapidly discharges the capacitor into the gate terminal of the SCR. This arrangement requires only relatively low power to charge the capacitor from some DC source, and yet a large power for a short time is available to reliably turn on the SCR. Several negative resistance devices are available with switching characteristics adaptable to this method.

The circuit shown in Figure 3.6 represents the basic means of slowly charging a capacitor and then rapidly releasing the stored energy to provide an SCR gate current suitable for SCR turn on. In the figure, a nonideal switch is modeled by an ideal switch in series with a resistor and a voltage source. The ideal switch is closed after the capacitor has been suitably charged. The capacitor then is discharged rapidly through the SCR's gate-cathode terminals. After a short interval, the switch is opened and the cycle repeats. It is assumed that, at some time during the capacitor-charging interval, the SCR is turned off and then is ready for turn on at the end of the next capacitor-charging interval.

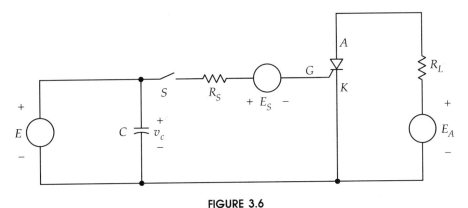

FIGURE 3.6

For analysis, the actual circuit shown in Figure 3.6 is replaced by the model in Figure 3.7. The gate-cathode terminal behavior of the SCR is modeled

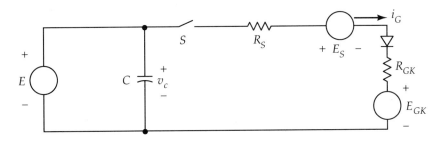

FIGURE 3.7

by an ideal diode in series with a resistor and a voltage source. These elements actually may be a Thévenin equivalent circuit if there is an additional resistor connected externally between the SCR's gate and cathode terminals.

After the capacitor has been charged to a suitable voltage, switch S is closed. The ideal switch S and elements R_S and E_S actually may represent a semiconductor switch. Such a switch may be a two-terminal device that is sensitive to voltage. The device switches into a conducting state when the voltage across the device terminals exceeds a certain value. The commercial two-terminal device commonly called a "DIAC" is such a voltage-sensitive switch.

The graph in Figure 3.8 shows the first quadrant that is characteristic of a typical DIAC element. Such devices usually are bidirectional and have a mirror-image characteristic in the third quadrant. The device can be modeled by using two states. In the first, the device is essentially an open circuit. The graph in Figure 3.8 is not to scale in the sense that the current at Point A is almost zero in comparison to current values that exist during conduction. Upon reaching a device voltage that corresponds to Point A, the device rapidly switches to operation along the second part of its characteristic along with the conduction of significant current. The slope of Line C of the characteristic is nearly vertical. Conduction continues as the capacitor is discharged until Point B is reached. At this point, further reduction in device current causes it to revert to the nonconducting state, and charging of the capacitor begins with the start of another cycle of operation. Typical dynamic operation is shown in the graphs of Figure 3.9.

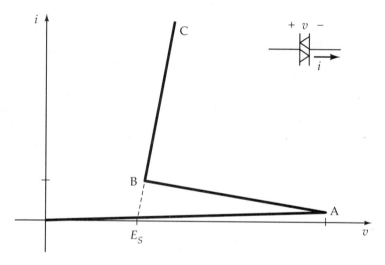

FIGURE 3.8

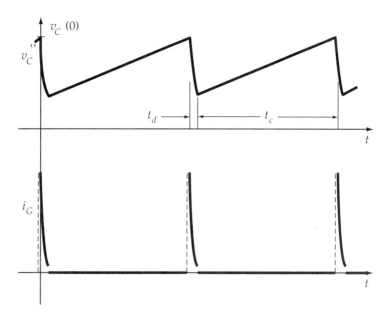

FIGURE 3.9

The conducting-state model for the DIAC element can be determined from the graph shown in Figure 3.8. The voltage source E_S is the intercept of the extension of the conducting characteristic with the voltage axis. The value of R_S is the reciprocal of the slope of the conducting portion of the characteristic.

After the switch is closed, linear circuit analysis can be used to determine gate current as a function of time. The element values used frequently are such that the contribution of the voltage source E may be neglected during this discharge interval with only a very small error. Of course, such an approximation is not absolutely necessary.

If the above approximation is made, the gate current can be determined from the remaining series circuit in Figure 3.7. A solution of this circuit for the transient current is given in Equations 3.8 and 3.9. In Equation 3.8, $V_C(0)$ is the capacitor voltage at the initiation of switch conduction.

$$i_G(t) = \left(\frac{v_C(0) - E_{GK} - E_S}{R_S + R_{GK}} \right)(e^{-t/\tau_d}) \tag{3.8}$$

$$\tau_d = (R_S + R_{GK})(C) \tag{3.9}$$

The semiconductor switch, which is modeled in Figure 3.7, ceases to conduct any significant current whenever the switch current decays to some value such as that represented by Point B. Substitution of this current value in Equation 3.8 yields the value of time t_d at which conduction ceases. A comparison of the gate current as function of time with the gate current–triggering require-ments determines whether the SCR has sufficient gate current for turn on. This comparison also allows us to assess the amount by which the minimum required gate current is exceeded.

At the end of the conduction interval, the capacitor is not fully discharged. The voltage remaining can be determined from a solution of the Kirchoff volt-age equation for the right-hand loop shown in Figure 3.7 for the instant just before switch opening. Equation 3.10 expresses the relation needed to determine this value of capacitor voltage:

$$v_C(t_d) = E_S + E_{GK} + [i_G(t_d)(R_S + R_{GK})]. \tag{3.10}$$

The next charging interval begins with the capacitor partly charged with a voltage as determined from the preceding operation. This charging interval is shorter than would be the case for an initial interval that started with the ca-pacitor fully discharged. Using the left-hand portion in Figure 3.7 with switch S open, the time to charge the capacitor to some specified voltage can be determined. Equation 3.11 expresses capacitor voltage as a function of time during the charging interval:

$$v_C(t) = E - [E - v_C(t_d)] e^{-t/\tau_c} \tag{3.11}$$

where

$$\tau_c = RC. \tag{3.12}$$

Substitution of $v_C(0)$ for $v_C(t)$ in Equation 3.11 enables the time for recharge to be determined in Equation 3.14. The time origin for Equation 3.13 is a new one that starts at the beginning of the recharge interval. At the time of switch turn on, the capacitor voltage is $v_C(0)$:

$$v_C(0) = E - [E - v_C(t_d)] e^{-t_c/\tau_c} \tag{3.13}$$

$$t_c = \tau_c \ln \left[\frac{E - v_C(t_d)}{E - v_C(0)} \right]. \tag{3.14}$$

Switch modeling and illustration of circuit calculations are given in Example 3.2. A design example is illustrated in Example 3.3.

EXAMPLE 3.2

In the circuit in Figure 3.10, the following data are known: $E = 100$ V, $R = 100$ kΩ, and $C = 0.1$ μF.

DIAC characteristic   Point A at 30 V
                        Point B at 12 V and 10 mA
                        Region C slope = 0.20 mho

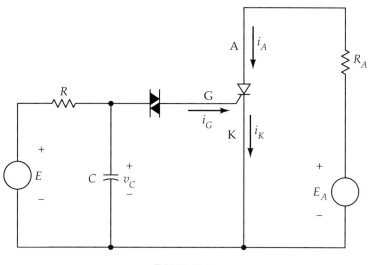

FIGURE 3.10

The SCR gate characteristic can be represented by

$$E_{GK} = 1.0 \text{ V in series with } R_{GK} = 20 \text{ } \Omega.$$

Find:

(a) DIAC conduction model
(b) capacitor peak voltage
(c) capacitor discharge current versus time
(d) time at which discharge ends
(e) capacitor voltage at end of discharge interval
(f) duration of recharge interval
(g) frequency at which gate pulses are produced.

Solution

(a) R_S = reciprocal of Region C slope = $\dfrac{1}{0.2}$ = 5 Ω

E_S = intercept of Region C slope extended to the voltage axis
$E_S = 12 - (0.01)(5) = 11.95$ V.

(b) Capacitor peak voltage = $E_A + E_{GK} = 30.0 + 1.0 = 31.0$ V.

(c) From Equations 3.8 and 3.9:

$$i_G(t) = \frac{(31.0 - 11.95 - 1.0)(e^{-t/\tau_d})}{5 + 20} = 0.722 \, e^{-t/\tau_d}$$

$$\tau_d = (5 + 20)(0.1) = 2.5 \ \mu s.$$

(d) The discharge ends when $i_G(t) = 0.01$:

$$0.01 = 0.722 \, e^{-t_d/2.5}$$

$$t_d = 10.7 \ \mu s.$$

(e) At the end of the discharge interval, the capacitor voltage can be found from the Kirchoff voltage relation of Equation 3.10:

$$v_C = (20 + 5)i_G(t) + 11.95 + 1.0$$

$$v_C = 13.2 \text{ V.}$$

(f) Recharging of the capacitor occurs from a starting value of 13.2 V and an ending value of 31 V. From Equations 3.13 and 3.14:

$$31 = 100 - (100 - 13.2)\, e^{-t_c/\tau_c}$$

$$\tau_c = (100,000)(0.1 \times 10^{-6}) = 0.01 \text{ s}$$

$$t_c = 0.002295 \text{ s.}$$

(g) The total period is the sum of the charge and discharge times:

$$T = 0.002295 + 0.0000107 = 0.002306 \text{ s}$$

$$\text{Frequency} = \frac{1}{T} = 433.7 \text{ Hz.} \qquad \blacksquare$$

EXAMPLE 3.3

Design a DIAC circuit to provide gate pulses to an SCR with a repetition frequency of 1000 Hz. The gate current must exceed 25 mA during an interval of 4 μs at each turn-on operation. The DIAC has the same characteristic as the one in Example 3.2. For the SCR, $E_{GK} = 1.2$ V and $R_{GK} = 35 \ \Omega$; $E = 80$ V.

Solution   The peak capacitor voltage is the sum of E_{GK} and the peak DIAC voltage, or 31.2 V. The gate current can be found by using Equation 3.8:

$$i_G(t) = \left(\frac{31.2 - 11.95 - 1.2}{5 + 35}\right) e^{-t/\tau_d}$$

$$= 0.451 \, e^{-t/\tau_d}.$$

For $t = 4 \ \mu s$, i_G must be 0.025 A. The time constant can be found to be $\tau_d = 1.383 \ \mu s$. The capacitor can be found from this time constant:

$$C = \frac{\tau_d}{R_{GK} + R_S} = \frac{1.383}{40} = 0.035 \ \mu F.$$

The DIAC continues to discharge the capacitor until the current reduces to 0.01 A. The total discharge time can be calculated by using Equation 3.8 again:

$$0.01 = 0.451 e^{-t_d/\tau_d}$$

$$t_d = 5.27 \ \mu s.$$

The remainder of the total period of 1000 μs is available for capacitor recharging. The lowest value of capacitor voltage can be found by using Equation 3.10 for the right side in Figure 3.7 at the end of the discharge interval:

$$v_C(t_d) = 11.95 + 1.2 + 0.01(5 + 35) = 13.55 \ \text{V}$$

$$t_c = T - t_d = 1000 - 5.3 = 994.7 \ \mu s.$$

Using Equation 3.14, the value of the charging time constant—and thus the value of R—can be determined:

$$994.7 = \tau_c \ln\left(\frac{100 - 13.55}{100 - 31.2}\right)$$

$$\tau_c = 4356 \ \mu s.$$

With a capacitor of 0.035 μF, this means that $R = 124.5 \ k\Omega$.   ∎

The SCR gate current from the capacitor discharge in the preceding examples is substantial, and even though it is not constant, it is large enough to provide SCR gate current for several microseconds. Thus, the gate current provided by this capacitor-discharge arrangement will be sufficient to turn on many SCRs. Some large devices may require larger gate current than in the above examples.

The data necessary for the above analysis usually are not available, but the analysis does serve to illustrate the discharge process. In most design situations, simplified methods are used. Because there is such a wide variation in the SCR gate current required for triggering, precise modeling of the SCR is not very useful. It is the designer's responsibility to obtain gate current that is several times larger than necessary and to get that current independent of the SCR gate-cathode model. It is, of course, necessary to impose some upper limit on gate current so that damage does not occur.

Basic Turnoff

The SCR recovers its blocking ability only by a circuit action that reduces the anode current to less than the holding current or by an attempt to cause reverse current in the anode lead. The two-transistor model in Figure 3.2 seems to predict turnoff capability by using negative gate current, but this does not happen with a standard SCR. The model does not represent the lateral geometry of the SCR, because SCR regions remote from the gate lead cannot be turned off by negative gate current. This effect results from the lateral bulk semiconductor resistance between the gate terminal and the most remote portion of the gate region's P-type material. This same resistance prevents the immediate turn on by gate current of these remote regions.

Turnoff by reduction of the anode current to less than the holding current is not the usual means. If this happens, it usually is inadvertent. A case can occur in which the anode current is variable and the anode current falls below the holding level. Design steps should be taken to prevent this. Turnoff by this method results in a recovery time that is quite long. Recovery time is defined here as the time during which forward voltage cannot be applied (at normal load-impedance value) without the SCR reverting to a conducting state.

In those circuits with alternating voltage sources, the reversal of source voltage provides an automatic turnoff of the SCR. The attempt to cause current reversal with subsequent reversal of V_{AK} causes a transient reverse anode current. This reverse current is necessary to transport the charges of the depletion zones of the reverse-biased junctions J_1 and J_3 that occur with reverse anode–cathode voltage. In low-frequency circuits at 60 Hz, this transient interval is so short in comparison to the source period that it has a negligible effect on circuit operation and generally is ignored. Thus, a first-order model treats the SCR ideally because there can be no reverse current, and the SCR turns off immediately upon any attempt to reverse the anode current.

In certain resonant converters, the SCR is turned off by an attempted anode current reversal because of the natural action of an LC-resonant circuit. Such circuits usually are quite underdamped and can be modeled approximately using the analysis techniques in Appendix A. For the circuit in Figure 3.11, the SCR is modeled by an ideal switch in the forward direction and by zero current in the reverse direction. Initial capacitor voltage is assumed to be zero and inductor resistance is neglected. The voltage and current for the various circuit elements are shown in Figure 3.12. At the end of the conduction interval, the SCR is reverse-biased by the combined source and capacitor voltages.

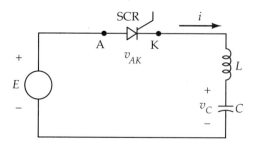

FIGURE 3.11

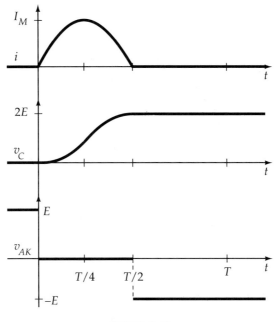

FIGURE 3.12

This is not a completely usable circuit in its present form, because there can be no further circuit function until the capacitor somehow is discharged. The circuit in Figure 3.11 can be incorporated as part of a series resonant inverter provided that a second switch element is used to discharge the capacitor.

One further aspect of such a commutation means by anode current reversal is illustrated by the circuit in Figure 3.13. At $t = 0$, the value of v_C is V_0. The SCR is turned on and natural circuit action causes the SCR to be turned off automatically. At the end of the conduction period, shown in Figure 3.14, the capacitor voltage has been reversed from its initial value. For the ideal models used in this analysis, there are no losses and the magnitude of the capacitor voltage is the same at the beginning and end of the conduction interval.

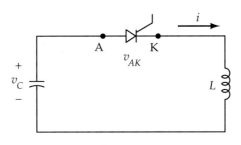

FIGURE 3.13

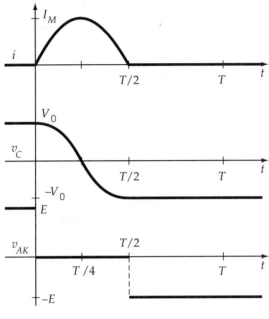

FIGURE 3.14

The reversal method illustrated here is useful in several of the commutation methods shown in the two following sections on turnoff and commutating capacitors.

In each of the circuits of this section, the SCR remains reverse-biased for an indefinite period. To remain in the blocking state upon subsequent forward voltage, the SCR must have been reverse-biased for a certain period. This period, generally identified as t_q, is specified on SCR datasheets and depends on the exact state of the SCR before and during turnoff. In repetitive on–off circuits, the specified value of t_q is important in determining that the SCR does not turn on until the desired time. The next two sections explore this in more detail.

EXAMPLE 3.4

In Figure 3.13, $v_C(0) = 200$ V, $L = 100$ μH, and $C = 5$ μF.

(a) What is the peak SCR current?

(b) How long does the SCR conduct?

Solution

(a) From Appendix A:

$$i = v_C(0)\left(\frac{C}{L}\right)^{0.5} \sin \omega t$$

where $\omega = (LC)^{-0.5} = 44{,}721 \text{ rad/s}$.

$$i = 200\left(\frac{5}{100}\right)^{0.5} \sin{(44721t)} = 44.7 \sin 44721t$$

Peak current is 44.7 A.

(b)
$$T = 2\pi(LC)^{0.5}$$
$$= 2\pi[(100 \times 10^{-6})(5 \times 10^{-6})]^{0.5} = 140 \times 10^{-6} \text{ s}.$$

The conduction period is $T/2$ or 70 μs. ∎

Turnoff: Commutating Capacitor

In those cases with DC sources, the SCR can be turned off by diverting the anode current to an alternate path for a sufficient time so that the SCR can recover its blocking ability. This time interval is important, because in SCR circuit design the alternate path is established only for a short interval, from perhaps 10 to 100 μs. A simple circuit is shown in Figure 3.15. The SCR current is diverted to the alternate path by closing switch S. This is not very practical for repetitive on–off operations because the SCR is not actually reverse-biased and turnoff is thus quite slow. A second arrangement as shown in Figure 3.16 provides reverse bias and is more useful.

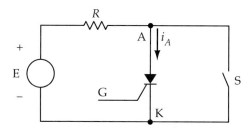

FIGURE 3.15

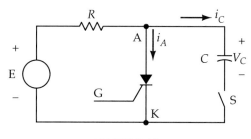

FIGURE 3.16

In Figure 3.16, the capacitor voltage has an initial negative value. Upon closure of switch S, the capacitor is in parallel with the SCR terminals in such an arrangement as to provide reverse v_{AK}. This causes the SCR to begin a recovery process and, if the duration of reverse bias is long enough, forward blocking ability will be recovered. A circuit analysis can be performed if the reverse anode current of the SCR is neglected. Upon switch closure, the circuit shown in Figure 3.17 results because i_A is identically zero thereafter. Upon performing a circuit analysis for Figure 3.16, the following equation for v_C results:

$$v_C = v_C(0)e^{-t/\tau} + E(1 - e^{-t/\tau}) \tag{3.15}$$

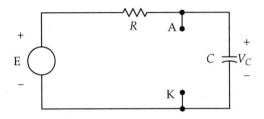

FIGURE 3.17

If the value of $v_C(0) = -E$, the graph in Figure 3.18 results. This initial value of capacitor voltage is selected because the circuit providing initial capacitor voltage frequently has the same magnitude as the source in Figure 3.17. The anode–cathode voltage, which is the same as v_C, changes exponentially from the initial negative value to become asymptotic to $+E$. The time interval of

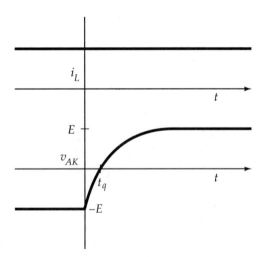

FIGURE 3.18

interest is that identified as t_q, during which the anode–cathode voltage is nega-tive. If this interval is long enough, then upon positive anode–cathode voltage, the SCR will have forward blocking ability and will not turn on again.

Values can be calculated for this time interval. At the time when $v_C = 0$ in Equation 3.15, the value of t_q is determined by the following equations:

$$0 = -Ee^{-t_q/\tau} + E(1 - e^{-t_q/\tau}) \tag{3.16}$$

$$t_q = 0.693\tau = 0.693RC. \tag{3.17}$$

EXAMPLE 3.5

In Figure 3.16, $E = 100$ V, $R = 5\ \Omega$, $C = 5\ \mu$F, and required $t_q = 15\ \mu$s. Is the SCR reverse-biased long enough for turnoff to occur?

Solution

$$\tau = RC = (5)(5 \times 10^{-6}) = 25\ \mu s$$

$$t_q = (0.693)(25) = 17.33\ \mu s.$$

Because the SCR is reverse-biased for longer than the required value of t_q, SCR turnoff occurs. ∎

It is more usual for the load to contain inductance rather than be entirely resistive. The charging of the capacitor changes in this case and a problem of overvoltage appears. To simplify the analysis and set a limit on circuit operation, the inductance in the load will be assumed large enough so that no appreciable change in load current occurs during the turnoff interval. Figure 3.19 is similar to Figure 3.16 except that the load contains inductance, and Figure 3.20 is similar to Figure 3.17 in the same manner. The capacitor current in Figure 3.20 remains constant during the short turnoff interval, and thus the capacitor voltage changes

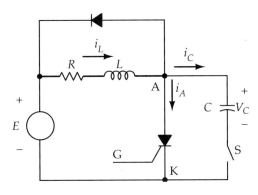

FIGURE 3.19

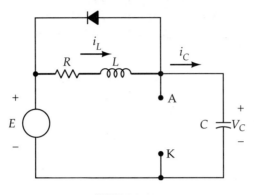

FIGURE 3.20

linearly with time as shown in Figure 3.21. The analysis is as follows:

$$\frac{dv_C}{dt} = \frac{i_C}{C} = \frac{I_L}{C} \tag{3.18}$$

where

$$I_L = \frac{E}{R} \tag{3.19}$$

and I_L is assumed constant for the short commutation interval;

$$v_C = -E + \left(\frac{I_L}{C}\right)t. \tag{3.20}$$

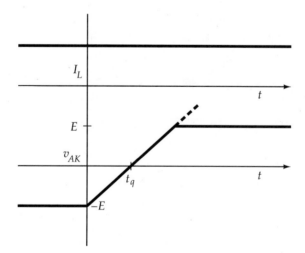

FIGURE 3.21

To find the time at which reverse bias ceases, set $v_C = 0$ in Equation 3.20:

$$0 = -E + \left(\frac{I_L}{C}\right)t_q \tag{3.21}$$

$$t_q = \frac{EC}{I_L} = RC. \tag{3.22}$$

The result is similar to the resistive load case except that the shape of the curve for v_C changes. For the previous numerical example, the time of SCR reverse bias is now 25 μs. The reason for the increase of time is that i_L remains constant during the turnoff interval. In the resistive case, the load current had an instantaneous doubling of value at the beginning of the turnoff. This meant the capacitor charged more rapidly in the resistive case.

But another problem now occurs. As the load current continues in the capacitor because of load inductance, the capacitor voltage continues to increase as shown by the dashed line in Figure 3.21. With large load inductance, the energy stored in the inductance is large and this energy is transferred to the capacitor. This could mean a damaging capacitor voltage. To limit this voltage, a diode known as a freewheeling diode (FWD), is placed in parallel with the load. When the capacitor voltage reaches the value $+E$, the diode then becomes forward-biased and load current is transferred to the diode. Further capacitor charging does not occur, and the capacitor voltage is clamped to the value $+E$. The orientation of the FWD in Figure 3.19 is such that normal load current is not affected.

A practical implementation for the circuit in Figure 3.20 is shown in Figure 3.22 for the case of an inductive load. A resistive load has the same

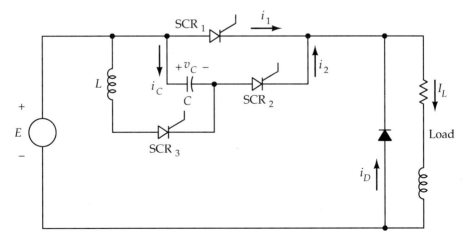

FIGURE 3.22

circuit except that the inductance is zero and the FWD plays no role in circuit operation. Most loads are inductive, however, so the following analysis for the inductive case generally is applicable.

The main switch is SCR_1, which is presently on and requires turnoff. This may be either a one-time operation or SCR_1 may be a switch that is repetitively turned on and off. At the time of turnoff, the capacitor is charged by previous circuit action with $v_C(0) = -E$. At $t = 0$, SCR_2 is turned on and SCR_1 is reverse-biased by this action. Reverse current in SCR_1 is neglected with a result that is identical to that shown in Figure 3.21 in turning off SCR_1. The behavior of the currents and voltages in the circuit in Figure 3.22 is shown in the graphs in Figure 3.23.

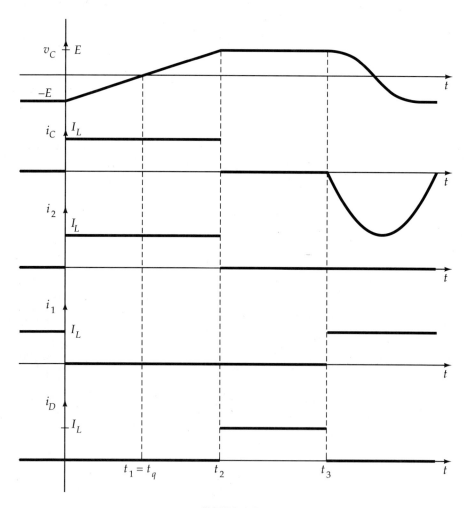

FIGURE 3.23

At time t_1, the anode-to-cathode voltage of SCR$_1$ becomes positive. This is the same as t_q in Figure 3.21. The interval of reverse bias must be long enough for SCR$_1$ to recover its blocking ability if turnoff is to be achieved.

When the FWD begins conduction at t_2, SCR$_2$ current goes to zero and SCR$_2$ begins to recover. If SCR$_2$ has not fully recovered its blocking ability by the next turn on of SCR$_1$, the action of turning on SCR$_1$ causes reverse voltage on SCR$_2$ from the voltage on the capacitor. At the same time that SCR$_1$ turns on, SCR$_3$ also can be turned on at t_3. The circuit consisting of L, C, and SCR$_3$ is a resonant circuit that acts to reverse the voltage on C. This voltage reversal is necessary so that the main SCR$_1$ can be turned off the next time. Proper circuit design requires that this reversal be accomplished before the next turnoff of SCR$_1$. The minimum on time of SCR$_1$ determines how long this reversal may require.

EXAMPLE 3.6

A circuit of the configuration shown in Figure 3.22 is used to supply a load current of 30 A to an inductive load from a 400-V DC source. The required value of t_q for SCR$_1$ is 30 μs. When SCR$_1$ is turned on the next time, it will be on for a minimum of 100 μs. Design the turnoff elements by determining the following:

(a) the capacitor C

(b) the inductor L

(c) the peak current in SCR$_3$.

Solution

(a) Because the circuit in Figure 3.22 and the graph in Figure 3.23 apply here, the value of C can be found using Equation 3.22:

$$C = \left(\frac{t_q I_L}{E}\right) = \frac{(30 \times 10^{-6})(30)}{400}$$

$$C = 2.25 \times 10^{-6} \text{ F.}$$

(b) The combination of L, C, and SCR$_3$ must reverse the voltage on C in 100 μs or less. Thus,

$$\frac{T}{2} = 100 \times 10^{-6} \text{ s}$$

$$T = 2\pi(LC)^{0.5} = 200 \times 10^{-6}$$

$$L = 450 \times 10^{-6} \text{ H.}$$

(c) Peak current in SCR_3 from Appendix A is given by

$$I_p = E\left(\frac{C}{L}\right)^{0.5}$$

$$I_p = 400\left(\frac{2.25 \times 10^{-6}}{450 \times 10^{-6}}\right)^{0.5}$$

$$I_p = 28.3 \text{ A}.$$

■

Turnoff: Commutating Capacitor with Inductor

The commutation method of the preceding section can be modified with the addition of an inductor as shown in Figure 3.24. This circuit reduces the rate at which the current increases in auxiliary SCR_2 by reason of the inductor in series with SCR_2. Therefore, there is a short delay before SCR_1 is reverse-biased by the commutation process. During this delay, the commutation capacitor discharges somewhat so that the initial reverse-bias voltage on the SCR is slightly less than the initial voltage on the commutating capacitor.

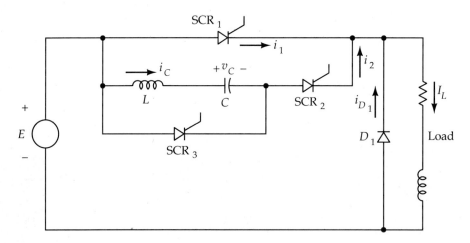

FIGURE 3.24

After the capacitor current reaches the value of the load current, the capacitor current remains constant at the load current value. The commutating inductor voltage is zero and the reverse voltage across SCR_1 equals the capacitor voltage. The relations are shown in the graphs in Figure 3.25.

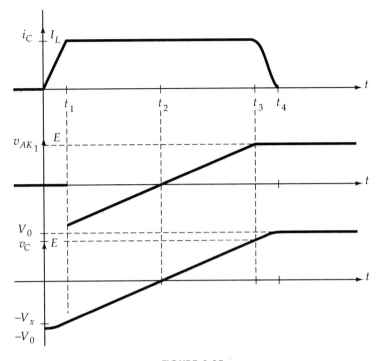

FIGURE 3.25

At time t_3 in this figure, the FWD begins conduction and i_C begins to decrease as determined by Equation 3.23:

$$i_C = I_L \cos \omega t. \qquad (3.23)$$

In Equation 3.23, ω is determined by the commutating circuit L and C. At the time that the capacitor current becomes zero at t_4, the capacitor voltage is greater than the circuit source voltage. This value can be calculated by equating stored energy in L and C at t_3 and t_4 with recognition of the energy supplied by the source. At $t = t_3$, the energy stored is given by Equation 3.24:

$$W_3 = 0.5LI_L^2 + 0.5CE^2. \qquad (3.24)$$

At $t = t_4$, the energy stored is given by Equation 3.25:

$$W_4 = 0.5CV_0^2. \qquad (3.25)$$

Energy supplied from the source is the product of the source voltage E and the charge represented by i_C between t_3 and t_4. In this interval, i_C is a sinusoid of

$T/4$ duration; this energy is given by Equation 3.26:

$$W_S = \frac{2}{\pi}(I_L)(t_4 - t_3)(E) = \frac{2}{\pi}EI_L\frac{T}{4} \tag{3.26}$$

$$W_4 = W_3 + W_S. \tag{3.27}$$

Combining Equations 3.24 through 3.26 with Equation 3.27 yields Equation 3.30:

$$0.5CV_0^2 = 0.5CE^2 + 0.5LI_L^2 + \left(\frac{2}{\pi}\right)EI_L\left(\frac{\pi}{2}\right)(LC)^{0.5} \tag{3.28}$$

$$V_0^2 = E^2 + \left(\frac{L}{C}\right)I_L^2 + 2EI_L\left(\frac{L}{C}\right)^{0.5} \tag{3.29}$$

$$\frac{V_0}{E} = 1 + \left(\frac{I_L}{E}\right)\left(\frac{L}{C}\right)^{0.5}. \tag{3.30}$$

The value of V_0 is greater than the value of E, and a suitable design must account for this in the voltage rating of the commutating capacitor, SCR_2, and SCR_3. SCR_3 is used to reverse the commutating capacitor voltage in preparation for the next turnoff operation.

E X A M P L E 3 . 7

In the circuit in Figure 3.24, $E = 250$ V, $V_0 = 375$ V, $I_L = 25$ A, $C = 3$ μF, and $L = 75$ μH. Find:

(a) reverse-bias time on SCR_1

(b) capacitor voltage at the end of the commutation period (t_4 in Figure 3.25).

Solution

(a) The initial value of v_C is -375 V.

$$I_P = 375\left(\frac{C}{L}\right)^{0.5} = 75 \text{ A.}$$

At $t = t_1$,

$$\theta = \sin^{-1}\left(\frac{25}{75}\right) = 0.340 \text{ rad}$$

$$V_X = -V_0\cos\theta = -353.6 \text{ V.}$$

From Equation 3.22:

$$t_q = \frac{(0 - V_X)(C)}{I_L} = \frac{(353.6)(3 \times 10^{-6})}{25} = 42.4 \times 10^{-6} \text{ s.}$$

(b) From Equation 3.30:

$$\frac{V_0}{E} = 1 + \left(\frac{25}{250}\right)\left(\frac{75 \times 10^{-6}}{3 \times 10^{-6}}\right)^{0.5}$$

$$\frac{V_0}{E} = 1.5$$

$$V_0 = (1.5)(250) = 375 \text{ V}.$$

This is the same magnitude as the starting value of v_C. Thus, when v_C is reversed by SCR_3, initial conditions are established for the next turnoff of SCR_1. ■

EXAMPLE 3.8

Design the commutating portion of a circuit such as that in Figure 3.24. Given values are $E = 400$ V, $I_L = 10$ A, and $t_q = 35$ μs. The value of the capacitor voltage is to be limited to 500 V.

(a) Find L and C values.

(b) If I_L is reduced to 5 A, how does the value of t_q change?

Solution

(a) From Equation 3.30:

$$\frac{V_0}{E} = \frac{500}{400} = 1 + \left[\left(\frac{I_L}{E}\right)\left(\frac{L}{C}\right)^{0.5}\right] = 1 + \left[\left(\frac{10}{400}\right)\left(\frac{L}{C}\right)^{0.5}\right]$$

$$\frac{L}{C} = 100$$

$$I_P = (V_0)\left(\frac{C}{L}\right)^{0.5} = 500\left(\frac{1}{100}\right)^{0.5} = 50 \text{ A}$$

$$\theta = \sin^{-1}\left(\frac{I_L}{I_P}\right) = \sin^{-1}\left(\frac{10}{50}\right) = 0.2014 \text{ rad}$$

$$V_X = -V_0 \cos\theta = -500[\cos(0.2014)] = -489.9 \text{ V}.$$

From Equation 3.22:

$$t_q = \frac{(0 - V_X)(C)}{I_L} = \frac{(489.9)(C)}{10} = 35 \times 10^{-6}$$

$$C = 0.714 \times 10^{-6} \text{ F}$$

$$L = 100 \, C = 71.4 \times 10^{-6} \text{ H}.$$

(b) If $I_L = 5$ A, V_0 changes to a new value;

$$\frac{V_0}{E} = 1 + \left[\left(\frac{I_L}{E} \right) \left(\frac{L}{C} \right)^{0.5} \right] = 1 + \left[\left(\frac{5}{400} \right) \left(\frac{71.4}{0.714} \right)^{0.5} \right] = 1.125$$

$$V_0 = 450 \text{ V}$$

$$I_P = (V_0) \left(\frac{C}{L} \right)^{0.5} = (450) \left(\frac{0.714}{71.4} \right)^{0.5} = 45 \text{ A}$$

$$\theta = \sin^{-1} \left(\frac{5}{45} \right) = 0.1113 \text{ rad}$$

$$V_X = -V_0 \cos \theta = (-450)(\cos 0.1113) = -447.2 \text{ V}$$

$$t_q = \frac{(0 - V_X)(C)}{I_L} = \frac{(447.2)(0.714 \times 10^{-6})}{5}$$

$$t_q = 63.86 \times 10^{-6} \text{ s.}$$

This value is much larger than the value obtained with I_L of 10 amperes.

∎

As shown by Example 3.8, the reverse-bias time of SCR_1 in Figure 3.24 depends on the load current. This reverse-bias time can be made nearly independent of load current by adding a diode as shown in Figure 3.26. The resulting

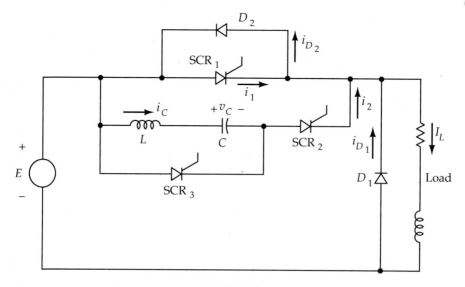

FIGURE 3.26

circuit operation causes a small reverse voltage across SCR_1 for a time that is almost independent of load.

During the commutation interval, either SCR_1 is conducting or D_2 is conducting until time t_3 in Figure 3.27. The LC-resonant circuit is designed so that the peak value of i_C exceeds I_L. During the time that i_C exceeds I_L, the part of i_C that is greater than I_L has a path through D_2 and for this interval SCR_1 is reverse-biased. The reverse-bias voltage is small, and the necessary value of t_q therefore is increased as compared to the case of a large reverse-bias voltage.

For the interval from $t = 0$ to $t = t_3$, the equation describing i_C is

$$i_C = V_0 \left(\frac{C}{L}\right)^{0.5} \sin \omega t = I_P \sin \omega t. \qquad (3.31)$$

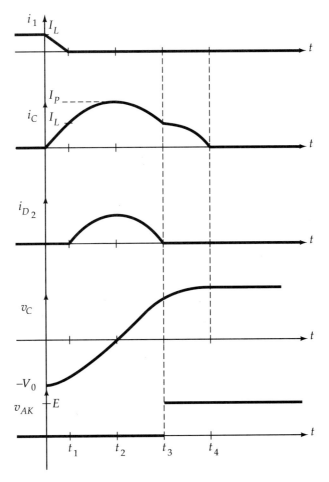

FIGURE 3.27

The reverse-bias time of SCR_1 is given by

$$t_q = t_3 - t_1 \qquad (3.32)$$

where

$$t_q = \left(\frac{\pi - 2\Theta_1}{2\pi}\right) T \qquad (3.33)$$

$$\Theta_1 = \omega t_1. \qquad (3.34)$$

The peak value of i_C is designed to be larger than the load current by a factor of 1.5 to 2.0. The next example will illustrate some of these relations.

At $t = t_3$ in Figures 3.26 and 3.27, conditions of total energy storage in L and C are the same as at $t = 0$ or at $t = t_1$. During the time from $t = 0$ to $t = t_3$, the voltage across the SCR terminals has been essentially zero, and no net energy has been transferred to or from L and C. During the time from t_3 to t_4, energy is added to the LC circuit from the voltage source. The final value of v_C therefore is greater than the beginning magnitude of V_0. This process causes the value of the capacitor voltage to increase with each commutation cycle unless steps are taken to recover the excess energy and return it to the voltage source. The inductor L can have a second magnetically coupled winding added to perform this function. The arrangement to recover this energy is not shown in Figure 3.26.

EXAMPLE 3.9

For a circuit like that in Figure 3.26, a value of 30 μs is required for SCR_1. $E = 300$ V and $V_0 = 450$ V.

(a) Design values for L and C with $I_L = 20$ A and with $I_P = 40$ A.

(b) For $I_L = 10$ A, find the new value of t_q.

Solution

(a)

$$I_P = 40 = V_0 \left(\frac{C}{L}\right)^{0.5} = 450 \left(\frac{C}{L}\right)^{0.5}$$

$$\frac{C}{L} = 7.90 \times 10^{-3}$$

$$\theta_1 = \sin^{-1}\left(\frac{I_L}{I_P}\right) = \sin^{-1} 0.5 = \frac{\pi}{6}$$

$$t_q = \left(\frac{\pi - 2\theta_1}{2\pi}\right) T = 30 \times 10^{-6}$$

$$T = 90.0 \times 10^{-6} = 2\pi(LC)^{0.5}$$

$$LC = 205.18 \times 10^{-12}.$$

Solving these two relations for L and C gives

$$L = 161.2 \times 10^{-6} \text{ H}$$

$$C = 1.273 \times 10^{-6} \text{ F}.$$

(b) Assuming V_0 remains unchanged at 450 V, the following relations hold:

$$\theta_1 = \sin^{-1}\left(\frac{I_L}{I_P}\right) = \sin^{-1}\left(\frac{10}{40}\right) = 0.2527 \text{ rad}$$

$$t_q = \left(\frac{\pi - 2\theta_1}{2\pi}\right)T = \left(\frac{\pi - (2)(0.2527)}{2\pi}\right)(90.0 \times 10^{-6})$$

$$t_q = 37.8 \times 10^{-6} \text{ s.} \qquad \blacksquare$$

In the graphs in Figure 3.27, the voltage of SCR_1 has an idealized discontinuity at $t = t_3$. In actual practice, however, this does not occur because of the finite recovery time of D_2 and the distributed junction capacitance of SCR_1. But the rate of increase of v_{AK} of SCR_1 still may be large enough to inadvertently turn on SCR_1. To prevent this, a snubber is required either in parallel with SCR_1 or in parallel with the FWD. This is discussed in the next section.

Rapid Changes of SCR Voltage

Two operating conditions may produce undesirable conditions for the SCR. Both can and should be prevented by proper design. The first is the dv_{AK}/dt effect cited earlier, which can cause unwanted SCR turn on and possible SCR or circuit damage. The second is the damage resulting from too large a value of di_A/dt. If the SCR anode current becomes too large immediately after turn on, the device may be damaged because the whole cross section of the SCR is not yet turned on. The anode current is crowded into a restricted region close to the gate, and the SCR may be destroyed.

The solution to the dv_{AK}/dt problem is to reduce the rate at which v_{AK} may change, usually with capacitors. Some commutation circuits automatically limit the rate of reapplication of forward voltage. Examples were shown in the circuits in Figures 3.16 and 3.19. There are commutation circuits, however, that do not so limit the reapplication of forward voltage, and none of the circuits prevents a sudden application of v_{AK} upon initial circuit energization. For these cases, a snubber is connected in parallel with the SCR. A snubber is basically a capacitor, but two elements are frequently added to the capacitor as shown in Figure 3.28. For increases in v_{AK}, the diode provides a path around the resistor, so the snubber is effectively the capacitor. If only the capacitor were used, then on subsequent SCR turn on, the capacitor would be rapidly discharged through the SCR. This probably would require too large an SCR current and also probably exceed the di_A/dt limit of the SCR. A resistor in series with the snubber

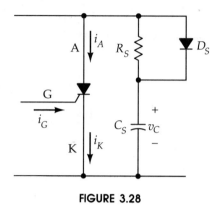

FIGURE 3.28

capacitor limits this current on SCR turn on. The diode prevents the resistor from reducing the effectiveness of the capacitor in performing its basic snubber function.

The basis of snubber design is to select a capacitor that limits the rate at which v_{AK} may change. This is done in conjunction with other existing circuit elements such as a load resistance or inductance. SCR datasheets contain information on the maximum rate at which v_{AK} may change without causing unwanted SCR turn on. The next example illustrates the basic process of snubber design.

E X A M P L E 3 . 1 0

In Figure 3.29, the SCR is able to withstand a dv_{AK}/dt value of 50 V/μs, and the initial discharge from the snubber capacitor must be limited to 3 A. The switch S may be closed to energize the circuit randomly on the sinusoid of v_S;

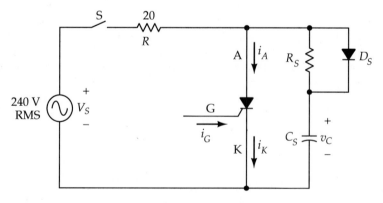

FIGURE 3.29

similarly in normal operation, the SCR may be gated on at any point on the voltage waveform of v_S. If $R_L = 20\ \Omega$, find:

(a) snubber capacitor value

(b) snubber resistor value.

Solution

(a) If v_S is at its peak value of 339.4 V at the closure of S, the circuit becomes as that shown in Figure 3.30. The diode is assumed to require zero voltage for forward current. The voltage v_C initially is zero and thus i_C can be found as

$$i_C(0) = \frac{339.4}{20} = 16.97\ \text{A}$$

$$\frac{dv_C}{dt} = \frac{i_C}{C} = \frac{16.97}{C}.$$

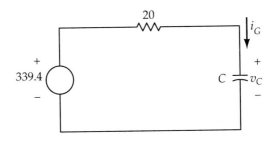

FIGURE 3.30

The problem requires that dv_C/dt be limited to 50×10^6 V/s:

$$50 \times 10^6 = \frac{16.97}{C}$$

$$C = 0.34 \times 10^{-6}\ \text{F}.$$

The time constant of the snubber capacitor and load resistor is 6.8 μs, so in 15–20 μs essentially full voltage is established on the SCR. This is a short enough time that the source voltage will not have changed appreciably from its peak value.

(b) If the SCR is turned on at peak source voltage, then the capacitor voltage is 339.4 V. To limit the snubber discharge current to 3 A requires a value of

$$R = \frac{339.4}{3} = 113.1\ \Omega. \qquad \blacksquare$$

Some commutating circuits are so arranged that, upon conduction of a load FWD, the forward voltage on the SCR suddenly is increased. The diagram in Figure 3.26 is representative of these circuits. At $t = t_3$ in Figure 3.27, i_C equals I_L, D_2 stops conducting, and forward voltage suddenly appears across SCR_1. In a nonideal case, this voltage is continuous although its rate of rise may still be so large as to cause SCR_1 to turn on. A snubber added in parallel with SCR_1 moderates this rate of rise and prevents an unwanted turn on. The following example illustrates some of the design principles involved.

EXAMPLE 3.11

In the circuit in Figure 3.26 and the graphs in Figure 3.27, the circuit conditions at $t = t_3$ are

$$I_L = 20 \text{ A} \qquad E = 200 \text{ V} \qquad v_C = 250 \text{ V}$$
$$i_C = 20 \text{ A} \qquad L = 70 \text{ } \mu\text{H} \qquad C_C = 3 \text{ } \mu\text{F}.$$

A snubber capacitor of 0.2 μF is added to prevent a rapid rise of v_{AK} as shown in Figure 3.31. Graphs of circuit operation are shown in Figure 3.32.

(a) Using a new time origin that corresponds to t_3 in Figure 3.27, find the time at which v_{AK} equals 200 V and at which the load FWD begins to conduct.

(b) Find the maximum rate at which v_{AK} changes during this interval.

Solution

(a) SCR_2 and D_2 are assumed to be ideal elements. The solution from Appendix A for the lossless LC circuit consisting of C_S, C_C, and L is

$$i_C = \left(\frac{C_C I_L}{C} \right) + \left(\frac{C_S I_L \cos \omega t}{C} \right) + v_C(0) \left(\frac{C}{L} \right)^{0.5} \sin \omega t$$

$$i_C = 18.75 + 1.25 \cos \omega t - 12.94 \sin \omega t$$

$$i_S = I_L - i_C = 1.25 - 1.25 \cos \omega t + 12.94 \sin \omega t$$

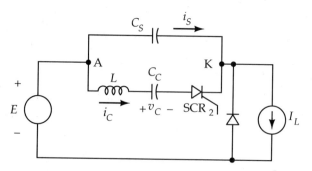

FIGURE 3.31

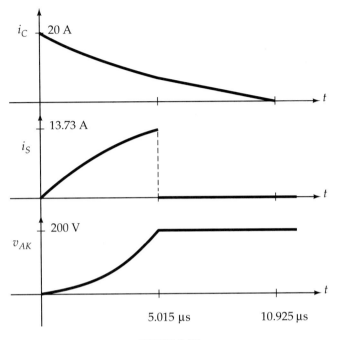

FIGURE 3.32

where

$$C = \left(\frac{C_S C_C}{C_S + C_C}\right) = 0.1875 \ \mu F$$

and

$$\omega = (LC)^{-0.5} = 276{,}000 \ \text{rad/s}.$$

$$v_{AK} = \left(\frac{1}{C_S}\right) \int_0^t i_S \, dt$$

$$v_{AK} = 6.25 \times 10^6 t - 22.64 \sin \omega t + 234.4(1 - \cos \omega t).$$

An iterative solution of this equation for $v_{AK} = 200$ V yields

$$t = 5.015 \ \mu s.$$

(b) The maximum rate at which v_{AK} changes occurs at the time when i_S is a maximum or else at the end of the interval for which $t = 5.015 \ \mu s$. From part (a),

$$i_S = 1.25 - 1.25 \cos \omega t + 12.94 \sin \omega t$$

$$i_S = 1.25 - 13.00 \cos (\omega t + 1.475).$$

The maximum occurs at

$$\cos(\omega t + 1.475) = -1$$

or at
$$t = 6.04 \ \mu s.$$

Because this value of t is greater than t in the interval, the maximum rate of change of v_{AK} occurs at $t = 5.015 \ \mu s$. At this time,

$$i_S = 13.74 \ \text{A}$$

$$\frac{dv_{AK}}{dt} = \frac{i_S}{C_S} = \frac{13.74}{0.2 \times 10^6}$$

$$= 68.68 \times 10^6 \ \text{V/s.} \qquad \blacksquare$$

Turn-On Limiting of Anode Current

At the time of SCR turn on, only the region near the gate lead conducts immediately. A certain time is required for the region of conduction to spread over the full SCR junction area. To prevent SCR damage, the anode current must not increase so rapidly that the current density exceeds some limiting value. This requirement means that the external circuit must be so arranged as to limit di_A/dt during the turn-on process.

This limiting can be accomplished by adding a small inductance in series with the SCR anode lead. In the circuit in Figure 3.33, the load essentially is resistive, and anode current may increase so rapidly as to cause damage at SCR turn on. A small-value inductor in series with the anode can eliminate the problem as shown in Example 3.12.

EXAMPLE 3.12

In Figure 3.33, a load of $R = 5 \ \Omega$ is controlled by an SCR with $V_S = 300$ V. What value of L should be used to limit the rate of rise of anode current to 5 A/μs?

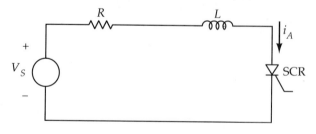

FIGURE 3.33

Solution   At turn on, $i_A = 0$, so the full source voltage appears across L. Therefore,

$$\frac{di_A}{dt} = \frac{V_S}{L} = 5 \times 10^6 \text{ A/s}$$

$$L = \frac{300}{5 \times 10^6} = 60 \times 10^{-6} \text{ H.} \qquad \blacksquare$$

If a snubber is used in parallel with the SCR, the inductor will not limit the initial anode current from discharging the snubber capacitor. The resistor portion of the snubber limits this current to a relatively small value that the SCR can handle without the need for limiting its rate of rise.

Other circuit configurations, in which the load is inductive and has a FWD in parallel with the load, cannot make use of the load inductance to limit the SCR current's rate of rise. Load current already exists in the load inductance. An added inductance in series with the SCR anode is required as shown in Figure 3.34. Without the added inductance of L_1, the SCR anode current ideally will equal the pre-existing load current in the FWD and L. Upon turnoff of the SCR, a snubber, a clamp circuit, or both will be necessary to reduce the current in L_1 to zero before the next turn on of the SCR.

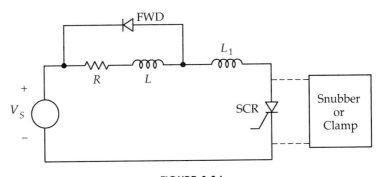

FIGURE 3.34

Latching Problem

A turn-on problem sometimes occurs with an inductive load when a short gate-current pulse is used for SCR turn on. The pulse is large enough and of sufficient duration to cause SCR turn on, but the circuit does not operate properly. The problem is that the SCR anode current has not reached the latching current level when the gate current pulse ends.

Latching current and holding current involve similar concepts: In either case, the anode current is not large enough for the SCR to remain on. Holding current is the anode current needed to maintain SCR conduction after the SCR is fully turned on. The anode current has been at a larger value and now is reduced slowly to the point where the SCR turns off. Latching current is the current value that must be reached during the turn-on process so that the SCR remains on when gate current is removed. At the latching point, the SCR is not fully turned on, junction equilibrium has not been obtained, and latching current thus is larger than holding current. The ratio of the two values is approximately 2:1. Datasheets do not typically give latching current, but they do give holding current values.

A snubber circuit provides a means to solve this problem. In the usual connection, the snubber capacitor discharge current decreases with time, while the load current increases with time. The anode current is the sum of these two currents, and it is possible to design the snubber so that the two changing component currents together provide a nearly constant anode current until the load current has reached the latching current level. The circuit is shown in Figure 3.35.

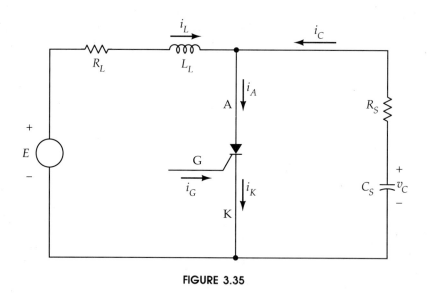

FIGURE 3.35

The snubber design suitable for this purpose may be different than the snubber design used for another purpose. The more effective of the two designs generally will be suitable for the other purpose.

In Figure 3.36, currents versus time for the low-current portion of the graph are shown. Because the final value of load current is much larger than shown on

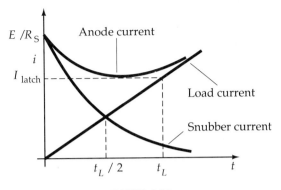

FIGURE 3.36

the graph, the portion shown is essentially linear with time, and its actual exponential character is not evident. A possible empirical design procedure follows. Determine the latching current for the SCR and the time after SCR turn on at which the load current equals the latching value; this is t_L in Figure 3.36. Select R_S of the snubber so that the initial capacitor discharge current is 1.5 times as large as the latching current. Select C_S by making the RC time constant of the snubber equal to $t_L/2$. The total anode current then will always be greater than the latching current even though the SCR gate pulse is of short duration.

The following equations may be written assuming that the initial value of capacitor voltage is E:

$$i_A = i_L + i_C \tag{3.35}$$

$$i_A = \left(\frac{E}{L}\right)t + \left(\frac{E}{R_S}\right)e^{-t/\tau} \tag{3.36}$$

$$\frac{di_A}{dt} = \left(\frac{E}{L}\right) - \left(\frac{E}{R_S\tau}\right)e^{-t/\tau}. \tag{3.37}$$

Setting the derivative to zero yields the time of minimum anode current. The added relations for τ and R_S are also used:

$$\tau = (I_{\text{latch}})\left(\frac{L}{2E}\right) \tag{3.38}$$

$$R_S = \frac{E}{1.5I_{\text{latch}}}. \tag{3.39}$$

Combining these relations gives t_{min}, at which the minimum value of i_A occurs:

$$t_{\text{min}} = \frac{(I_{\text{latch}})(L)(\ln 3)}{2E}. \tag{3.40}$$

If this result is substituted in Equation 3.36, the value of i_L is given by

$$i_A = 1.0493I_{latch}.$$ (3.41)

EXAMPLE 3.13

Using the circuit in Figure 3.35, determine whether latching occurs with a short SCR gate pulse. The snubber values are determined by the preceding equations; $E = 200$ V, $L_L = 0.5$ H, and $I_{latch} = 0.04$ A.

Solution

$$\frac{di_L}{dt} = \frac{200}{0.5} = 400 \text{ A/s}$$

$$t_L = \frac{I_{latch}}{di_L/dt} = \frac{(0.04)}{400} = 100 \text{ } \mu s$$

$$\frac{E}{R_S} = (1.5)(0.04) = 0.06 \text{ A}$$

$$R_S = \frac{200}{0.06} = 3,333 \text{ } \Omega$$

$$\tau = R_S C_S = \frac{t_L}{2} = 50 \text{ } \mu s$$

$$C_S = \frac{50 \times 10^{-6}}{3,333} = 0.015 \times 10^{-6} \text{ F}.$$

Using these values, the anode current is given by

$$i_A = 400t + 0.06 \, e^{-t/\tau} \qquad \text{where } \tau = 50 \text{ } \mu s.$$

A few computed values for i_A are:

t	i_A
0	0.0600
25	0.0464
50	0.0421
75	0.0434
100	0.0481
125	0.0549

It can be observed that the anode current is always greater than the latching value and that the minimum current is approximately 5% greater than the required latching current. ∎

3.2

OTHER THYRISTORS

Two other widely used thyristors are the TRIAC and the GTO. The TRIAC is a three-terminal bidirectional conducting thyristor. It has a gate terminal to provide turn-on control. The GTO is similar to an SCR but with the added feature that it is capable of being turned off with negative gate current.

TRIAC Basic Model

As stated, a TRIAC is a three terminal thyristor with bidirectional current capability and can be turned on in either direction by gate current either in or out of the gate terminal for either direction of main terminal current. The symbols shown in Figure 3.37 are commonly used for the TRIAC. In the figure, MT_1 refers to Main Terminal 1 and MT_2 refers to Main Terminal 2.

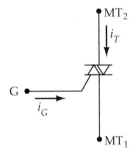

FIGURE 3.37

TRIAC turn on is possible in any of the four quadrants of operation as shown in Figure 3.38. Any of the four possible combinations of gate-current polarity together with sign of the voltage between MT_2 and MT_1 represents a possible turn-on condition. The sensitivity of turn on to gate current value is different for the four possible quadrants. Operation in Quadrant IV requires about four times as much gate current as in Quadrant I and this mode usually is avoided where possible. Quadrants II and III are only slightly less sensitive to turn on as compared to the sensitivity of Quadrant I. Certain phase-control circuits automatically reverse the direction of gate current as the AC source voltage reverses so that operation is always in Quadrants I or III.

The basic on-state model for the TRIAC is similar to that for the SCR. The voltage between MT_2 and MT_1 can either be set to zero as an approximation or set equal to some on-state voltage, typically around 1 V. The TRIAC differs from the SCR in that the voltage exists for either direction of current and, of course, changes polarity with reversal of main terminal current.

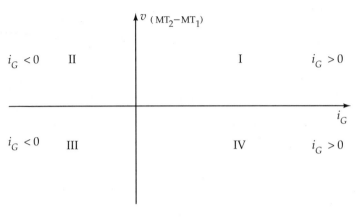

FIGURE 3.38

Triggering

The gate current needed for TRIAC turn on is specified on a device's datasheet. This value depends on temperature, voltage between main terminals, gate-current duration for pulse operation, and the quadrant being used. Values also vary among individual TRIAC devices. Worst-case values are given for specific operating conditions; good design requires that the gate drive circuit be capable of triggering a worst-case device. To minimize turn-on losses, the TRIAC should be turned on as rapidly as possible by means of a gate current that is several times the minimum required value. This generally means a gate-current pulse of large amplitude but short duration. This pulse can be conveniently provided in several ways, but two common ways are (1) to rapidly discharge a capacitor into the gate terminal and (2) to use a pulse transformer to couple such pulses into the gate terminal.

The TRIAC is most commonly used in a phase-control application with a 60-Hz source voltage. Phase control requires repetitively triggering the TRIAC at some fixed point after the zero crossings of the source voltage for both positive and negative half-cycles of operation. This means that the triggering circuit must be synchronized to the 60-Hz source voltage so that timing can begin from the zero crossings of the source voltage. To use as little average power as possible for triggering, a large current pulse should be provided to the gate circuit for a short time to initiate TRIAC conduction. Example 3.14 illustrates this point.

EXAMPLE 3.14

In the circuit in Figure 3.39(a), find values of R and C that cause the TRIAC to turn on $90°$ after the source voltage becomes zero in each half-cycle. The TRIAC can be turned on by a gate current that delivers a charge of 500 nC within 2 μs,

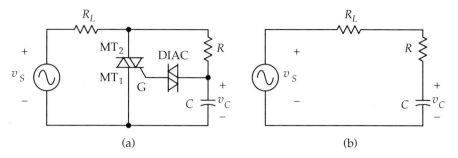

FIGURE 3.39

provided the gate current is not less than 50 mA during the interval. Data for the source voltage, the DIAC, and the TRIAC gate circuit are given below. E_G and R_G for the TRIAC gate circuit are similar to those for the SCR gate model shown in Figure 3.7. The difference here is that model polarity reverses on alternate half-cycles. E_A is the peak DIAC voltage.

$$E_S = 11.5 \text{ V} \qquad R_S = 15 \text{ }\Omega \qquad E_G = 1.0 \text{ V} \qquad R_G = 15 \text{ }\Omega$$

$$V_S = 120 \text{ V RMS} \qquad f = 60 \text{ Hz} \qquad R_L = 10 \text{ }\Omega \qquad E_A = 30 \text{ V.}$$

Solution   The capacitor discharge is from a peak voltage of 31 V ($E_A + E_G$) to the voltage that exists for $i_G = 50$ mA. This latter value of v_C is

$$v_C = E_S + E_G + i_G(R_S + R_G)$$
$$= 11.5 + 1.0 + 0.05(15 + 15) = 14 \text{ V.}$$

The charge removed from the capacitor for this voltage change allows us to determine the minimum capacitor value. This value is sufficient provided the gate current is at least 50 mA during the 2 μs following initiation of gate current:

$$(31 - 14)C = 500 \times 10^{-9}$$

$$C = 0.029 \text{ }\mu\text{F.}$$

The value of R is determined by the need to delay the increase in capacitor voltage to 31 V by 90° beyond the time when the source voltage is zero. The circuit in Figure 3.39(b) is the model to use for this calculation. We assume that during the TRIAC conduction in the previous half-cycle the capacitor voltage has decayed to zero. Thus, the starting point for the next half-cycle is with the capacitor voltage equal to zero. This may not be the case for some values of triggering delay angle.
   The equation for capacitor voltage in Figure 3.39(b) is as follows:

$$v_C = \left[\frac{V_m \omega RC}{1 + (\omega RC)^2} \right] e^{-t/\tau} + \frac{V_m}{1 + (\omega RC)^2} (\sin \omega t - \omega RC \cos \omega t)$$

where

$$v_C(0) = 0$$

$$v_S = 169.7 \sin \omega t$$

$$\omega = 120\pi$$

$$\tau = RC.$$

The value of R that sets v_C equal to 31 V at $\omega t = \pi/2$ can be determined from an iterative solution of the above relations:

$$\omega RC = 4.885.$$

The value of C already is known, so R can be found:

$$R = 447 \text{ k}\Omega.$$

The gate current at the end of the 2-μs interval must be determined:

$$i_G = \left[\frac{(31 - 11.5 - 1.0)}{(15 + 15)} \right] e^{-t/\tau} = 0.6167 \, e^{-t/\tau}$$

$$\tau = RC = (447000)(0.029 \times 10^{-6}) = 0.870 \; \mu s.$$

At $t = 2 \; \mu s$,

$$i_G = 0.6167 \, e^{-2/0.87} = 0.062 \text{ A}$$

$$v_C = 11.5 + 1.0 + (0.062)(15 + 15) = 14.36 \text{ V}.$$

The gate current at the end of this interval is adequate, but the capacitor has not quite discharged to the 14-V level used in determining the value of C. A slightly larger value of C can be used to meet the charge requirement.

If an additional margin of gate overdrive is desired, the value of C can be increased with a corresponding decrease in R. In comparison to the value of R, the value of R_L has been neglected in this analysis. ∎

Turnoff

TRIAC turnoff occurs automatically as the TRIAC current passes through zero value as the load current tries to reverse. For an inductive load, the zero current value occurs later than the source voltage zero value. At the time of a current zero, the TRIAC begins blocking in the opposite direction provided that suitable external conditions exist: First, the TRIAC is not retriggered to maintain conduction; second, the rate of voltage increase across the TRIAC terminals does not exceed the TRIAC capability. In the case of an inductive load, the voltage between the main terminals may increase rapidly at turnoff and the TRIAC may

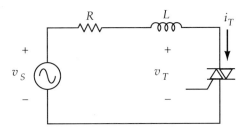

FIGURE 3.40

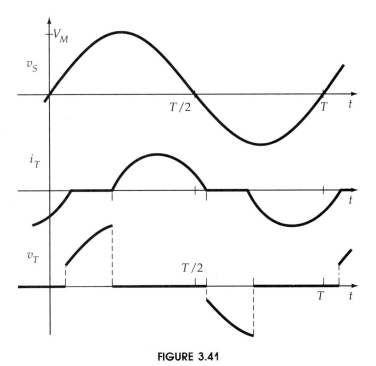

FIGURE 3.41

begin conduction in the opposite direction. This is illustrated by the circuit in Figure 3.40 and the graph in Figure 3.41.

Desired circuit operation is depicted in the graphs. At the time the current reaches and remains at zero, the voltage across the load becomes zero and the voltage across the TRIAC changes from a very small value to the present value of the source voltage. This forces a very large rate of change of main terminal voltage, which is limited only by stray circuit elements of capacitance and inductance.

The TRIAC probably will turn on again at this current zero without any gate current. This is undesirable, of course, and may even be hazardous. The rapid change in terminal voltage can be limited by the addition of a snubber circuit in parallel with the TRIAC. Because the TRIAC is a bidirectional element, the snubber also must be bidirectional and thus contains only a capacitor and resistor. The snubber elements in conjunction with the load impedance limit the rate at which the TRIAC terminal voltage may change. An example illustrates such a snubber design.

EXAMPLE 3.15

In a circuit such as that in Figure 3.40, the TRIAC is turned on repetitively $50°$ after the source voltage passes through zero on both half-cycles. The current goes to zero in each half-cycle when the source voltage has a magnitude of 201 V. Circuit waveforms are similar to those in Figure 3.41. The TRIAC has a parallel snubber circuit of R_S and C_S:

V_S is a 240-V RMS, 60-Hz sinusoid

$$R_L = 10 \ \Omega \qquad L_L = 0.02 \ H \qquad R_S = 800 \ \Omega \qquad C_S = 0.025 \ \mu F.$$

Find:

(a) the equation for voltage across the TRIAC each time the TRIAC current becomes zero

(b) maximum TRIAC voltage

(c) maximum rate at which TRIAC voltage changes.

Solution

(a) A representation of the problem is the RLC circuit in Figure 3.42(a). Solving the second-order system with the time origin being the time of TRIAC current zero gives the following result:

$$i = 0.252 \, e^{-\alpha t} \sin \omega t$$

$$v_C = 201 + e^{-\alpha t}(-201 \cos \omega t - 102.1 \sin \omega t)$$

$$v_X = 201 + e^{-\alpha t}(-201 \cos \omega t + 99.5 \sin \omega t)$$

where $\alpha = 20{,}250$ Np/s and $\omega = 39{,}874$ rad/s.

(b) By an iterative process, maximum TRIAC voltage can be found at $t = 55 \ \mu s$

$$v_X = 266 \ V.$$

(c) By differentiating the equation for v_X, we obtain

$$\frac{dv_X}{dt} = e^{-\alpha t}(8.04 \times 10^6 \cos \omega t + 6.00 \times 10^6 \sin \omega t)$$

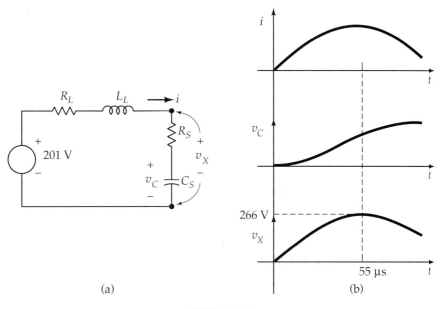

FIGURE 3.42

The maximum for this function occurs at

$$t = 0, \text{ and is } 8.1 \times 10^6 \text{ V/s.}$$

To prevent undesirable turn on at this time, this rate of change of TRIAC voltage must be within the device's capability. ∎

GTO Basic Model

The gate turnoff thyristor (GTO) is externally very similar to the SCR in most operating aspects, although it can turn off by means of a negative gate current. A considerable advantage is gained by the ability to turn off the GTO by gate control. Certain auxiliary circuits, including such components as commutation capacitors and thyristors, are no longer necessary. The amount of power needed to effect gate turnoff is much less than the power being controlled in the anode circuit. The major disadvantage of the GTO device is that appreciable negative gate current is required to achieve turnoff.

The same circuits that are used to model the forward characteristics of the diode or SCR are useful in the case of the GTO. If circuit voltages are very large, then zero anode-to-cathode voltage may be a good model for determining current. For better accuracy, a model using a voltage source in series with a resistor may be necessary. In general, the GTO thyristor has a higher ON-state voltage than the SCR, and this voltage also is more dependent upon anode current than is the SCR.

Turn On

The same circuits used for triggering the gate of an SCR also are useful for GTO turn on. The only notable difference would be in the required value of the gate current's rise time.

Turnoff

GTO turnoff usually is accomplished by a negative gate current of a few microseconds duration. The value of the gate current required to cause turnoff is relatively large. The turnoff gain, denoted by I_A/I_G, may be on the order of 5. For a GTO anode current of 100 A, the required gate current pulse would be -20 A maximum amplitude although for only a few microseconds. The gate circuit components needed to provide this large current operate in a low-voltage circuit. Thus, the cost of these components may be low compared to commutation capacitors that otherwise would be required in the anode circuit of an SCR.

The rate of negative gate current increase at turnoff must be controlled to achieve uniform turnoff of the GTO. An extremely rapid rise of negative gate current turns off the device near the gate and crowds remaining anode current into a restricted region. If this were to occur, the result would be increased localized heating and possible device failure. A suitable arrangement is shown in Figure 3.43(a), with typical graphs in Figure 3.43(b).

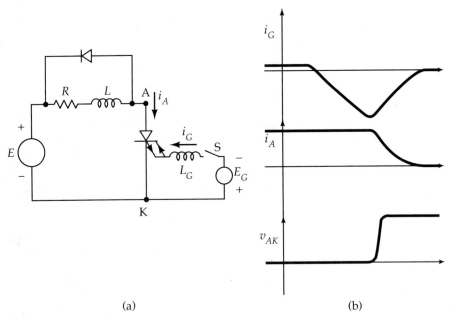

(a)   (b)

FIGURE 3.43

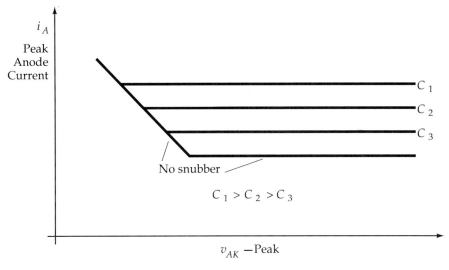

FIGURE 3.44

The forward voltage that can be blocked after turnoff is a function of both prior anode current and the snubber capacitor. A GTO can operate capably at a reduced current or voltage without any snubber circuit, but to achieve full device capability a snubber is required. The graph shown in Figure 3.44 reveals some of these relations.

EXAMPLE 3.16

The GTO in Figure 3.45 operates in a periodic on–off arrangement. The value of L is large enough that the load current essentially is constant at a value of 40 A.

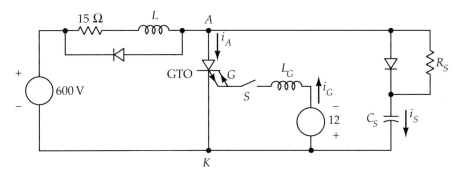

FIGURE 3.45

(a) For a turnoff gain of 6, find the required value of negative gate current.

(b) Find the value of L_G such that the gate current at turnoff changes at the rate of 2 A/μs. Neglect v_{GK}.

(c) Find the value of C_S that limits dv_{AK}/dt to 500 V/μs after turnoff.

(d) Find R_S to limit subsequent discharge current from C_S to 5 A.

(e) Find the power dissipated in R_S if the GTO is turned off 1000 times per second.

Solution

(a) At turnoff, $i_A = 40$ A, so the gate current can be determined:

$$i_G = -\left(\frac{i_A}{6}\right) = -\left(\frac{40}{6}\right) = -6.67 \text{ A.}$$

This is the minimum value of peak negative gate current.

(b) This calculation neglects the value of v_{GK}:

$$\frac{di_G}{dt} = \frac{-12}{L_G} = -2 \text{ A/}\mu\text{s}$$

$$L_G = 6 \text{ }\mu\text{H.}$$

(c) The i_S value is 40 A at turnoff assuming the GTO turns off in negligible time:

$$\frac{dv_{AK}}{dt} = 500 \times 10^6 = \frac{i_S}{C_S} = \frac{40}{C_S}$$

$$C_S = 0.08 \times 10^{-6} \text{ F.}$$

(d) The capacitor is charged to 600 V at the time the FWD begins conduction. Thus, on GTO turn on, C_S discharges through R_S:

$$i_A = \frac{600}{R_S} = 5 \text{ A} \qquad R_S = 120 \text{ }\Omega.$$

(e) Each time the GTO turns on, the energy stored in C_S is dissipated in R_S:

$$\text{Energy} = \tfrac{1}{2}C_S v_C^2 = \tfrac{1}{2}(0.08 \times 10^{-6})(600)^2$$
$$= 0.0144 \text{ J.}$$

The power that results depends on the number of such occurrences per second:

$$P_{\text{avg}} = (f)\left(\frac{\text{energy}}{\text{discharge}}\right) \qquad\blacksquare$$

$$P_{\text{avg}} = (1000)(0.0144) = 14.4 \text{ W.}$$

3.3

PROBLEMS

3.1 In the circuit in Figure 3.4, the SCR has values of maximum required $V_{GK} = 1.5$ V and $I_G = 200$ mA. $E_G = 20$ V and maximum average gate power is 1 W. Find a suitable value of R if an overdrive of $2:1$ is required.

3.2 Repeat Problem 3.1 with $V_{GK} = 1.3$ V and $I_G = 300$ mA. $E = 15$ V and maximum average gate power is 1.5 W.

3.3 Repeat Problem 3.1 using an SCR of type 2N4170. $E = 20$ V and $T_C = -40°$ C.

3.4 An SCR is used in the circuit shown in Figure 3.46. To reliably turn on the SCR, a total gate charge of 40 nC is required within 2 μs after S closes. The GK model to be used is 1.4 V in series with 8 Ω. The capacitor is charged to 15 V when S closes. Find values of R and C that are sufficient to turn on the SCR. The maximum permitted gate current is 100 mA.

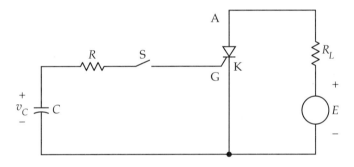

FIGURE 3.46

3.5 In an arrangement like that in Figure 3.10, $E = 70$ V, $R = 50$ kΩ, and $C = 0.25$ μF. The DIAC model is the same as in Example 3.2. The G–K model is 1.0 V in series with 25 Ω.

(a) Find the peak gate current.

(b) Find the charge delivered to the gate terminal within 3 μs after the beginning of DIAC conduction.

(c) Find the frequency of gate pulses.

3.6 An SCR is to be turned on using an arrangement like that in Figure 3.10. The DIAC model is the same as in Example 3.2. The SCR requires delivery of 50 nC to the gate terminal within 2.5 μs to cause turn on. The SCR model for the G–K circuit is 1.5 V in series with 20 Ω. $E = 80$ V. Design the remainder of the circuit to repetitively turn on the SCR at a rate of 500 Hz.

3.7   In a circuit like that in Figure 3.16, find the value of t_q for the following conditions:

$$E = 300 \text{ V}, \quad R = 20 \text{ } \Omega, \quad C = 2.0 \text{ } \mu\text{F}, \quad \text{and} \quad v_C(0) = -300 \text{ V}.$$

3.8   Repeat Problem 3.7 with $v_C(0) = -400$ V and $E = 300$ V.

3.9   In a circuit like that in Figure 3.19, find the value of t_q for the following conditions:

$$E = 300 \text{ V}, \quad R = 20 \text{ } \Omega, \quad C = 3.0 \text{ } \mu\text{F}, \quad \text{and} \quad v_C(0) = -300 \text{ V}.$$

The SCR has been on long enough that i_L is at its steady-state value.

3.10   In the circuit in Figure 3.11 with $E = 200$ V, select values of L and C to achieve a peak current of 20 A and a conduction interval of 300 μs.

3.11   In the circuit in Figure 3.22, the SCR is repetitively turned on and off;

$$E = 400 \text{ V and } I_L = 30 \text{ A}.$$

(a) Select a value of C to obtain t_q of 30 μs.

(b) Select a value for L such that the frequency of sign reversal for v_C is 5000 Hz.

3.12   In the circuit in Figure 3.24, $E = 400$ V and $I_L = 20$ A. With $L = 100 \text{ } \mu$F and $C = 3 \text{ } \mu$F, find the following quantities:

(a) the value of t_1 in Figure 3.25

(b) the interval that SCR_1 is reverse-biased

(c) the time required to reverse the voltage on C after $t = t_4$ in Figure 3.25

(d) the value of V_0.

3.13   In a circuit like that in Figure 3.24, $E = 200$ V and $I_L = 30$ A. The required value of t_q is 25 μs. Capacitor voltage may not exceed 275 V. Find appropriate values of L and C.

3.14   In Example 3.10, $C_S = 0.5 \text{ } \mu$F, $R = 10 \text{ } \Omega$, $R_S = 25 \text{ } \Omega$, and $V_S = 460$ V RMS.

(a) Find the maximum dv_{AK}/dt to which the SCR is subjected.

(b) Find the maximum value of the discharge current of C_S.

3.15   In the circuit in Figure 3.29, $V_S = 460$-V RMS and $R = 15 \text{ } \Omega$. The SCR is able to withstand voltage increasing at 40 V/μs. Initial discharge of C_S should be limited to 5 A at SCR turn on. Design the snubber circuit values if switch S may close at any point on the input voltage waveform.

3.16   Repeat Problem 3.15 for a 230-V source with $R = 10 \text{ } \Omega$. Other conditions remain the same.

3.17 In the circuit in Figure 3.33, $V_S = 400$ V and $R = 20\ \Omega$. Find a value of L to limit the SCR's di_A/dt to 10 A/μs.

3.18 An SCR requires anode current of 100 mA to latch into conduction. In the circuit in Figure 3.35, $R_L = 10\ \Omega$, $E = 400$ V, and $L_L = 0.1$ H. Design a snubber circuit that helps latching occur even if the gate current is a short-duration pulse.

3.19 In the circuit in Figure 3.39(a), $R_L = 20\ \Omega$ and V_S is a 480-V RMS sinusoid. DIAC characteristics are the same as in Example 3.2. Find values of R and C that cause a delay in TRIAC turn on of $40°$ in each half-cycle.

3.20 Repeat Problem 3.19 with $V_S = 240$-V RMS.

3.21 In Example 3.14, do not assume that the capacitor is completely discharged at the end of each half-cycle. Find the effect on the design values computed in Example 3.14.

3.22 In Figure 3.40, TRIAC current zero occurs $40°$ later than the voltage zero. The source is a 240-V RMS sinusoid. Find snubber circuit values such as those in Figure 3.42 to limit the rate of increase of TRIAC voltage to 10 V/μs. TRIAC turn on occurs at $\alpha = 80°$, and the snubber's initial discharge current should be limited to 3 A or less. $R_L = 20\ \Omega$ and $L_L = 0.045$ H.

3.23 Repeat Problem 3.22 with a 480-V source. The rate of increase of voltage is limited to 15 V/μs.

3.24 In a circuit like that in Figure 3.45, $E = 800$ V, $R = 25\ \Omega$, $L = 2.5$ mH, and $E_G = -10$ V.

 (a) For a turnoff gain of 5, find the required peak value of negative gate current.

 (b) Find a value for L to limit gate current change to -1.5 A/μs.

 (c) Find C_S to limit dv_{AK}/dt to 400 V/μs at turnoff.

 (d) Find R_S to limit peak snubber discharge current to 4 A.

 (e) Find the power dissipated in R_S if the GTO is turned off 2000 times per second.

CHAPTER · 4

Power
Transistor
Switches

In this chapter we will examine some of the characteristics of transistor semi-conductor devices. We will do this from the viewpoint of how well these devices approximate the ideal switch that will be used in many of the circuit analyses performed in later chapters. Further considerations concern the devices' limitations in current and voltage capability, as well as in temperature.

4.1
BIPOLAR JUNCTION TRANSISTOR

The bipolar junction transistor (BJT) in a power version is used widely as a switching device to provide characteristics that approach the ideal switch. In this section, transistor properties are considered, the transistor is compared to the ideal switch, and elementary models of the transistor are introduced. In contrast to other uses of the bipolar junction transistor, the normal active region is of little interest for switching purposes. Rather, the cutoff and saturation states are primary regions of operation; these two states correspond to the open and closed states of the ideal switch being approximated. The relatively high current gain of the linear region thus is usually not significant to the BJT's operation as a switch.

Unless otherwise stated, all devices are NPN and have the usual polarities for such devices. Figure 4.1 shows reference directions for the device currents. Voltages are specified using a double-subscript notation.

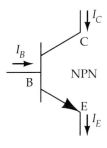

FIGURE 4.1

ON-State Model

In the conducting region, the transistor is in either the saturation state or a quasi-saturated state. The transition from the linear to the saturated state is not abrupt, so a region of quasi-saturation exists in which V_{CE} decreases with increasing base current and for which the concept of a current gain is not valid. In Figure 4.2, these regions are identified as 1—the saturated region, 2—the quasi-saturated region, and 3—the linear region.

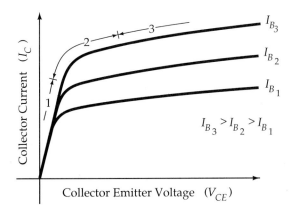

FIGURE 4.2

For a given value of collector current in the saturation region (large base current), the value of V_{CE} is almost independent of base current. In the quasi-saturation region, the value of V_{CE} is small and a function of the base current.

The distinction between these regions is not precise, and there is a gradual change from one condition to the other as base current is varied. Most transistor datasheets do not specifically identify these regions. Nevertheless, the distinction is important for the effect on transistor losses and on the transistor's switching speed. In the linear region, the value of V_{CE} varies widely and depends on the nature of the collector circuit.

For the purpose of operating in or near saturation, a forced gain is defined in Equation 4.1:

$$\text{Forced gain} = \beta_F = \frac{I_C}{I_B}. \tag{4.1}$$

In such saturation, the collector current is determined almost entirely by the external circuit and to only a very limited degree (if at all) by the base current. The lower the value of the forced gain, the deeper into the saturation region the transistor operates and to a lesser extent the lower the value of V_{CE} that is obtained. To achieve saturated operation, a relatively large base current is required, such that the forced current gain is normally small and in the range of 3 to 10. This may be surprising when one considers the current gain of 50 to 500 that may be obtained in small-signal transistors. Note also that large currents greater than 1 A are being considered. Transistor current gain normally decreases significantly with increased collector current in power transistors.

In the circuit in Figure 4.3, the transistor current can be found from the circuit equation:

$$I_C = \frac{V_{CC} - V_{CE}}{R}. \tag{4.2}$$

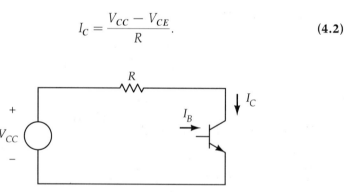

FIGURE 4.3

A first approximation for the collector current can be made by setting V_{CE} equal to zero. For a known value of base current, the value of β_F can be calculated. From the characteristics of the transistor, the actual value of V_{CE} can be determined. Perhaps the datasheet gives a value of 2.0 V for collector-to-emitter voltage for a particular combination of base and collector current at the transistor's case temperature. Thus, the original value of zero for V_{CE} is in error, and the actual value of collector current is somewhat smaller than first calculated. The approximation of an ideal switch causes little error (and one that is frequently accepted as reasonable) in the value of the collector current.

Suitable means must be provided to remove the heat developed in the device so that the junction temperature is safely limited. It is also unlikely that the device would continue to have a case temperature of $25°$ C (essentially room temperature) when operated at any significant level of power dissipation. Therefore, datasheet values at $25°$ C must be modified appropriately to account for the actual temperature at which the device operates.

In addition to power supplied in the collector region, another component of power is represented by the base current and base-to-emitter voltage. The total power to the transistor is given by Equation 4.3:

$$P = V_{CE}I_C + V_{BE}I_B. \tag{4.3}$$

EXAMPLE 4.1

A transistor with the characteristics shown in Figure 4.5 is used in the circuit in Figure 4.4 to provide current to a load resistor. Operating conditions are $R_L = 25 \ \Omega$ and $\beta_F = 5$. Find:

(a) I_C with $V_{CE} = 0$

(b) V_{CE} with this I_C

(c) new I_C

(d) V_{BE}

(e) total transistor power loss.

Solution

(a) The collector current may be found by noting that the transistor is in a state of saturation. Using Equation 4.2 gives

$$I_C = \frac{V_{CC} - V_{CE}}{R_L} = \frac{300 - 0}{25} = 12 \text{ A}$$

because $V_{CE} \sim 0$ as compared to 300 V.

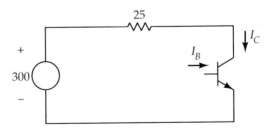

FIGURE 4.4

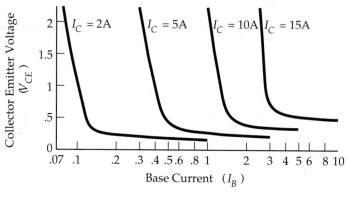

(a)

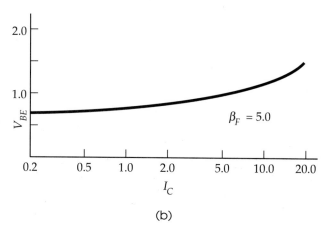

(b)

FIGURE 4.5

(b) $I_B = \dfrac{I_C}{\beta_F} = \dfrac{12}{5} = 2.4$ A.

From the graph in Figure 4.5(a), the value of V_{CE} is found to be approximately 0.5 V.

(c) $I_C = \dfrac{300 - 0.5}{25} = 11.98$ A.

(d) From the graph in Figure 4.5(b) at $I_C = 12$ A, the typical value of V_{BE} is 1.2 V.

(e) From Equation 4.3:

$$P = V_{CE}I_C + V_{BE}I_B$$
$$= (0.5)(12) + (1.2)(2.4) = 8.88 \text{ W}.$$

For the transistor to operate safely, the junction temperature must be held within safe limits by removing the heat developed in normal operation. ∎

Cutoff Model

In many situations, the OFF-state of a BJT is approximated by an open circuit. For situations when this is not sufficiently accurate, the actual collector current may be modeled by a cutoff current. This current is nearly independent of V_{CE} but is strongly dependent upon junction temperature. As an example, the 2N6547, which is rated for 400 V and 15 A, has maximum collector currents at cutoff as shown in Table 4.1. In the data in Table 4.1, V_{BE} is the voltage between base and emitter, R_{BE} is the resistance between base and emitter, I_{CEV} is the collector cutoff current with a specified value for V_{BE}, and I_{CER} is the collector cutoff current with a specified base-to-emitter resistance.

V_{CE}	*Temperature*	*Base Condition*	*Current*	*Value*
850	$25°\,C$	$V_{BE} = -1.5\text{ V}$	I_{CEV}	1.0 mA
850	$100°\,C$	$V_{BE} = -1.5\text{ V}$	I_{CEV}	4.0 mA
850	$100°\,C$	$R_{BE} = 50\ \Omega$	I_{CER}	5.0 mA

TABLE 4.1

Whether this transistor constitutes a sufficiently close approximation to the open circuit of an ideal switch can be answered only in the context of a specific design requirement. It is sufficient, however, to say that the bipolar junction transistor is widely used in power-control circuits as an approximation to an ideal switch.

Safe Operating Area

In addition to observing constraints such as temperature, other limits on the operating point are identified by a *safe operating area* (SOA). One of these is the forward-biased safe operating area (FBSOA). This requirement results from the need to avoid a condition known as "second breakdown," or a localized heating of the collector base junction resulting from a nonuniform distribution of the collector current over the transistor cross section. At large values of V_{CE}, this can be so severe as to cause immediate transistor failure. The manufacturer of high-voltage transistors (greater than approximately 40 V) publishes an FBSOA curve that establishes the devices' capabilities for successful operation. There are, in fact, several curves, depending upon the duration of the collector current at a given value of V_{CE}. A typical curve is shown in Figure 4.6.

Both A line sections in Figure 4.6 are current limits set by the bonding wires to the device. Lines B and C apply for continuous operation. The limit for B is set by power dissipation at the given case temperature; for C, the limit is set

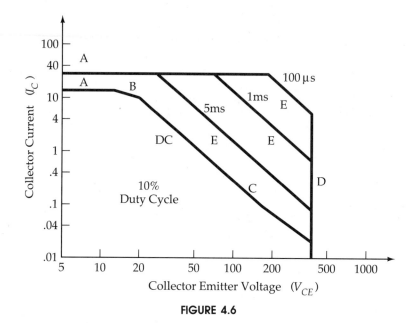

FIGURE 4.6

by second breakdown limitations. Line D is set by the device's V_{CE} limit. Lines labeled E are also second breakdown limits, applying for specified pulse conditions of pulse duration and duty cycle. An example of typical pulse conditions could be 100 μs on with a 10% duty cycle. Different curves apply for each pulse length.

These characteristics generally are not limiting for applications in which the transistor is used as a switch. When the transistor is turned on (generally within a few microseconds), the value of V_{CE} does not remain high long enough for a problem to develop. The only limit is one of maximum collector current, provided that maximum junction temperature is not exceeded.

Another constraint that does become important is the reverse-biased safe operating area (RBSOA). This limit applies during transistor turnoff when reverse bias is applied to the base emitter junction but before the collector current has decayed to zero. Two cases might be considered here. The first is a resistive load, but this almost never occurs in practice, and does not occur if stray wiring inductance is considered. The second case is a load consisting of inductance in series with a resistive element. The inductance tends to maintain collector current as the transistor tries to turnoff, thereby causing v_{CE} to be greater than would otherwise be the case without the inductive load. Generally, added circuit elements are necessary to safely turnoff this inductive load. In Figure 4.7, the collector-to-emitter voltage is clamped to the value of E_2 on turnoff of the transistor ($E_2 > E_1$). Idealized graphs of several quantities are shown in Figure 4.8. Actual nonidealized results with an expanded time scale are shown in Figure 4.9.

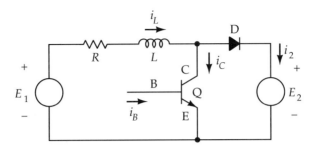

FIGURE 4.7

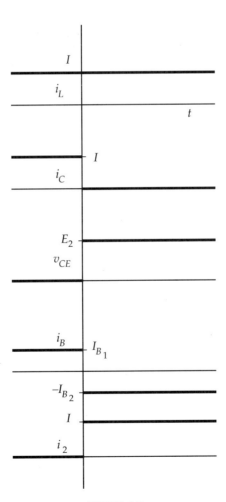

FIGURE 4.8

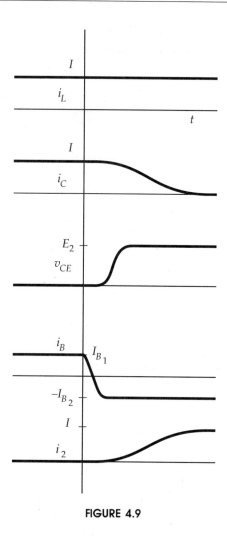

FIGURE 4.9

In Figure 4.9, note the time delay from $t = 0$ until the time at which i_C and v_{CE} begin to change. There also is a fall time in which the major part of the change of i_C occurs. The actual value of these times is a function of the transistor, especially the base drive circuit as we will discuss in the section on "Dynamic Base Current Requirements."

The RBSOA sets limits on collector current that may exist during the transistor's turnoff period. Curve 1 in Figure 4.10 shows such a limit. The designer must ensure that the transistor remains within those limits by adding auxiliary circuit elements as well as by appropriate base circuit design. As an example, the circuit in Figure 4.7 sets an upper limit on v_{CE} by the clamping action of the

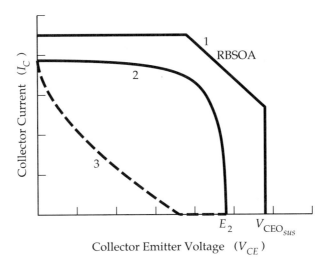

FIGURE 4.10

diode and the voltage source of value E_2. The graph of v_{CE} and i_C versus time in Figure 4.9 gives Curve 2 in Figure 4.10 for transistor turnoff. Without a snubber, the value of v_{CE} equals E_2 as soon as the collector current decreases to less than I as shown in Figure 4.9.

The addition of a snubber circuit as shown in Figure 4.11(a) allows the path on the RBSOA graph to be shifted to a position such as that of Curve 3 in Figure 4.10. The capacitor requires time to charge and thus holds v_{CE} to a relatively small value until the collector current has decreased to a low value. The collector current may be less than i_L because i_S exists to satisfy the Kirchoff current law at the collector node. The graphs in Figure 4.11(b) show the effect of the snubber in delaying the increase in v_{CE} until i_C is reduced in value. In this graph, the curve for v_{CE} is quadratic from $t = 0$ to $t = t_f$. After this, i_S is constant, and the graph of v_{CE} is linear until i_S becomes zero.

For subsequent transistor turn on, the snubber in Figure 4.11(a) must include a resistor and diode in addition to C_S. This is not shown in the figure.

EXAMPLE 4.2

In Figure 4.11, $E_1 = 200$ V, $E_2 = 350$ V, and $i_L = 20$ A at the instant of transistor turnoff. What C_S value should be used to limit v_{CE} to less than 100 V at the time i_C becomes 5 A? In effect, this puts a point on the graph in Figure 4.10 that causes less turnoff stress than permitted by the manufacturer's RBSOA. It is assumed that the collector current decay is linear with a fall time, t_f, of 2 μs.

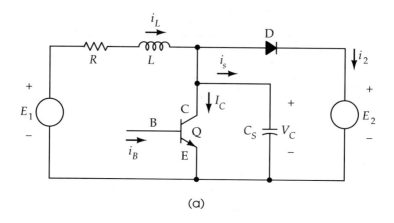

(a)

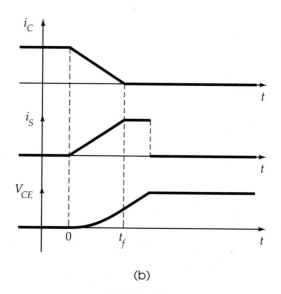

(b)

FIGURE 4.11

Solution   In the interval of collector current fall time, the collector current can be expressed as

$$i_C = I_{CM}\left(1 - \frac{t}{t_f}\right),$$

where I_{CM} is maximum collector current of 20 A and t_f is the collector current fall time. During this time, the snubber capacitor current changes as in the following relation:

$$i_S = \frac{I_{CM}t}{t_f}.$$

Solve the above equations to find the following result for $i_C = 5$ A:

$$t = 1.5 \ \mu s$$

$$i_S(t) = 20 - i_C(t) = 20 - 5 = 15 \ A$$

$$q_S = \tfrac{1}{2}(15)(1.5 \times 10^{-6}) = 11.25 \times 10^{-6} \ C$$

where q_S is the charge on the snubber capacitor at $t = 1.5 \ \mu s$;

$$q_S = v_C C_S$$

$$C_S = \frac{11.25 \times 10^{-6}}{100} = 0.1125 \times 10^{-6} \ F. \qquad \blacksquare$$

Dynamic Base Current Requirements

The idealized base current for a BJT is shown in Figure 4.12(a). A positive base current of value I_{B_1} is required to turn on the transistor and achieve the desired level of saturation. To turnoff the transistor at a later time, it is usual to reverse the base current for a short interval. The reverse current of magnitude I_{B_2} causes the transistor to turnoff more rapidly than it would by simply reducing the base current to zero. Collector current continues for a short interval after reversal of base current until cutoff-equilibrium conditions can be established.

A large I_{B_1} value reduces the time required for the collector current to change from its initial value to its final value. The saturated value of the collector-to-emitter voltage also decreases, as we discussed in an earlier section. Thus, the device operates in a more saturated condition with reduced power loss. The undesirable effect is that the transistor requires a longer time to turnoff. In particular, the storage time increases. *Storage time* is defined as the interval after reversal of base current, during which the collector current remains essentially constant. A design conflict exists because a large value of I_{B_1} normally is desirable except for the adverse effect on storage time. A large I_{B_2} value reduces storage time, but only at the cost of the increased power required for the base drive circuit.

As long as the transistor is conducting collector current, the base-to-emitter junction can be modeled approximately by a voltage source of about 1 V. Thus, both normal and reverse base currents are determined largely by the external base circuit. The ratio I_{B_2}/I_{B_1} generally is selected in the range from 0.5 to 2.0. Figure 4.12(b) shows a more realistic graph of base current versus time, with nonzero rise times as shown.

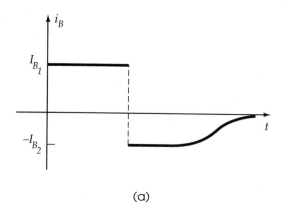

(a)

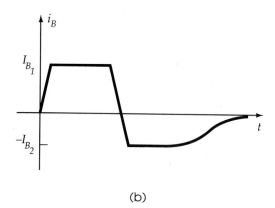

(b)

FIGURE 4.12   (a) Idealized Base Current and (b) Actual Base Current

Resistive Load Circuit   Figure 4.13 shows a transistor switching circuit with a resistive load. The base circuit elements are selected to achieve the desired values of I_{B_1} and I_{B_2}. In practice, the switch is a semiconductor device and should open and close in a shorter time than the switching time of the transistor being driven. Generally, this is not a problem because the main transistor is a power device and probably is slower in operation than the element represented by the switch. Voltage source V_X provides negative base current during the turnoff interval, and diode D_Y limits the base-to-emitter reverse voltage to an acceptable value. Diode D_Y in the test circuit is a Schottky barrier type and limits the reverse base-to-emitter voltage to a small value.

Circuit modeling of the transistor is relatively simple during the switching interval. During transistor turn on, the value of v_{BE} may be considered as fixed at a value found from the transistor's datasheet. This value probably will be on

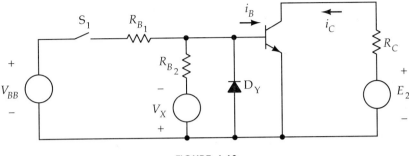

FIGURE 4.13

the order of 1 V for a power transistor. In comparison to the relatively large value of V_{BB}, the exact value of v_{BE} is not especially important.

During the turnoff process, two time intervals must be considered. The first is the storage time during which the transistor is still in saturation. For this interval, the collector-to-emitter voltage remains essentially zero, the base-to-emitter voltage remains at about the same value as during the ON state, and the reverse base current is determined by the external circuit. The reverse base current is needed to remove charge from the base region and to bring the transistor out of saturation. The larger the value of I_{B_2}, the more rapidly the base charge can be removed and thus the turnoff process completed.

After the storage interval ends, the collector current begins decreasing to zero. At the same time, the negative base current also decreases in magnitude to the essentially zero value corresponding to cutoff. This interval, known as the *fall time*, completes the transistor turnoff process.

The effect that may be observed in a circuit such as that in Figure 4.13 is the effect of changes in I_{B_1} and I_{B_2}. An increase in I_{B_1} causes a decrease in the transistor turn-on time and an increase in the storage time. An increase in I_{B_2} causes a decrease in storage time and to a lesser extent a decrease in the collector current fall time.

Obviously, there are design conflicts in the base circuit design. It is desirable to have a large value of I_{B_1} to reduce turn-on time and to have the saturated value of v_{CE} as low as possible. But a large I_{B_1} value may produce an unacceptably long storage time. The effect of I_{B_1} on storage time can be reduced by increasing the value of I_{B_2}, but economic constraints limit this solution. In addition, a larger I_{B_2} value means larger power dissipation and larger ratings for the components that form the turnoff circuit.

The photographs in Figures 4.14, 4.15, and 4.16 show the effects of various I_{B_1} and I_{B_2} values. A decrease in the value of β_F reduces the transistor turn-on time and causes an increase in the storage time for a given value of I_{B_2}. Note the especially long storage time for the case of $V_X = 0$ in Figure 4.16. This corresponds to one commonly used circuit in which the only provision for I_{B_2} is a resistor from base to emitter.

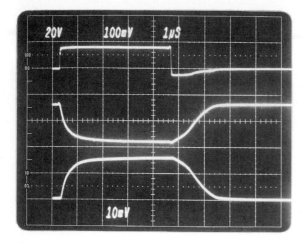

Upper Trace (i_B):
$I_{B_1} = 0.2$ A $I_{B_2} = 0.05$ A

Middle Trace (v_{CE}):
20 V/Division

Lower Trace (i_C):
2 A/Division

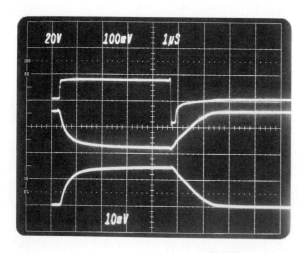

Upper Trace (i_B):
$I_{B_1} = 0.2$ A $I_{B_2} = 0.2$ A

Middle Trace (v_{CE}):
20 V/Division

Lower Trace (i_C):
2 A/Division

FIGURE 4.14

The graphs in Figures 4.17 and 4.18 show the manner in which turn-on and turnoff times vary with I_{B_1} and I_{B_2}. These graphs are obtained for the circuit in Figure 4.13 by using photographs similar to those in Figures 4.14 and 4.15. The circuit in Figure 4.13 was chosen for simplicity and does not necessarily represent an optimum configuration.

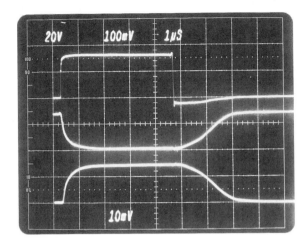

Upper Trace (i_B):
$I_{B_1} = 0.4$ A $I_{B_2} = 0.05$ A

Middle Trace (v_{CE}):
20 V/Division

Lower Trace (i_C):
2 A/Division

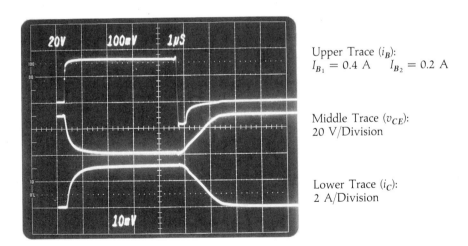

Upper Trace (i_B):
$I_{B_1} = 0.4$ A $I_{B_2} = 0.2$ A

Middle Trace (v_{CE}):
20 V/Division

Lower Trace (i_C):
2 A/Division

FIGURE 4.15

A "Speed-Up" Capacitor The circuit in Figure 4.13 can be varied by using a "speed-up" capacitor as shown in Figure 4.19. Upon closure of switch S, with capacitor C_B initially discharged, the base current's value is determined by the parallel combination of R_{B_3} and R_{B_4}. The capacitor begins charging and, after a time determined by element values, the base current is determined by

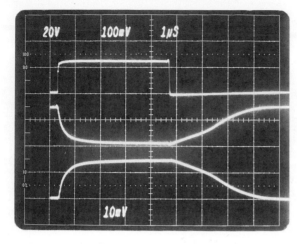

Upper Trace (i_B):
$I_{B_1} = 0.3$ A
$R_{B_2} = 56\ \Omega$ $V_X = 0$

Middle Trace (v_{CE}):
20 V/Division

Lower Trace (i_C):
2 A/Division

FIGURE 4.16

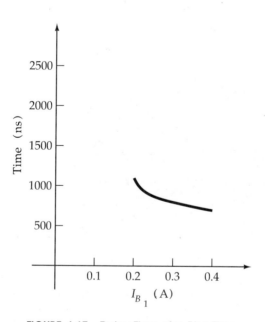

FIGURE 4.17 Delay Time plus Rise Time

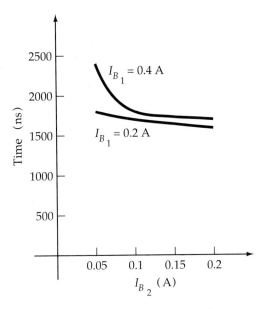

FIGURE 4.18 Storage Time plus Fall Time

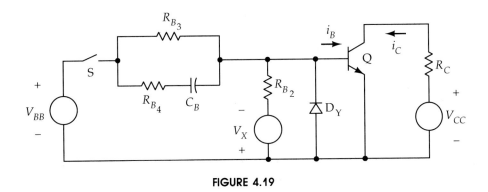

FIGURE 4.19

the value of R_{B_3}. This smaller base current value can be designed so that the transistor is not too deeply into saturation at the end of its conduction interval and at turnoff the storage time is relatively short. Thus, by design, a rapid turn on of the transistor can be obtained without the penalty of an overly long storage time. There is, however, a small penalty in that the collector-to-emitter voltage at the reduced saturation is somewhat larger than in a more saturated state. The conduction losses thereby are increased somewhat.

Oscilloscope photographs corresponding to the circuit in Figure 4.19 are shown in Figures 4.20 and 4.21 for conditions without and with the speed-up capacitor. The elements in the circuit are such that I_{B_1} and I_{B_2} at turnoff are 0.2 A each. For the case with the speed-up capacitor, I_{B_1} essentially is 0.4 A during the turn-on interval. The value of C_B is such that the base current does not decay much during the interval of collector current rise time, and yet the base current has decayed to essentially steady-state value by the time the transistor is to be turned off. Design requirements can be conflicting, and such a capacitor value may not exist.

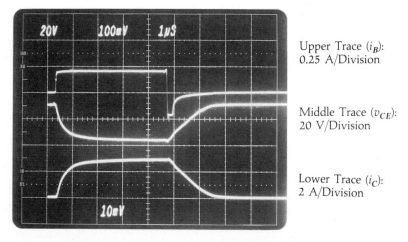

Upper Trace (i_B):
0.25 A/Division

Middle Trace (v_{CE}):
20 V/Division

Lower Trace (i_C):
2 A/Division

FIGURE 4.20 Oscillogram without Speed-up Capacitor

The photograph in Figure 4.21 shows a rise time of 700 ns. This is the same time interval as obtained from the graph in Figure 4.17 for I_{B_1} of 0.4 A. In both Figures 4.20 and 4.21, just before transistor turnoff, I_{B_1} is 0.2 A and the resulting storage plus fall time in both cases is 1600 ns. There has been no significant effect on the speed of transistor turnoff. If the base current had been maintained at 0.4 A during the conduction interval, the transistor turnoff time would have been longer.

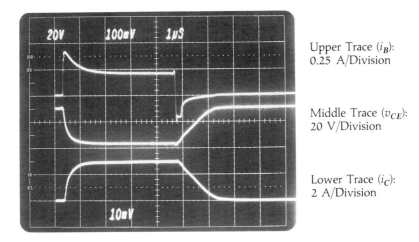

FIGURE 4.21 Oscillogram with Speed-up Capacitor

Upper Trace (i_B):
0.25 A/Division

Middle Trace (v_{CE}):
20 V/Division

Lower Trace (i_C):
2 A/Division

EXAMPLE 4.3

In the circuit in Figure 4.19, the transistor requires a β_F of 8 to achieve the desired collector current rise time of 0.8 μs. The transistor remains in saturation for a β_F of 20. Total transistor on time is 20 μs, after which turnoff is initiated. For a collector current of 5 A and with $I_{B_2}/I_{B_1} = 1$ at turnoff, design a possible circuit for this application. Positive and negative 10-V sources are available.

Solution   At the beginning of turn on,

$$I_{B_1} = \frac{I_C}{\beta_F} = \frac{5}{8} = 0.625 \text{ A.}$$

At the end of the turn-on interval,

$$I_{B_1} = I_{B_2} = \frac{I_C}{\beta_F} = \frac{5}{20} = 0.25 \text{ A.}$$

Using the circuit in Figure 4.22, the following design equations can be written assuming $v_{BE} = 0.8$ V. This figure is drawn for the initial instant with capacitor voltage equal to zero:

$$i_X = I_{B_2} = 0.25 \text{ A}$$

$$R_{B_2}i_X - 10 - 0.8 = 0$$

$$R_{B_2} = 43.2 \ \Omega.$$

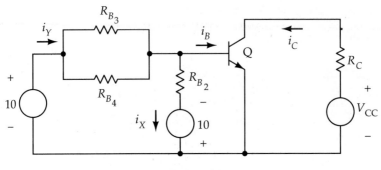

FIGURE 4.22

A voltage equation for the circuit in Figure 4.22 allows a solution for the parallel combination of R_{B_3} and R_{B_4}:

$$10 - (R_{B_3} \| R_{B_4})i_Y - 0.8 = 0$$

$$i_Y = i_X + I_{B_1} = 0.25 + 0.625 = 0.875 \text{ A}$$

$$(R_{B_3} \| R_{B_4}) = 10.51 \text{ } \Omega.$$

At the end of the turn-on interval, the current in R_{B_4} has decayed to essentially zero. The circuit shown in Figure 4.23 applies:

$$10 - R_{B_3}i_Y - 0.8 = 0$$

$$i_Y = i_X + I_{B_1} = 0.25 + 0.25 = 0.50 \text{ A}$$

$$R_{B_3} = 18.40 \text{ } \Omega$$

$$R_{B_4} = 24.51 \text{ } \Omega.$$

Select a time constant of 5 μs for the capacitor. This is relatively long compared to the collector current rise time of 0.8 μs, and yet only one-fourth of the time the transistor is on. The base current will have decayed nearly to its final value in

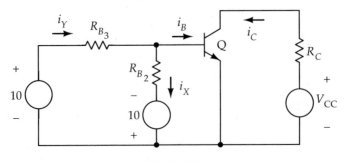

FIGURE 4.23

the 20 μs that the transistor is on. The circuit in Figure 4.24 can be used to calculate the time constant:

$$R_{B_4}C_B = 5 \times 10^{-6} \text{ s}$$

$$C_B = 0.204 \times 10^{-6} \text{ F.}$$

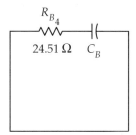

FIGURE 4.24

Because the voltage on C_B is unidirectional, this capacitor can be an electrolytic type and thus its physical size is not overly large. ∎

Inductive Collector Circuit   Similar requirements on base drive currents exist for inductive loads as compared to resistive loads. The circuit in Figure 4.25 is an example of a clamped inductive load, and the graphs in Figures 4.8 and 4.9 are representative of the turnoff part of the process. The turn-on part of the process requires separation into two cases, depending upon the circuit arrangement. If the inductor current in Figure 4.25 is zero at the start of the turn-on process, then at turn on collector current starts at zero and rises slowly as limited by load inductance. This is not a demanding application insofar as base current is concerned, because the base current need not rapidly increase in value.

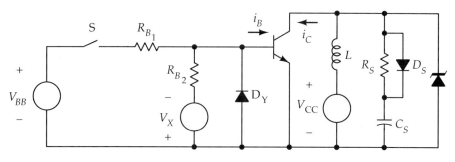

FIGURE 4.25

If the inductor current is not zero when the transistor turns on, then the base current rise time is critical. The transistor must turn on rapidly to have a short turn-on time and thus limit the time during which large losses occur. The previous section for resistive loads applies in regard to values of I_{B_1} to achieve rapid turn on.

The circuit in Figure 4.13 has the collector circuit modified to match that in Figure 4.11(a), with the addition of a resistor to control snubber-capacitor discharge. This new circuit is shown in Figure 4.25.

Circuit operation without a snubber circuit is depicted in the oscillogram in Figure 4.26 and shows that the transistor operates at one point in time at 3.0 A and approximately 56 V. The modeling of a linear collector current versus time, as we did in the section on safe operating areas, is seen to be a fairly good representation of collector current behavior. A reduction in storage time or collector current fall time would not appreciably change the locus of operation on the RBSOA graph.

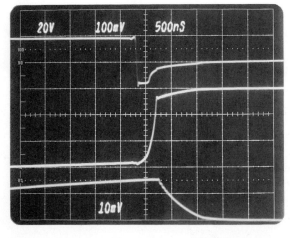

Upper Trace (i_B):
$I_{B_1} = 0.2$ A $I_{B_2} = 0.2$ A

Middle Trace (v_{CE}):
20 V/Division

Lower Trace (i_C):
2 A/Division

FIGURE 4.26

The addition of a snubber circuit delays the collector-to-emitter voltage increase and thus alters the locus on the RBSOA graph. Oscilloscope graphs with a snubber capacitor of 50 nF are shown in Figure 4.27. The improvement is evident in the collector-to-emitter voltage value that corresponds to any given value of collector current. The previous calculations for the appropriate snubber capacitance values are valid here.

The effects shown in the previous oscillograms are plotted on an RBSOA graph in Figure 4.28. The graph of collector current versus collector-to-emitter

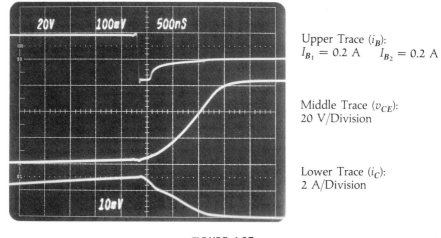

Upper Trace (i_B):
$I_{B_1} = 0.2$ A $\qquad I_{B_2} = 0.2$ A

Middle Trace (v_{CE}):
20 V/Division

Lower Trace (i_C):
2 A/Division

FIGURE 4.27

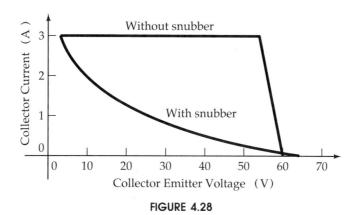

FIGURE 4.28

voltage is a measure of the reverse-bias stress on the transistor. The second curve, which shows the effect of the snubber capacitor, is significantly different from the curve for the case without the snubber capacitor.

Switching Losses

During transistor turn on and turnoff, there can be appreciable power dissipation that generally cannot be neglected. At turn on, there is a short delay time before any change in collector current occurs. At turnoff, there is a storage time before collector-to-emitter voltage can change. The loss during both intervals is essentially the same as during the prior "off" or "on" state, and thus these intervals do not contribute to the switching loss. Switching loss occurs only during the interval of significant change in collector current or collector-to-emitter voltage.

Resistive Loads   The graph in Figure 4.29 shows idealized waveforms for turn on and turnoff in the case of a resistive load such as that in Figure 4.3. Current rise and fall times are controlled by both the transistor base drive and the actual transistor type.

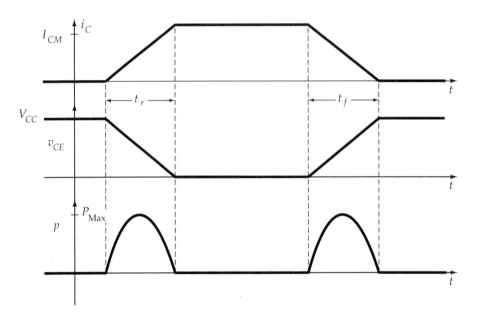

FIGURE 4.29

If an origin is selected at the beginning of the collector current rise time, then the following equations can be written:

$$i_C = I_{CM}\left(\frac{t}{t_r}\right) \qquad 0 < t < t_r \tag{4.4}$$

where

$$I_{CM} = \frac{V_{CC}}{R} \tag{4.5}$$

$$v_{CE} = V_{CC} - Ri_C \tag{4.6}$$

$$v_{CE} = V_{CC}\left(1 - \frac{t}{t_r}\right) \qquad 0 < t < t_r. \tag{4.7}$$

We will assume that v_{CE} in saturation is negligible in comparison to V_{CC}. The instantaneous power to the transistor during this interval is given by

$$p = v_{CE}i_C = V_{CC}I_{CM}\left(\frac{t}{t_r}\right)\left(1 - \frac{t}{t_r}\right) \qquad 0 < t < t_r. \qquad \textbf{(4.8)}$$

The energy, W_r, dissipated in the transistor during the rise time is given by an integration of power during the fall-time interval, with the result given in Equation 4.9:

$$W_r = \left(\frac{V_{CC}I_{CM}}{4}\right)\left(\frac{2t_r}{3}\right). \qquad \textbf{(4.9)}$$

In a similar manner, the energy (W_f) dissipated in the transistor during the current fall time is given by Equation 4.10:

$$W_f = \left(\frac{V_{CC}I_{CM}}{4}\right)\left(\frac{2t_f}{3}\right). \qquad \textbf{(4.10)}$$

The first term in these two energy expressions is the peak power occurring at one-half the rise or fall time; it is independent of the switching time. Because this can be a very appreciable power, it is important to reduce the duration of the rise or fall time to keep the switching energy loss as limited as possible. The shape of the actual collector-current versus time curve may not be exactly as the idealized waveform in Figure 4.29. Therefore, the $\frac{2}{3}$ factor in the equations may be somewhat different, although the requirement to minimize rise and fall times still holds to minimize switching losses.

If the transistor is turned on and off in a periodic manner, this switching loss occurs for each operation. The average power that results depends on the frequency of these switching operations:

$$P_{avg} = (\text{frequency})(\text{loss per operation}) \qquad \textbf{(4.11)}$$

$$P_{avg} = (f)(W_r + W_f). \qquad \textbf{(4.12)}$$

EXAMPLE 4.4

In the circuit in Figure 4.3, the transistor is turned on and off at a frequency of 10 kHz. Collector current rise time is 0.8 μs and fall time is 1.0 μs. $V_{CC} = 400$ V and $R = 20\ \Omega$. Find:

(a) rise-time energy loss

(b) fall-time energy loss

(c) switching loss power.

Solution

(a) $I_{CM} = \dfrac{V_{CC}}{R} = \dfrac{400}{20} = 20$ A.

From Equation 4.9, the rise-time energy loss is determined:

$$W_r = \left[\frac{(400)(20)}{4}\right]\left[\left(\frac{2}{3}\right)(0.8 \times 10^{-6})\right] = 0.00107 \text{ J.}$$

(b) From Equation 4.10, the fall-time energy loss is determined:

$$W_f = \left[\frac{(400)(20)}{4}\right]\left[\left(\frac{2}{3}\right)(1 \times 10^{-6})\right] = 0.00133 \text{ J.}$$

(c) $W_r + W_f = 0.00107 + 0.00133 = 0.00240$ J.

From Equation 4.11, the switching power loss is found:

$$P_{avg} = (0.00240)(10,000) = 24 \text{ W.}$$ ∎

Inductive Loads   With inductive loads, switching losses depend on the specific case. If the initial inductor current is zero, then at the start of transistor turn on the collector current is zero. Because the load is inductive, collector current is essentially zero during the entire turn-on process and the switching power is negligibly small. Turn-on losses thus may be neglected.

The situation is quite different if the initial inductor current is not zero. In the circuit in Figure 4.7, the initial inductor current is not zero, and the idealized graphs in Figure 4.30 apply at turn on. In the graph for transistor power loss, maximum power is the product of E_2 and I_{CM}. Again, it is important to minimize switching energy by decreasing switching time.

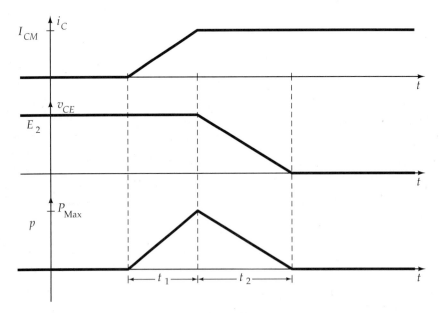

FIGURE 4.30

In the graph in Figure 4.30, t_1 and t_2 represent current rise time and voltage fall time, respectively. The energy supplied to the transistor during turn on is represented by the area under the power versus time curve. This energy is given by Equation 4.13:

$$\text{Turn-on energy} = \tfrac{1}{2}E_2 I_{CM}(t_1 + t_2). \tag{4.13}$$

During an inductive load's turnoff, transistor voltage and current variations are similar to those at turn on except for the order of the changes. Figure 4.31 shows idealized versions of the process. In these graphs, t_1 and t_2 represent voltage rise time and current fall time, respectively. Their sum is similar to the crossover time defined on transistor datasheets. The equation for turnoff energy loss is the same as that for turn on:

$$\text{Turnoff energy} = \tfrac{1}{2}E_2 I_{CM}(t_1 + t_2). \tag{4.14}$$

The power from these switching losses in a periodic situation is given by Equation 4.15:

$$P_{\text{avg}} = (\text{frequency})(\text{turn-on loss} + \text{turnoff loss}). \tag{4.15}$$

One difference between actual datasheet parameters and idealized waveforms is the abrupt slope changes shown in the latter. These do not occur in the actual devices. To take measurements, it is customary to select the 10% and 90% points on a waveform as a practical means of defining the beginning and end of an event.

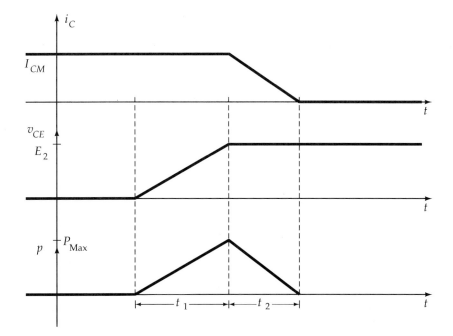

FIGURE 4.31

E X A M P L E 4 . 5

In a circuit similar to that in Figure 4.7, the inductor current is 20 A and may be assumed constant during the switching interval. $V_{CC} = 200$ V, and $E_2 = 400$ V. During turn on, $t_1 = 0.4$ μs and $t_2 = 0.2$ μs. During turnoff, $t_1 = 0.1$ μs and $t_2 = 0.3$ μs. Find:

(a) energy loss during turn on

(b) energy loss during turnoff

(c) total switching loss at a frequency of 10 kHz.

Solution

(a) From Equation 4.13:

$$\text{Energy} = \tfrac{1}{2}[(400)(20)(0.4 + 0.2)(10^{-6})] = 0.0024 \text{ J.}$$

(b) From Equation 4.14:

$$\text{Energy} = \tfrac{1}{2}[(400)(20)(0.1 + 0.3)(10^{-6})] = 0.0016 \text{ J.}$$

(c) Total energy $= 0.00240 + 0.00160 = 0.0040$ J.

From Equation 4.15:

$$\text{Power} = (0.0040)(10{,}000) = 40 \text{ W.} \qquad \blacksquare$$

E X A M P L E 4 . 6

In Example 4.5, add a snubber of 0.0075 μF along with a suitable diode and a resistor of 1000 Ω. Assume no change in collector current fall time at turnoff. The voltage rise on turnoff is controlled by the snubber capacitor. Find:

(a) energy loss during turn on

(b) energy loss during turnoff

(c) snubber resistor energy loss

(d) total switching loss at a frequency of 10 kHz.

Solution

(a) There is essentially no change at turn on as compared with Example 4.5. The transistor must conduct an additional small current to discharge the snubber. This current cannot exceed $400/1000 = 0.4$ A, and there is little effect on transistor turn on loss:

$$\text{Turn-on energy} = 0.0024 \text{ J.}$$

(b) During turnoff, the collector current decreases linearly from 20 A to 0 as the snubber current increases linearly from 0 to 20 A. The graphs in Figure 4.32 apply.

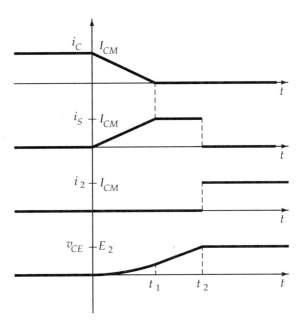

FIGURE 4.32

The following equations apply with a time origin beginning at the start of the collector current fall time of 0.3 μs:

$$i_C = 20(1 - 3.33 \times 10^6 t) \qquad 0 < t < 0.3 \ \mu s$$

$$i_S = 66.67 \times 10^6 t$$

$$v_{CE} = \left(\frac{1}{C}\right) \int_0^t i_S \, dt = 4.44 \times 10^{15} t^2$$

$$p = v_{CE} i_C$$

$$p = 88.89 \times 10^{15} t^2 (1 - 3.333 \times 10^6 t).$$

At the end of the collector current fall time, the value of v_{CE} is just equal to E_2. The load current is diverted to the clamp voltage source and i_S becomes zero. By integrating the power over the collector current fall time, the energy to the transistor can be found:

$$\text{Energy} = \int_0^{t_1} v_{CE} i_C \, dt$$

$$= \int_0^{0.3 \times 10^{-6}} 88.89 \times 10^{15} t^2 (1 - 3.333 \times 10^6 t) \, dt = 0.0002 \ \text{J}.$$

(c) The energy stored in the snubber capacitor is essentially dissipated in the snubber resistor each time the transistor is turned on. The snubber capacitor is charged to 400 V at the end of each turnoff interval:

$$\text{Energy stored} = \tfrac{1}{2}Cv_C^2 = \tfrac{1}{2}(0.0075 \times 10^{-6})(400^2)$$
$$= 0.0006 \text{ J.}$$

(d) The three energy losses of parts (a), (b), and (c) occur each cycle. Thus, the switching power loss is given by

$$P_{\text{avg}} = (\text{sum of losses})(\text{frequency})$$

$$P_{\text{avg}} = (0.0024 + 0.0002 + 0.0006)(10,000) = 32 \text{ W.}$$

Note that this value is less than the loss calculated in Example 4.5. Energy is supplied to the clamp voltage source, E_2, during the remaining time the transistor is off. For good system efficiency, this energy must be returned to the system source or otherwise utilized.   ■

4.2
POWER MOSFETs

The emergence of power MOSFET (metal-oxide semiconductor field-effect transistor) devices in the past several years has caused the displacement of the BJT in certain applications. In situations in which high switching frequencies are required, the MOSFET may have lower total losses than a corresponding BJT even though its conduction losses are greater. In addition, the MOSFET is not subject to the second breakdown effects that are of serious concern for the BJT.

    Unless otherwise stated, all devices are of N-channel construction and have the usual polarities associated with such construction. Figure 4.33 shows reference directions for device currents. Voltages are specified using a double-subscript notation for gate, source, and drain.

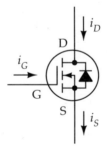

FIGURE 4.33

MOSFET Modeling

The static characteristics of the power MOSFET are quite similar to those of any small signal MOSFET except for the increase in current and voltage values associated with a power device. The curves in Figure 4.34 are typical of a power MOSFET and show a threshold value of v_{GS} such that i_D is essentially zero for values of v_{GS} less than the threshold value. For a device with rated drain current of several amperes, the drain current can be reduced to less than 1 mA for v_{GS} less than the threshold value.

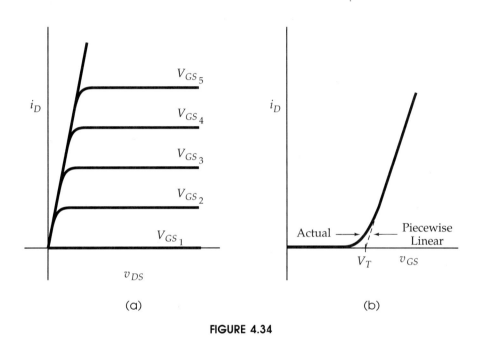

(a)

(b)

FIGURE 4.34

The graph in Figure 4.34(b) approximately represents the drain current by a piecewise linear function. For v_{GS} less than V_T, the drain current is zero; for v_{GS} greater than V_T, the drain current is a linear function of v_{GS}:

$$i_D = 0 \quad \text{for} \quad v_{GS} < V_T \tag{4.16}$$

$$i_D = G(v_{GS} - V_T) \quad \text{for} \quad v_{GS} > V_T. \tag{4.17}$$

In Equation 4.17, G is the slope of the linear approximation of the characteristic in Figure 4.34(b). A further restriction on Equation 4.17 is that the value of v_{DS} must be large enough that $R_{DS(ON)}$ is not a limiting parameter.

For values of v_{GS} greater than the threshold value, the MOSFET may be either in the linear region or in a "constant resistance" region. The first of these regions, in which the drain current essentially depends on v_{GS} only, has a relatively large value for v_{DS}. This region normally is not used in a power-electronics application because there are large losses in this mode of operation. The region in which the MOSFET is essentially fully turned on is of much greater usefulness. The value of v_{DS} is related to i_D by a resistance value, $R_{DS(ON)}$, which is nearly constant. This conducting region corresponds to the saturation region of the bipolar junction transistor and is represented in Figure 4.34(a) by the nearly vertical line:

$$v_{DS(ON)} = R_{DS(ON)}i_D. \tag{4.18}$$

In either ON or OFF state, the input gate terminal requires essentially zero gate current statically. There is an insulator between the gate terminal and the remainder of the MOSFET, with a resulting nonlinear input capacitance. Even though the static gate current is zero, the gate current required to charge this capacitance in time-varying situations may be quite substantial.

These two MOSFET states correspond to two states of an on–off switch. The MOSFET is not an ideal switch, of course, but it is sufficiently close to ideal to be a very useful and practical device. The MOSFET is capable of a faster transition between the two states than a bipolar junction transistor and thus has become useful at higher switching frequencies.

In the graph in Figure 4.34(a), which is for a 2N6762, the reciprocal of the typical slope of the ohmic region is approximately 1.35 Ω. This ohmic region is not strictly a straight line, although it is close. At large values of drain current, the resistance value does become somewhat larger. The datasheet for the 2N6762 lists a maximum value of 1.5 Ω for $R_{DS(ON)}$ at a drain current of 3.0 A at 25° C. For this value of drain current, the value of V_{DS} is equal to or less than 4.5 V. In comparison to the maximum V_{DS} of 500 V, this ON-state value of 4.5 V is less than 1% of maximum voltage. The switch has a reasonably small ON-state voltage, but it is certainly not an ideal switch for which V_{DS} is zero.

E X A M P L E   4 . 7

For an MTM15N40 (its datasheet is given in Appendix B), find typical values for V_T, G, and $R_{DS(ON)}$ that are suitable for drain currents up to 15 A.

Solution   From Appendix B, a piecewise linear approximation to the transfer characteristic of this MOSFET, which is shown in Figure 3 (p. 485) at 25° C, could be a straight line through the point at $i_D = 18$ A and $v_{GS} = 6$ V. This line also intersects the v_{GS} axis at 3.8 V. Therefore,

$$V_T = 3.8 \text{ V}$$

$$G = \frac{18}{6.0 - 3.8} = 8.18 \text{ A/V}.$$

The measured slope of the characteristic in Figure 1 of this datasheet using $v_{GS} = 10$ V is 16 A/3.2 V = 5 mho. Therefore, $R_{DS(ON)}$ is 0.2 Ω as a typical value. The maximum datasheet value is 0.3 Ω for a similar condition.　　　　■

MOSFET Capacitance

Two capacitors are important in a MOSFET's off–on switching. These are C_{gs} between the gate and source and C_{gd} between gate and drain. Each capacitance value is a nonlinear function of voltage. The value for C_{gs} has only relatively small variation, but the variation in C_{gd} as v_{DG} passes through zero is substantial. Any neglect of these variations creates substantial error in the gate charge that is required to establish a given operating condition.

The data for an MTP8N60 is replotted in the graphs in Figure 4.35, which were found by using the following relations and replotting data as a function of v_{DG}:

$$C_{gs} = C_{iss} - C_{rss} \tag{4.19}$$

$$C_{gd} = C_{rss} \tag{4.20}$$

where C_{iss} is the small signal capacitance from gate to source with zero drain-to-source voltage, and C_{rss} is the small signal capacitance between gate and drain.

A reasonable approximation to the actual nonlinear capacitance uses two values for each capacitance. A suitable estimated value can be used for $v_{DG} > 0$

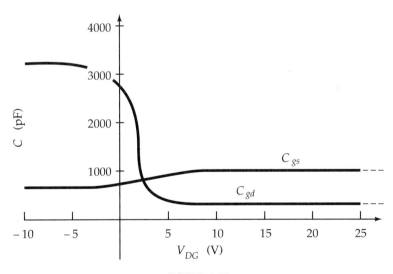

FIGURE 4.35

and another value for the region $v_{DG} < 0$. In Figure 4.35, values of 1000 pF and 600 pF for C_{gs} are reasonable. For C_{gd}, the corresponding values are 150 pF and 3600 pF.

The value of C_{gd} is small for $v_{DG} > 0$, but the excursion of drain-to-gate voltage is large compared to gate-to-source voltage; therefore, the charge involved for C_{gd} may be appreciable.

Turn On

In most MOSFET circuits, the objective is to turn on the MOSFET as quickly as possible to minimize switching loss. To do this, the gate drive circuit must be capable of supplying sufficient current to quickly increase the gate voltage to the required level. To calculate circuit behavior at turn on, the process is divided into several time intervals. The circuit to be analyzed is that in Figure 4.36. The graphs of circuit variables versus time are shown in Figure 4.37.

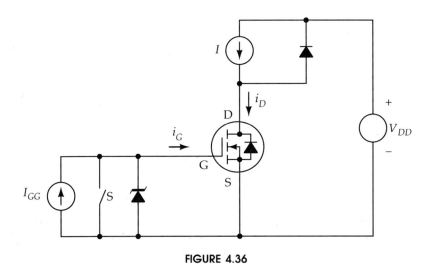

FIGURE 4.36

In Figure 4.36, the turn-on process begins with opening of switch S. There is no drain current until v_{GS} reaches V_T. At t_1 in Figure 4.37, drain current begins, increasing until it reaches the value of I at t_2. Because the FWD in Figure 4.36 remains in conduction during this interval, there is no change in the drain-to-source voltage. During these two intervals, C_{gs} and C_{gd} are effectively in parallel for the change in voltage and are charged by the gate current:

$$i_G = (C_{gs} + C_{gd})\left(\frac{dv_{GS}}{dt}\right). \tag{4.21}$$

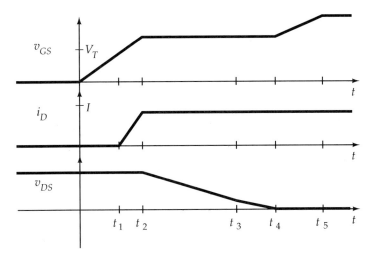

FIGURE 4.37

For $t > t_2$, the FWD is reverse-biased, and the drain-to-source voltage may decrease. The drain current is constant, and the value of v_{GS} must remain constant. Therefore, all gate current is directed to charging C_{gd} as the drain-to-source voltage decreases. During the interval from t_2 to t_3, Equation 4.21 is replaced by Equation 4.23. Note that v_{GS} is constant in Equation 4.22:

$$i_G = C_{gd}\left(\frac{dv_{GD}}{dt}\right) = C_{gd}\left(\frac{dv_{GS}}{dt} - \frac{dv_{DS}}{dt}\right) \tag{4.22}$$

$$i_G = -C_{gd}\left(\frac{dv_{DS}}{dt}\right) \tag{4.23}$$

This reduction in v_{DS} continues until the device is fully turned on at $t = t_4$. As the value of v_{DG} changes, so does the value of C_{gd} as described in the preceding section. The rate at which v_{DS} changes becomes appreciably smaller as v_{DG} passes through a value of zero at $t = t_3$. For the interval from t_3 to t_4, a much larger value of C_{gd} should be used, although Equation 4.23 still applies. This interval is very short compared to that from t_2 to t_3 and may even be zero. This depends on the numbers for a particular device and circuit. The next example will demonstrate the relative times involved. During the interval from t_4 to t_5, the gate voltage is increased to some limiting value. During this interval, both C_{gs} and C_{gd} are involved in the charging process, so Equation 4.21 applies.

EXAMPLE 4.8

In the circuit shown in Figure 4.36, the source current is 15.0 A. Using a gate drive of 0.2 A, find the time required to turn on the MOSFET and drive the gate-to-source voltage to 10 V. The MOSFET is Motorola MTM15N40 operating at $T_J = 100°$ C. The source voltage is 250 V.

Solution From the datasheet in Appendix B, the following values are determined.

$$
\begin{array}{llll}
C_{gs} = 1000 \text{ pF} & v_{DG} < 0 & C_{gd} = 7000 \text{ pF} & v_{DG} < 0 \\
C_{gs} = 1800 \text{ pF} & v_{DG} > 0 & C_{gd} = 200 \text{ pF} & v_{DG} > 0 \\
V_T = 3.8 \text{ V} & & G = 8.33 \text{ A/V}. &
\end{array}
$$

For the interval from 0 to t_2, total capacitance is 2000 pF. Using Equation 4.17, the value of v_{GS} that corresponds to the maximum drain current can be determined:

$$
v_{GS} = V_T + \frac{I_D}{G} = 3.8 + \frac{15}{8.33} = 5.6 \text{ V}.
$$

From Equation 4.21,

$$
\frac{dv_{GS}}{dt} = \frac{0.2}{2000 \times 10^{-12}} = 100 \times 10^6 \text{ V/s}
$$

$$
t_2 = \frac{v_{GS}}{dv_{GS}/dt} = \frac{5.6}{100 \times 10^6} = 56.0 \times 10^{-9} \text{ s}.
$$

For the interval from t_2 to t_3, C_{GS} is 200 pF. The value of v_{DG} must change from 244.4 V to zero. Equation 4.23 applies:

$$
\frac{dv_{GD}}{dt} = \frac{-0.2}{200 \times 10^{-12}} = -1 \times 10^9 \text{ V/s}
$$

$$
t_3 - t_2 = \frac{-244.4}{-1 \times 10^9} = 244 \times 10^{-9} \text{ s}.
$$

For the interval from t_3 to t_4, the value of $v_{DS(ON)}$ must be determined. The datasheet gives a typical value: $R_{DS(ON)} = 0.37 \ \Omega$ at $T_J = 100°$ C. The value of $v_{DS(ON)}$ therefore is 5.6 V. This is the same as v_{GS} for i_D of 15 A. The interval from t_3 to t_4 thus happens to be zero in this case. This may be the case if the device is used near its rated current.

For the interval from t_4 to t_5, both C_{gs} and C_{gd} are once again in parallel because v_{DS} is constant at $v_{DS(ON)}$. Both C_{gs} and C_{gd} are set to values that correspond to $v_{DG} < 0$. Using Equation 4.21 gives

$$\frac{dv_{GS}}{dt} = \frac{0.2}{8000 \times 10^{-12}} = 25 \times 10^6 \text{ V/s}$$

$$t_5 - t_4 = \frac{10 - 5.6}{25 \times 10^{-6}} = 176 \times 10^{-9} \text{ s.}$$

The total time required to reach the overdrive indicated by $v_{GS} = 10$ V at t_5 is therefore 476 ns.   ∎

The switching time found in Example 4.8 can be estimated using the gate charge curve given in a MOSFET datasheet if the operating point corresponds to the given data. In the characteristics for the MTM15N40, the gate charge curve gives a value of 105 nC to turn on the MOSFET under the conditions of Example 4.8. With a gate current of 0.2 A, this charge requires an interval of 525 ns to t_5. This compares very favorably to the 476 ns calculated in the example. For those conditions that do not correspond to datasheet values, the previous analysis can be used to provide reasonable predictions.

Turnoff

To turn off the MOSFET, the gate-to-source voltage must be reduced in reverse order of the actions that occur during turn on. The particular sequence of currents and voltages depends on the external circuit arrangements, but one such frequently occurring arrangement is represented by the circuit in Figure 4.38.

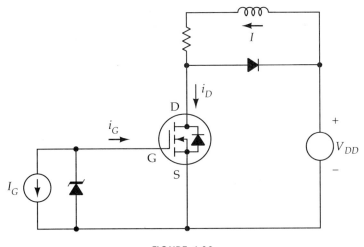

FIGURE 4.38

Several actual circuits with inductive loads can be represented by this idealized circuit.

The graph in Figure 4.39 shows the significant currents and voltages during the turnoff process. From the time origin to time t_1, the gate-to-source voltage is reduced until it is just sufficient to maintain the drain current. This requires a gate current to discharge C_{gs} and C_{gd} to this value of v_{GS}. During the interval from the time origin to t_1, the drain-to-source voltage remains essentially constant at a low value, so the "Miller" effect does not occur. During this interval, Equation 4.21 applies.

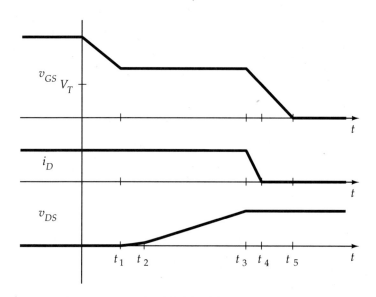

FIGURE 4.39

At t_1, the gate-to-source voltage is just sufficient to maintain the drain current. Further reduction of gate-to-source voltage is not possible because this would mean a reduction in drain current, and this latter reduction is not yet possible until the drain-to-source voltage increases to the drain supply voltage. To make this change, gate current must be used solely to change the value of v_{DS} according to the relation in Equation 4.23. At time t_3, the value of v_{DS} equals the drain supply voltage and further change in v_{DS} is no longer required. For the interval from t_1 to t_2, v_{DG} is less than zero and C_{gd} is large. This interval actually may be zero in length, as was the case in Example 4.8. The interval from t_2 to t_3 has v_{DG} greater than zero with C_{gd} having a relatively small value.

For time greater than t_3, the gate-to-drain voltage essentially is constant, and the gate current is available to reduce the gate-to-source voltage. At time

t_4, the MOSFET is at the threshold voltage, the drain current is essentially zero, and the turnoff process has been completed. In the interval from t_4 to t_5, the gate-to-source voltage is further reduced to zero or any other desired OFF-state value. For the interval from t_3 to t_5, Equation 4.21 once again applies.

EXAMPLE 4.9

The MOSFET of Example 4.8 is to be turned off by a gate current of -0.1 A. Find the time for each interval shown in Figure 4.39 with the final value of v_{GS} equal to zero.

Solution

$$t_1 = \frac{-(10 - 5.6)(8000 \times 10^{-12})}{-0.1} = 352 \times 10^{-9} \text{ s}$$

$$t_2 - t_1 = \frac{-(5.6 - 5.6)(7000 \times 10^{-12})}{-0.1} = 0 \text{ s}$$

$$t_3 - t_2 = \frac{-(250 - 5.6)(200 \times 10^{-12})}{-0.1} = 488 \times 10^{-9} \text{ s}$$

$$t_4 - t_3 = \frac{-(5.6 - 3.8)(2000 \times 10^{-12})}{-0.1} = 36 \times 10^{-9} \text{ s}$$

$$t_5 - t_4 = \frac{-(3.8 - 0)(2000 \times 10^{-12})}{-0.1} = 76 \times 10^{-9} \text{ s.}$$

The calculations of this example show a total time of 876 ns to turn off the MOSFET at $t = t_4$. The major effect of the gate-to-drain capacitance is apparent even though its actual capacitance value is small when compared to the capacitance from gate to source. The calculations in this example are approximate because the capacitances are continuous functions of voltage, but the calculated results still are quite useful in determining values for the MOSFET's switching times.

A further approximation has been made in this calculation and in Example 4.8. The lead inductance in the source terminal has been neglected. The typical datasheet value for this inductance is 12.5 nanohenries. The effect of this inductance occurs during the interval from t_3 to t_4 as the source current decreases. For a change of 15 A in this current in approximately 36 ns, the voltage across this inductance is 5 V. This voltage is sufficiently large to have an appreciable effect on the net gate-to-source voltage and thus on the time it takes for the drain current to fall to zero. This effect is examined later in the section on source inductance. ∎

Safe Operating Area

A MOSFET's safe operating area is limited by three variables that form the boundary of acceptable operation. In Figure 4.40, these limits are:

1. maximum pulsed drain current

2. maximum drain-to-source voltage

3. maximum junction temperature.

There is no severely restricted region that is similar to the second breakdown that occurs in bipolar junction transistors.

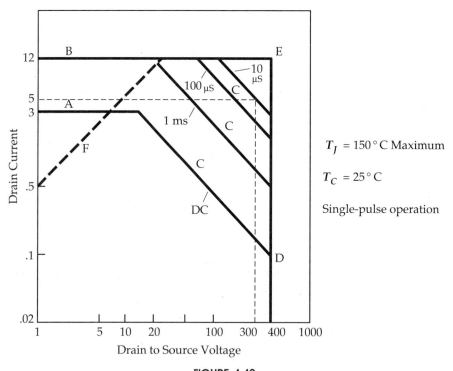

FIGURE 4.40

Section A in Figure 4.40 is the limit imposed by the device's continuous drain current rating. Operation at a much larger drain current is possible in a pulsed or noncontinuous mode, as shown by Section B in the graph. Maximum drain-to-source voltage has the limit shown by the vertical Section D. Further limitation occurs because of maximum junction temperature as shown by the Sections labeled C; each corresponds to a particular length of MOSFET conduction time. The shorter the conduction time, the larger the permitted power dissipation. For a sufficiently short pulse duration, it is even possible to operate at Point E with simultaneously maximum values of v_{DS} and i_D. The restrictions that must be met are certainly less of a problem for the MOSFET than for the BJT.

The high current region to the left of Line F does not represent a region of possible operating points. The value of $R_{DS(ON)}$ sets a lower limit for v_{DS} for each value of i_D, and the points in this region represent values of v_{DS} less than the lower limit.

EXAMPLE 4.10

The MOSFET in Figure 4.41 is turned on in a single-pulse mode with a drain current of 5 A. The MOSFET has the properties previously shown in Figure 4.40. $V_{DD} = 400$ V, $R = 20 \ \Omega$, and $i_D = 5$ A. How long can the MOSFET remain in the on state without exceeding the maximum permitted value of junction temperature?

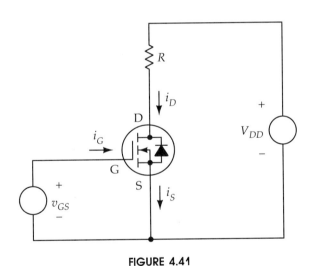

FIGURE 4.41

Solution

$$v_{DS} = 400 - (5)(20) = 300 \text{ V}.$$

The point that corresponds to these values of v_{DS} and i_D falls on the 10-μs line for pulse length. This is the device's maximum safe duration of on time.   ■

MOSFET Losses

A power MOSFET's losses are a factor in selecting a switching device from among the semiconductor types that might be used for a given switch. The choice is not simple because it cannot be said that the MOSFET has lower or higher losses than a BJT at a specific current value. The switching losses at turn on and turnoff play a major role in the assessment. The switching frequency is especially important.

During continuous conduction at constant drain current, the MOSFET loss is found simply by calculating $(I_D)^2 R_{DS(ON)}$. The energy lost during turn on and turnoff is not found so easily and, in fact, depends on both the drain and gate circuit conditions. The circuits shown in Figures 4.36 and 4.38 can be used as models to calculate such losses for a particular circuit arrangement.

For circuit turn on, the current and voltage variations with time were shown in Figure 4.37. The product of v_{DS} and i_D in that figure during turn on yields turn-on power as a function of time; this is shown in Figure 4.42. The area under the curve is the energy supplied to the MOSFET during turn on. A small amount of energy is required from the gate drive, but generally this is negligible compared to the other losses and will not be considered here. Each time the MOSFET is turned on, this same energy loss occurs, so the power represented is found as the product of switching frequency and energy loss per turn-on operation.

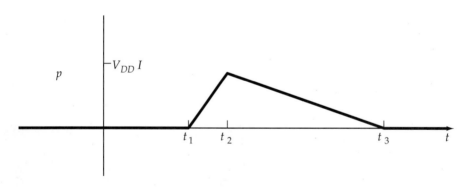

FIGURE 4.42

The energy equation is for the area under the curve in Figure 4.42:

$$\text{Energy(turn on)} = (0.5)(V_{DD})(I)(t_3 - t_1). \qquad (4.24)$$

In Equation 4.24, t_1 and t_3 are as defined earlier in the section on MOSFET turn on. The MOSFET is not turned on fully in the interval from t_3 to t_4, but the value of v_{DS} is very nearly equal to $V_{DS(ON)}$ during this period. The difference is neglected in this model for losses. The same approximation is used below in Equation 4.25 for the interval from t_1 to t_2 during turnoff.

In a very similar manner, we determine the loss associated with turnoff by finding a graph of the product of v_{DS} and i_D as a function of time. The curves in Figure 4.39 are used to plot the graph shown in Figure 4.43, which shows the energy found as the area under the curve:

$$\text{Energy(turnoff)} = (0.5)(V_{DD})(I)(t_4 - t_2) \qquad \textbf{(4.25)}$$

where t_2 and t_4 have been defined previously for the turnoff process.

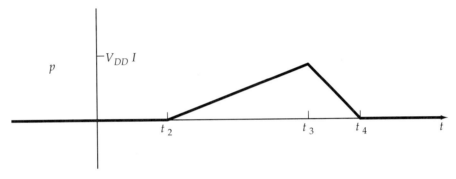

FIGURE 4.43

The total loss now may be found by summing the results of Equations 4.24 and 4.25:

$$\text{Switching power loss} = (f)[\text{energy(turn on)} + \text{energy(turnoff)}] \qquad \textbf{(4.26)}$$

$$\text{Switching power loss} = 0.5(f)(V_{DD})(I)[(t_3 - t_1)_{ON} + (t_4 - t_2)_{OFF}]. \qquad \textbf{(4.27)}$$

One fact to consider about the losses is the relatively small increase in total loss as the switching frequency increases. In many cases, the MOSFET is at a comparative disadvantage with a BJT at a low switching frequency. This results from the relatively high ON-state losses of the MOSFET. As the switching frequency is increased, the BJT switching losses increase more than do the MOSFET switching losses. At some frequency, the two losses are equal, and for a higher switching frequency the MOSFET has lower total losses than the BJT. This becomes especially significant in those applications for which a higher switching frequency is desirable to allow smaller inductors and capacitors and thus lowered circuit cost.

In Equation 4.27, the time interval is the only switching loss factor that can be controlled. A reduction in switching time is reflected directly in a reduction of loss. This requires careful design of the gate drive circuit to provide sufficient gate current for rapid turn on and turnoff.

EXAMPLE 4.11

In Figure 4.44, the MOSFET is turned on and off periodically at 50 kHz. The gate current supply is $+100$ mA for 5 μs and then -60 mA for 15 μs. The value of v_{GS} is limited to $+10$ or 0 V by the action of the zener diode connected to the gate. The load inductance is large enough that the load current may be assumed constant during each cycle. Find the MOSFET switching and conduction loss for this operating condition.

$R_{DS(ON)} = 0.5\ \Omega$ $\qquad I_L = 10$ A $\qquad C_{gs} = 1200$ pF with $V_{DG} > 0$

$V_T = 3.8$ V $\qquad\qquad V_{DD} = 200$ V $\qquad C_{gd} = 50$ pF with $V_{DG} > 0$

$G = 4.0$ mho $\qquad\qquad\qquad\qquad\qquad C_{gs} = 500$ pF with $V_{DG} < 0$

$\qquad\qquad\qquad\qquad\qquad\qquad\qquad C_{gd} = 2000$ pF with $V_{DG} < 0.$

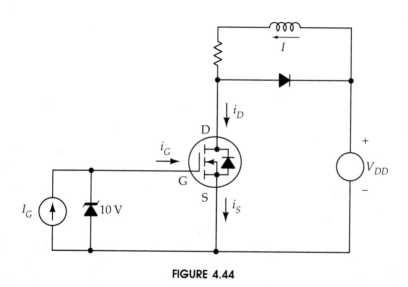

FIGURE 4.44

Solution *Turn on.* At full drain current,

$$v_{GS} = \left(\frac{10}{4}\right) + 3.8 = 6.3\ V$$

$$t_1 = (3.8)\frac{1250 \times 10^{-12}}{0.1} = 47.5 \times 10^{-9}\ s$$

$$t_2 - t_1 = \frac{(6.3 - 3.8)(1250 \times 10^{-12})}{0.1} = 31.3 \times 10^{-9}\ s$$

$$t_3 - t_2 = \frac{(200 - 6.3)(50 \times 10^{-12})}{0.1} = 96.9 \times 10^{-9} \text{ s}$$

$$t_4 - t_3 = \frac{(6.3 - 5.0)(2000 \times 10^{-12})}{0.1} = 26.0 \times 10^{-9} \text{ s}$$

$$t_5 - t_4 = \frac{(10 - 6.3)(2500 \times 10^{-12})}{0.1} = 92.5 \times 10^{-9} \text{ s}.$$

Turnoff (with new time origin)

$$t_1 = \frac{(10 - 6.3)(2500 \times 10^{-12})}{0.06} = 154.2 \times 10^{-9} \text{ s}$$

$$t_2 - t_1 = \frac{(6.3 - 5.0)(2000 \times 10^{-12})}{0.06} = 43.3 \times 10^{-9} \text{ s}$$

$$t_3 - t_2 = \frac{(200 - 6.3)(50 \times 10^{-12})}{0.06} = 161.4 \times 10^{-9} \text{ s}$$

$$t_4 - t_3 = \frac{(6.3 - 3.8)(1250 \times 10^{-12})}{0.06} = 52.1 \times 10^{-9} \text{ s}$$

$$t_5 - t_4 = \frac{(3.8 - 0)(1250 \times 10^{-12})}{0.06} = 79.2 \times 10^{-9} \text{ s}.$$

Any significant switching loss will occur during the interval from t_1 to t_3 during turn on and from t_2 to t_4 during turnoff. At t_3 during turn on, $v_{DS} = 6.3$ V, and the corresponding power is 63 W. This compares to peak power of 2000 W during turn on. From Equation 4.24:

Turn-on energy $= (0.5)(200)(10)(128.2 \times 10^{-9}) = 0.0001282$ J.

Similarly, from Equation 4.25:

Turnoff energy $= (0.5)(200)(10)(213.5 \times 10^{-9}) = 0.0002135$ J.

Conduction loss occurs essentially from t_3 in turn on to t_2 in turnoff, as shown in Figure 4.45. This time is

$$t = 5000 + 197.5 - 175.6 = 5021.9 \text{ ns.}$$

During conduction,

$$P = V_{DS(ON)}I_D = (10)(0.5)(10) = 50 \text{ W}$$

$$\frac{\text{Conduction loss}}{\text{cycle}} = (50)(5021.9 \times 10^{-9}) = 0.0002511 \text{ J}$$

Total loss $= 0.0001282 + 0.0002135 + 0.0002511 = 0.0005928$ J/cycle.

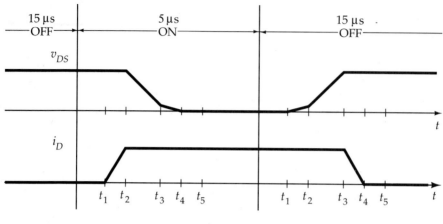

FIGURE 4.45

With a switching frequency of 50 kHZ, the power loss is

$$P = (50000)(0.0005928) = 29.64 \text{ W}.$$ ∎

As in Example 4.11, a BJT would have lower conducting losses, although the switching losses would be much larger. The BJT turn-on and turnoff times would be several times as long as those for the MOSFET and result in substantially increased switching loss. The application of a BJT to this situation would be more difficult and require a more complex circuit to provide the necessary base current for proper turn on and turnoff.

Source Inductance

As mentioned earlier in the section on turnoff (p. 129), the source inductance may have an appreciable effect on the time required to change drain current from one value to another. A relatively simple analysis can be done to calculate the actual time if one assumption is made: That the gate current can be neglected in comparison to the drain current during the period in which the drain current changes. This is quite reasonable to assume when comparing a gate current of perhaps 200 mA to a drain current of several amperes.

The circuit in Figure 4.46 is used for the analysis, with the gate source represented as a voltage source in series with a resistance. The inductance shown represents any inductance in series with the MOSFET internal source terminal, which has an internal minimum value because of the device package. To the extent that the gate source can be represented by a current source, the problem becomes of lesser importance.

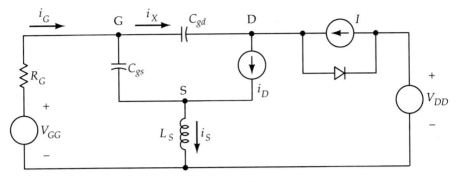

FIGURE 4.46

Equations for the circuit in Figure 4.46 during the time interval in question are given by Equations 4.28 through 4.32:

$$i_G + i_D = i_S + i_X \tag{4.28}$$

$$i_D = G(v_{GS} - V_T) \tag{4.29}$$

$$R_G i_G + v_{GS} + L_S\left(\frac{di_S}{dt}\right) = V_{GG} \tag{4.30}$$

$$i_G = C_{gs}\left(\frac{dv_{GS}}{dt}\right) + C_{gd}\left(\frac{dv_{GD}}{dt}\right) \tag{4.31}$$

$$v_{GD} = v_{GS} + L_S\left(\frac{di_S}{dt}\right) - V_{DD}. \tag{4.32}$$

During the drain-current change interval, the drain-to-circuit common voltage is constant because the FWD remains in conduction. An approximation also is made by replacing i_S by i_D because these two currents differ by only a very small amount. Using this approximation and differentiating Equation 4.32 yields

$$\frac{dv_{GD}}{dt} = \frac{dv_{GS}}{dt} + L_S\left(\frac{d^2 i_D}{dt^2}\right). \tag{4.33}$$

Eliminating i_D and i_G in the preceding equations permits a solution for one equation in v_{GS}:

$$(R_G G L_S C_{gd})\left(\frac{d^2 v_{GS}}{dt^2}\right) + \left(R_G + \frac{L_S G}{C}\right)(C)\left(\frac{dv_{GS}}{dt}\right) + v_{GS} = V_{GG} \tag{4.34}$$

$$(R_G G L_S C_{gd})\left(\frac{d^2 v_{GS}}{dt^2}\right) + (R_G + R')(C)\left(\frac{dv_{GS}}{dt}\right) + v_{GS} = V_{GG} \tag{4.35}$$

where

$$C = C_{gs} + C_{gd} \tag{4.36}$$

and

$$R' = \frac{L_S G}{C}. \tag{4.37}$$

The coefficient of the second derivative term in Equation 4.35 is negligible when compared to other terms using the usual values for the circuit elements. With this approximation, Equation 4.35 becomes the result expressed in Equation 4.38:

$$[(R_G + R')C]\left(\frac{dv_{GS}}{dt}\right) + v_{GS} = V_{GG}. \tag{4.38}$$

The principal effect on the equation that governs the time behavior of v_{GS} is that it adds an equivalent resistance in series with the actual gate-drive source resistance. The effect reduces the rate at which the gate-to-source voltage can be increased and hence increases the time needed to increase drain current from one value to another. The same process also works to increase the time during which the drain current reduces from one value to another. For a gate-drive circuit that approximates a current source, the addition of this equivalent resistance in series with the gate drive may have little effect on the circuit performance.

EXAMPLE 4.12

In the circuit in Figure 4.47, the source inductance, L_S, is included in the calculations. Find the drain current as a function of time for the interval of $t > 0$ after the switch is opened.

$V_{DD} = 300$ V	$R_{DS(ON)} = 0.9\ \Omega$	$C_{gs} = 570$ pF with $v_{DG} > 0$
$V_{GG} = 15$ V	$R_G = 200\ \Omega$	$C_{gd} = 30$ pF with $v_{DG} > 0$
$V_T = 4$ V	$I = 6.5$ A	$C_{gs} = 400$ pF with $v_{DG} < 0$
$G = 3.5$ mho	$L_S = 12.5$ nH	$C_{gd} = 600$ pF with $v_{DG} < 0$.

Solution   During the interval from $t = 0$ to $t = t_1$, the two capacitors are charging to the threshold value with $v_{DG} > 0$:

$$C = C_{gs} + C_{gd} = 570 + 30 = 600 \text{ pF}$$

$$\tau = R_G C = (200)(600 \times 10^{-12}) = 120 \times 10^{-9} \text{ s}$$

and

$$v_{GS} = 15(1 - e^{-t/\tau})$$

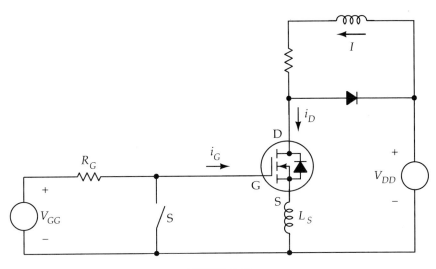

FIGURE 4.47

The time, t_1, for $v_{GS} = V_T$ must be found first:

$$4 = 15(1 - e^{-t_1/\tau})$$

$$t_1 = 37.2 \text{ ns.}$$

The time from t_1 to t_2 is the interval during which the drain current changes. From Equation 4.37,

$$R' = \frac{LG}{C} = \frac{(12.5 \times 10^{-9})(4)}{600 \times 10^{-12}}$$

$$R' = 83.3 \text{ }\Omega.$$

The final value of drain current equal to 6.5 A requires a gate-to-source voltage as calculated below:

$$v_{GS} = \left(\frac{i_D}{G}\right) + V_T$$

$$v_{GS} = \left(\frac{6.5}{3.5}\right) + 4.0 = 5.86 \text{ V.}$$

The new effective time constant is found to be

$$\tau = (R_G + R')C = (200 + 83.3)(600 \times 10^{-12})$$
$$= 170.0 \times 10^{-9} \text{ s.}$$

The value of the gate-to-source voltage changes from 4.0 to 5.86 V during the interval from t_1 to t_2, using the time constant calculated above:

$$v_{GS} = 15 - (15 - 4) e^{-t/\tau}$$

$$5.86 = 15 - 11 e^{-(t_2 - t_1)/\tau}$$

$$t_2 - t_1 = 31.5 \times 10^{-9} \text{ s.}$$

If the source inductance were not present, the time constant would have been the original value without R'. The value of $(t_2 - t_1)$ then would have been 22.2×10^{-9} seconds. The result of the source inductance is to increase the current rise time by 9.3 nanoseconds. Although this time may be negligible in many circuits, the effect needs to be included in those circuits that require very high performance.

The approximation made in obtaining Equation 4.38 can be examined using the numbers of this example. Equation 4.35 becomes

$$300 \times 10^{-18} \left(\frac{d^2 v_{GS}}{dt^2} \right) + 170 \times 10^{-9} \left(\frac{d v_{GS}}{dt} \right) + v_{GS} = 15.$$

The roots of the characteristic equation are

$$s_1 = -560.7 \times 10^6 \qquad s_2 = -5.95 \times 10^6.$$

The value of s_1 is so large in comparison to s_2 that the corresponding part of the solution decays very rapidly in comparison to the second part. Equation 4.38 therefore may be used with little error from this approximation.

To complete the turn-on process, the drain-to-source voltage now must be reduced to $v_{DS(ON)}$. During this change, v_{GS} is constant at 5.86 V and the gate current also is constant:

$$i_G = \frac{15 - 5.86}{200} = 0.0457 \text{ A}$$

and

$$v_{DS(ON)} = R_{DS(ON)} i_D = (0.9)(6.5) = 5.85 \text{ V}$$

$$t_3 - t_2 = \left[\frac{(V_{DD} - v_{DS(ON)})(C_{gd})}{i_G} \right]$$

$$= \frac{(300 - 5.85)(30 \times 10^{-12})}{0.0457} = 193.1 \times 10^{-9} \text{ s.}$$

This value of $v_{DS(ON)}$ is essentially the same as v_{GS} for this drain current; there-fore, the interval from t_3 to t_4 is zero. The total turn-on time is the sum of the four interval times:

$$t_4 = 37.2 + 31.5 + 193.1 + 0 = 261.8 \text{ ns.}$$

In terms of the total turn-on process, the 9.3 nanoseconds that result from source inductance has little effect in this example. This may not be true in every situation. ∎

4.3

PROBLEMS

4.1   In Figure 4.3, $R = 15\ \Omega$ and $V_{CC} = 225$ V. The transistor has the characteristics shown in Figure 4.5. Using a β_F value of 4, find:

(a) I_C with $V_{CE} \sim 0$ (b) V_{CE}

(c) the new value for I_C (d) I_B

(e) the total transistor power loss.

4.2   A transistor operating in the circuit in Figure 4.11 has a collector current
fall time of 1.8 μs; $C_S = 0.075\ \mu$F, $E_2 = 350$ V, and $i_C(0) = 10$ A. Find:

(a) v_{CE} at the time the transistor collector current becomes zero

(b) the time at which i_S becomes zero.

4.3   In the circuit in Figure 4.11, the transistor has a collector current fall time
of 1.2 μs; $i_C(0) = 10$ A and $E_2 = 350$ V.

(a) Select a value of C_S so that v_{CE} does not exceed 200 V at the time
the collector current becomes zero.

(b) Find the time at which D begins conduction.

4.4   In Figure 4.13, the following circuit elements are given:

$$V_{CC} = 300\ \text{V} \qquad R_{B_1} = 4.75\ \Omega \qquad V_{BB} = 20\ \text{V}$$
$$R_C = 10\ \Omega \qquad R_{B_2} = 8\ \Omega \qquad V_X = 15\ \text{V}.$$

$v_{BE} = 1.0$ V during both transistor operation and the initial stage of turnoff. Find values of I_{B_1} with S closed and I_{B_2} with S open.

4.5   Design a circuit like that in Figure 4.13 for values of R_{B_1} and R_{B_2}. The
desired values are 0.3 A for I_{B_1} and 0.45 A for I_{B_2}. $V_{BB} = 15$ V and
$V_X = 10$ V.

4.6   In Figure 4.13, required values are $I_{B_1} = 1$ A and $I_{B_2} = 0.75$ A.
$V_{BB} = 20$ V and $V_X = 12$ V. Find values for R_{B_1} and R_{B_2}.

4.7   Design a circuit like that in Figure 4.19 so that β_F at turn on is 10,
β_F at the end of conduction is 25, $I_{B_2}/I_{B_1} = 1.5$ at turnoff, and C_B is of
such value that its effect has a 15-μs time constant. The collector current
is 10 A. Positive and negative 15-V supplies are available.

4.8   In the circuit arrangement in Figure 4.3, the transistor achieves a rise time
of 1.2 μs and a fall time of 1.7 μs. The switching frequency is 5 kHz.
$V_{CC} = 200$ V and $R = 10\ \Omega$. Find:

(a) turn-on loss   (b) turnoff loss   (c) switching power loss.

4.9 In Problem 4.8, the switching frequency is changed to 10 kHz. During the transistor's ON state, $v_{CE} = 1.1$ V. The transistor is fully on for 40 μs of each period. Find:

(a) switching loss in watts   (b) average conduction loss in watts.

4.10 In Figure 4.7, $E_2 = 300$ V, $I = 10$ A, and the switching frequency is 7.5 kHz. Current rise time is 700 ns, and current fall time is 900 ns. Both voltage fall and rise times are 500 ns. Find:

(a) energy loss at turn on
(b) energy loss at turnoff
(c) total switching power loss in watts.

4.11 In Problem 4.10, a polarized snubber with $C_S = 0.05$ μF and $R_S = 1000$ Ω is added to the circuit. Find the total switching loss, including the power dissipated in the snubber resistor. Assume no change in collector current rise and fall times.

4.12 For an MTM15N40 MOSFET with data given in Appendix B, find piecewise linear values of C_{gs} and C_{gd} that are suitable for $V_{DG} > 0$ and $V_{DG} < 0$.

4.13 The circuit in Example 4.8 is changed to a gate-drive current of 50 mA. The inductor current is 8 A, and the gate voltage limit is 12 V. Find the duration of the five periods in the turn-on process.

4.14 Use the data in Problem 4.13 to find the five intervals during turnoff. The gate-drive current is changed to -75 mA.

4.15 Use the MOSFET data in Example 4.11. The gate current is 75 mA for turn on and -50 mA for turnoff. $V_{DD} = 300$ V and $I_L = 5$ A. Find:

(a) turn-on energy loss
(b) turnoff energy loss
(c) conduction power loss
(d) average MOSFET power loss if the gate current is positive for 20 μs and negative for 30 μs in a periodic manner.

4.16 In the circuit arrangement in Figure 4.47, the following data are given:

$V_{DD} = 200$ V	$I = 10$ A	$C_{gs} = 600$ pF for	$V_{DG} > 0$
$V_{GG} = 12$ V	$R_G = 50$ Ω	$C_{gd} = 50$ pF for	$V_{DG} > 0$
$V_T = 3.5$ V	$L_S = 15$ nH	$C_{gs} = 450$ pF for	$V_{DG} < 0$
$G = 4.0$ mho	$R_{DS(ON)} = 1$ Ω	$C_{gd} = 1000$ pF for	$V_{DG} < 0$

Find the time necessary to get v_{DS} equal to $v_{DS(ON)}$.

CHAPTER · 5

Phase-Controlled Rectifiers

One widespread use of power semiconductor devices is that of the SCR in phase-controlled rectifiers. In such applications, the AC line voltage is rectified, and the beginning of conduction is delayed in each half-cycle to achieve a variable output voltage. The reverse-blocking capability and the ability to control large currents with a relatively small pulsed gate current makes the SCR uniquely adapted for use in this power-control mode.

5.1
ASSUMPTIONS

In the power-circuit analysis in this chapter, we will emphasize primary circuit behavior. The SCR (and any diodes) thus will be considered ideal except where nonideal aspects are specifically considered. The following assumptions are made about SCR circuit characteristics:

(a) The SCR is turned on by a negligibly short gate-current pulse.

(b) The turn on occurs in zero time.

(c) When conducting, the anode-to-cathode voltage is zero.

(d) At turnoff, there is no reverse anode current, even for a short transient interval, during the time that the anode-to-cathode voltage is reversed.

(e) The turnoff state is achieved in zero time.

(f) In the OFF state, the anode current is zero.

Figure 5.1 shows (c), (d), and (f) of these ideal characteristics for the steady-state case.

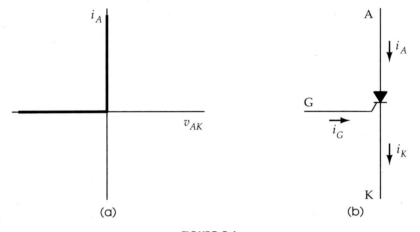

(a)   (b)

FIGURE 5.1

5.2

DIODE RECTIFIER CIRCUIT ANALYSIS

Before we analyze controlled rectifier circuits, we will find it useful to study certain noncontrolled rectifier circuits. The diodes used have the same ideal characteristics as those in part (a) of Figure 5.1.

Half-Wave Resistive Load

In Figure 5.2(a), a very simple half-wave rectifier circuit is shown. Part (b) shows graphs of current and load voltage. The source voltage is a sinusoid of maximum value V_m and period T.

The circuit equation is

$$v_S = v_D + v_R. \tag{5.1}$$

Because $v_D = 0$ for $i(t) > 0$, the equation for current is

$$i(t) = \frac{v_S}{R} = \frac{V_m \sin \omega t}{R}. \tag{5.2}$$

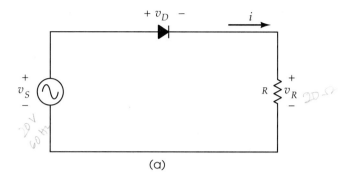

(a)

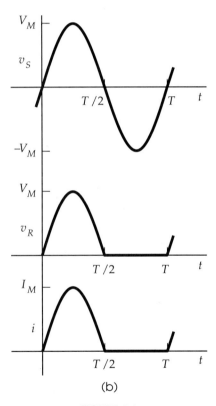

(b)

FIGURE 5.2

In Equation 5.2, ω corresponds to the specified source frequency, and the equation is valid only for $i(t) > 0$. Thus, maximum current occurs for v_S equal to V_m; it is given by

$$I_m = \frac{V_m}{R}. \tag{5.3}$$

During conduction, $v_D = 0$, so

$$v_R = v_S \quad \text{for} \quad i(t) > 0. \tag{5.4}$$

During the half-cycle when $v_S < 0$, the diode is reverse-biased, the current is zero, and thus v_R is zero. During this half-cycle, then,

$$v_D = v_S. \tag{5.5}$$

The quantities of interest for this circuit are average load current and voltage. Average current is found by integration of $i(t)$ over the period of the waveform:

$$I_{\text{avg}} = \frac{1}{T} \int_0^T i(t)\, dt. \tag{5.6}$$

Because $i(t) = 0$ for the second half-period, this integral is evaluated over a half-period from 0 to $T/2$:

$$I_{\text{avg}} = \frac{1}{T} \int_0^{T/2} I_m \sin \omega t\, dt \tag{5.7}$$

where

$$\omega = (2\pi)(f) = \frac{2\pi}{T}.$$

Integration of Equation 5.7 yields Equation 5.8, which is characteristic of the half-wave circuit:

$$I_{\text{avg}} = \frac{I_m}{\pi}. \tag{5.8}$$

Because the voltage waveform has the same shape as the current waveform, a relation similar to Equation 5.8 holds for the average load voltage:

$$V_{\text{avg}} = \frac{V_m}{\pi}. \tag{5.9}$$

Occasionally, the root-mean-square (RMS) value of the current is required. This is found by using the definition for an RMS value:

$$I_{\text{RMS}} = \left[\frac{1}{T} \int_0^T [i(t)]^2\, dt \right]^{0.5}. \tag{5.10}$$

Once again, the integral is evaluated over the half-period:

$$I_{RMS} = \left[\frac{1}{T} \int_0^{T/2} (I_m \sin \omega t)^2 \, dt \right]^{0.5} \tag{5.11}$$

$$= \frac{I_m}{2}. \tag{5.12}$$

The result in Equation 5.12 is characteristic of the half-wave circuit waveform.

The graph in Figure 5.2(b) shows that the diode must block a reverse voltage that is equal to the peak source voltage. This value is necessary for selecting the proper diode rectifier in a given circuit.

EXAMPLE 5.1

A half-wave rectifier with resistive load as shown in Figure 5.2(a) has a load of 20 Ω and a source voltage of 240-V RMS, 60 Hz. Find:

(a) peak load voltage

(b) peak load current

(c) average load voltage

(d) average load current

(e) RMS load current

(f) power to the load.

Solution

(a)   Peak load voltage $= V_m = 1.414 V_{RMS} = (1.414)(240)$
$= 339.4$ V

(b)   Peak load current $= \dfrac{V_m}{R} = \dfrac{339.4}{20} = 16.97$ A

(c)   Average load voltage $= \dfrac{V_m}{\pi} = \dfrac{339.4}{\pi} = 108.0$ V

(d)   Average load current $= \dfrac{I_m}{\pi} = \dfrac{16.97}{\pi} = 5.4$ A

(e)   RMS load current $= \dfrac{I_m}{2} = \dfrac{16.97}{2} = 8.48$ A

(f)   Power to the load $= (I_{RMS})^2(R) = (8.48)^2(20) = 1440$ W.   ■

Half-Wave Inductive Load

The half-wave circuit in Figure 5.2 is modified to include an inductive load as shown in Figure 5.3. The load current may exist for somewhat more than half of the entire period. No matter how large the load inductance, conduction may

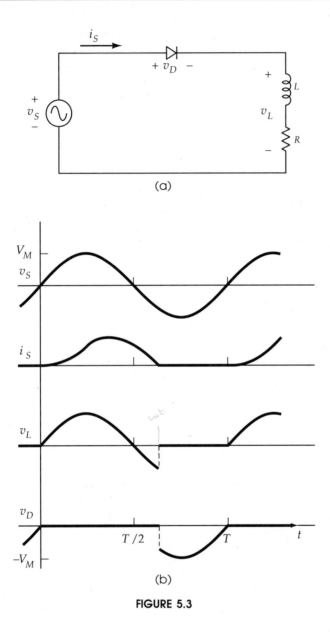

(a)

(b)

FIGURE 5.3

not exist for the full period; if it did, the diode would conduct continuously, the voltage across the diode would be essentially zero for the entire period, and the values of v_S and v_L would be equal. There would be no rectifier action and the current would be alternating. This condition is a contradiction and cannot exist. The load current must be zero for some interval that is less than one-half of the period.

A solution for the transient load current may be determined as follows from the methods in Appendix A. In the circuit in Figure 5.3, the current is zero at $t = 0$. The relation for current is given in Equation 5.13:

$$i = \left(\frac{V_m}{|Z|}\right)[\sin(\omega t - \theta) + (\sin \theta) e^{-t/\tau}] \tag{5.13}$$

$$|Z| = (R^2 + \omega^2 L^2)^{0.5} \tag{5.14}$$

$$\theta = \tan^{-1}\left(\frac{\omega L}{R}\right). \tag{5.15}$$

The current in Equation 5.13 becomes zero at some time greater than $T/2$. This time can be found by a numerical iteration of this equation.

For large power rectification, this method is not very useful. No amount of inductance can produce a load current that is not zero for some part of each cycle. Furthermore, the AC source current is unidirectional and may cause a saturation problem in a transformer that supplies the rectifier circuit, especially if the load current is large.

EXAMPLE 5.2

In Figure 5.3, find the average value of the load voltage and the load current; $V_S = 120$-V RMS, 60-Hz; $R = 20\ \Omega$; and $L = 0.0531$ H.

Solution   Solution of Equations 5.13 through 5.15 by iteration provides the time at which the current becomes zero:

$$\theta = \tan^{-1}\left[\frac{(120\pi)(0.0531)}{20}\right] = \frac{\pi}{4}\ \text{rad}$$

$$|Z| = [(20)^2 + (20)^2]^{0.5} = 28.28\ \Omega$$

$$\omega\tau = \tan \theta = 1$$

$$i = \left[\frac{(120)(2)^{0.5}}{28.28}\right]\left[\sin\left(\omega t - \frac{\pi}{4}\right) + 0.707\ e^{-\omega t/\omega\tau}\right].$$

The solution for ωt that makes $i = 0$ is at $\omega t = 3.9407$ radians.

The load voltage is the same as the source voltage for $0 < \omega t < 3.9407$, and is zero for the remainder of the cycle. The average value of v_L may be determined by integration, with an angle variable substituting for the variable:

$$V_L = \frac{1}{2\pi}\int_0^{3.9407} (120)(1.414) \sin \theta\ d\theta = 45.84\ \text{V}.$$

The average load current can be found from the average load voltage and the resistance:

$$I_L = \frac{V_L}{R} = \frac{45.84}{20} = 2.29\ \text{A}. \qquad \blacksquare$$

A modification of Figure 5.3 as shown in Figure 5.4 produces a circuit that is useful for loads requiring a relatively small amount of power. It remains a half-wave circuit, but the load current now may exist for the full period of operation. The graphs in this figure show the circuit currents and voltages and are drawn with the assumption of a large load inductance.

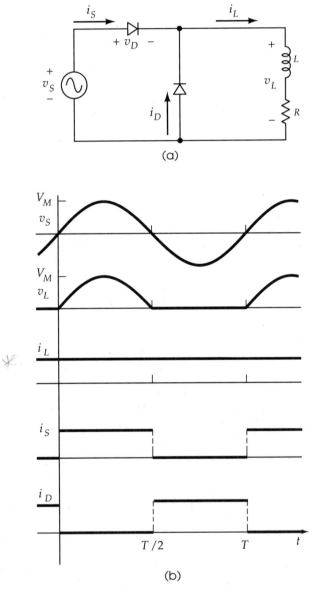

(a)

(b)

FIGURE 5.4

The diode in parallel with the load is known as a *freewheeling-diode*, or FWD. The circuit action of this diode prevents v_L from being negative. During the second half-cycle—when source voltage is negative—the load current may exist in the FWD. During this interval of FWD conduction, the voltage equation through the source and the main diode shows that the main diode is reverse-biased and thus the source current is zero for this half-period.

The average values for the load voltage and load current are the same as those for the half-wave resistive case. A comparison of the graphs for the two cases shows the same waveform for load voltage as a function of time. Equation 5.9 thus applies for this case.

EXAMPLE 5.3

The circuit in Figure 5.4 has the following values: $V_S = $ 120-V RMS, 60-Hz; and $R = 20\ \Omega$. The load inductance is large. Find:

(a) the average load voltage

(b) the average load current

(c) the load power.

Solution

(a) From Equation 5.9:

$$V_L = \frac{(120)(1.414)}{\pi} = 54.0\ \text{V}$$

(b) $$I_L = \frac{V_L}{R} = \frac{54}{20} = 2.7\ \text{A}$$

(c) $$P = I_L^2 R = (2.7)^2(20) = 145.8\ \text{W}.$$

This last calculation is correct: The load current is nearly constant because of the large value of the load inductance.   ∎

Full-Wave Resistive Load

The full-wave function can be obtained by using either a bridge rectifier or a transformer with a center-tapped secondary. The circuit in Figure 5.5(a), for illustration, uses a bridge-rectifier arrangement.

The source voltage and load resistor are the same as in the half-wave case. The full-wave circuit causes current in the load as before, but current also exists in the load during the second half-cycle. This second half-cycle portion is identical to the current that occurs during the first half-cycle, except that it is shifted to the right on the time axis. The diode bridge acts in a current steering mode so that the source current i_S, which is alternating, becomes a unidirectional current in the load resistor. Figure 5.5(b) shows appropriate waveforms, with the maximum current I_m still given by Equation 5.3.

Average and RMS values can be found in a manner similar to that for the half-wave case:

$$I_{avg} = \frac{1}{T} \int_0^T i_L(t)\, dt \tag{5.16}$$

$$I_{avg} = \frac{1}{T} \left[\int_0^{T/2} I_m \sin \omega t\, dt + \int_{T/2}^T -I_m \sin \omega t\, dt \right] \tag{5.17}$$

$$I_{avg} = \left(\frac{2}{\pi}\right) I_m. \tag{5.18}$$

We can note here that the full-wave average is twice the half-wave average. This is obvious by inspection of the two graphs of current versus time. Similarly, the average load voltage is given by the same factor, so

$$V_{avg} = \left(\frac{2}{\pi}\right) V_m. \tag{5.19}$$

The RMS current is found again using the RMS definition:

$$I_{RMS} = \left[\frac{1}{T} \int_0^T [i_L(t)]^2\, dt \right]^{0.5} \tag{5.20}$$

$$I_{RMS} = \left[\frac{1}{T} \int_0^{T/2} (I_m \sin \omega t)^2\, dt + \frac{1}{T} \int_{T/2}^T (-I_m \sin \omega t)^2\, dt \right]^{0.5}. \tag{5.21}$$

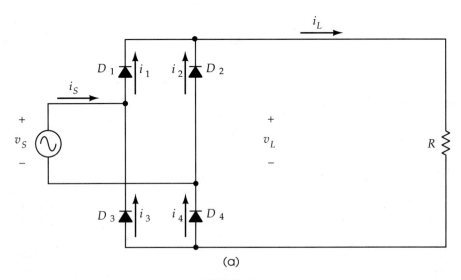

(a)

FIGURE 5.5

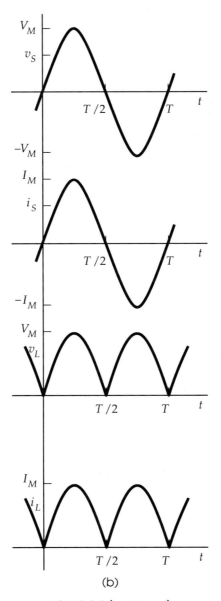

(b)

FIGURE 5.5 (continued)

Inspection of Equation 5.21 shows that the negative sign for the second half-period makes no difference, and the result of the mathematical process is the same as for the RMS of any sinusoid. Thus,

$$I_{RMS} = \frac{I_m}{(2)^{0.5}}. \qquad \qquad (5.22)$$

Once again, as in the half-wave case, the graph in Figure 5.5(b) shows that the diode must block a reverse voltage equal to V_m. Because there are two paths for the load current, average diode current is just one-half of the average load current.

EXAMPLE 5.4

A full-wave rectifier with resistive load as shown in Figure 5.5(a) has a load of 20 Ω and a source voltage of 240-V RMS, 60 Hz. Find:

(a) peak load voltage
(b) peak load current
(c) average load voltage
(d) average load current
(e) RMS load current
(f) power to the load.

Solution

(a)   Peak load voltage $= V_m = 1.414 V_{RMS} = (1.414)(240)$
$$= 339.4 \text{ V}$$

(b)   Peak load current $= \dfrac{V_m}{R} = \dfrac{339.4}{20} = 16.97 \text{ A}$

(c)   Average load voltage $= \left(\dfrac{2}{\pi}\right) V_m = \left(\dfrac{2}{\pi}\right) 339.4 = 216.0 \text{ V}$

(d)   Average load current $= \left(\dfrac{2}{\pi}\right) I_m = \left(\dfrac{2}{\pi}\right) 16.97 = 10.8 \text{ A}$

(e)   RMS load current $= \dfrac{I_m}{(2)^{0.5}} = \dfrac{16.97}{(2)^{0.5}} = 12.0 \text{ A}$

(f)   Power to load $= (I_{RMS})^2(R) = (12.0)^2(20) = 2880 \text{ W}.$ ∎

Full-Wave Inductive Load

The addition of inductance in series with the load resistance changes the current waveform. Only the full-wave case is considered here. Figure 5.6 is Figure 5.5(a) redrawn with an inductive load.

To make the analysis simple, an initial solution is done with an infinite load inductance. In practice this means that the load inductance is large enough that there is negligible ripple in the load current versus time. As we will see in a later example, the required inductance is not so large as to be unreasonable.

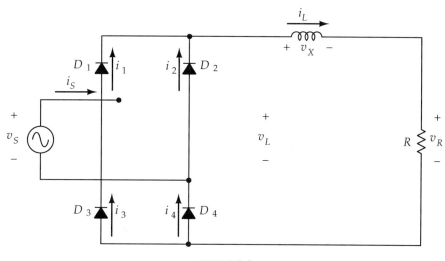

FIGURE 5.6

With this assumption, the circuit behavior is as shown in the graphs in Figure 5.7. Constant load current means that two of the diodes conduct a constant current on alternate half-cycles while the other two diodes do the same on the remaining half-cycles. The source current is alternating and of rectangular waveform. The load is connected to the source at all times, except that on alternate half-cycles, the connection is reversed. The load voltage again is the familiar full-wave rectified version of a sinusoid.

Circuit currents and voltages are evaluated easily. The average voltage to the load is the same value as for the resistive case. The load current now is essentially constant, and its value in relation to the load resistance must be found. The instantaneous voltage equation for Figure 5.6 allows this determination:

$$v_L = v_X + v_R. \tag{5.23}$$

If this equation is integrated over one period, the result is an equation in average voltages.

$$V_{L_{\text{avg}}} = V_{X_{\text{avg}}} + V_{R_{\text{avg}}}. \tag{5.24}$$

The average value of V_X is the average voltage across an ideal inductor. In periodic operation, the average voltage across an inductor must be zero. Note that if there is any resistance in the inductor, it may be included as part of the load resistor. Thus, from Equation 5.24:

$$V_{R_{\text{avg}}} = V_{L_{\text{avg}}} = \left(\frac{2}{\pi}\right) V_m \tag{5.25}$$

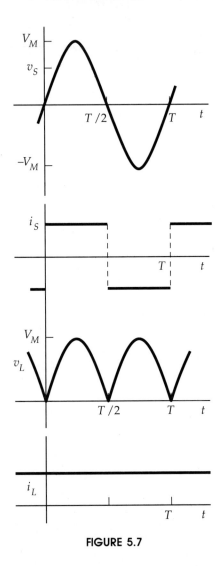

FIGURE 5.7

and

$$I_{avg} = \frac{V_{R_{avg}}}{R} \tag{5.26}$$

or

$$I_{avg} = \left(\frac{2}{\pi}\right)\left(\frac{V_m}{R}\right). \tag{5.27}$$

Because the load current is constant, its RMS and average values are the same.

EXAMPLE 5.5

A full-wave diode rectifier with an inductive load—as in Figure 5.6—has the resistive part of the load equal to 20 Ω and a source voltage of 240-V RMS, 60-Hz. Find:

(a) peak load voltage
(b) average load voltage
(c) peak load current
(d) average load current
(e) RMS load current
(f) power to the load
(g) average current in each diode.

Solution

(a) Peak load voltage $= V_m = 1.414 V_{RMS} = (1.414)(240)$
$$= 339.4 \text{ V}$$

(b) Average load voltage $= \left(\dfrac{2}{\pi}\right) V_m = \left(\dfrac{2}{\pi}\right) 339.4 = 216.0 \text{ V}$

(c) Peak load current $= \dfrac{V_{avg}}{R} = \dfrac{216.0}{20} = 10.80 \text{ A}$

(d) Average load current $=$ peak load current $= 10.80 \text{ A}$

(e) RMS load current $=$ average load current $= 10.80 \text{ A}$

(f) Power to load $= (I_{RMS})^2(R) = (10.80)^2(20) = 2334 \text{ W}$

(g) Diode average current $= \frac{1}{2} I_{avg} = \dfrac{10.80}{2} = 5.4 \text{ A}.$

The $\frac{1}{2}$ factor in item (g) results from the fact that the diodes in the bridge conduct on alternate half-cycles.   ■

5.3

PHASE CONTROL

In the process of phase control, the diode rectifiers in the circuits in the previous section are replaced by SCRs. Now as the source voltage reverses and SCR current becomes zero during each half-cycle, the SCR recovers its blocking ability and will not conduct until a gate current is provided. If that gate current is not provided at the time when the anode-to-cathode voltage becomes positive but is delayed, and if this process is done repeatedly, then the rectifier's output is reduced. This process is called *phase control of the rectifier output.* If the circuit is full-wave, it is usual to provide the same delay on both half-cycles. The delay usually is specified in terms of the angle α measured on the scale of $360°$ per cycle.

Phase Control: Half-Wave, Resistive

If in Figure 5.2 the diode is replaced by an SCR as shown in Figure 5.8(a) and if the SCR conduction each half-cycle is delayed by the angle α, the graphs in Figure 5.8(b) result. In these graphs, the SCR is turned on at time t_1, which is given by α/ω.

In the real world, the SCR does not turn on in zero time and no load resistance is truly without inductance, so the current cannot have a discontinuity as shown. On the time scale of the period T, however, these actions occur in such a short time that the idealization shown is a very good approximation.

The average values of the voltage and current are again of interest. These are found in a manner similar to the previous calculations:

$$I_{\text{avg}} = \frac{1}{T} \int_0^T i_L(t)\, dt \qquad (5.28)$$

$$I_{\text{avg}} = \frac{1}{T} \int_{t_1}^{T/2} I_m \sin \omega t\, dt. \qquad (5.29)$$

In Equation 5.29, the integration is done starting at t_1 because the current is nonzero only from t_1 to $T/2$:

$$I_{\text{avg}} = \left(\frac{I_m}{2\pi}\right)(1 + \cos \alpha). \qquad (5.30)$$

The same equation applies for voltage with V_m replacing I_m:

$$V_{\text{avg}} = \left(\frac{V_m}{2\pi}\right)(1 + \cos \alpha). \qquad (5.31)$$

The RMS value of the load current is found using the basic definition and is given in Equation 5.32:

$$I_{\text{RMS}} = \left[\frac{1}{T} \int_{t_1}^{T/2} (I_m \sin \omega t)^2\, dt\right]^{0.5}. \qquad (5.32)$$

After simplifying, this results in Equation 5.33:

$$I_{\text{RMS}} = \left(\frac{I_m}{2}\right)\left[1 - \left(\frac{\alpha}{\pi}\right) + \left(\frac{\sin 2\alpha}{2\pi}\right)\right]^{0.5}. \qquad (5.33)$$

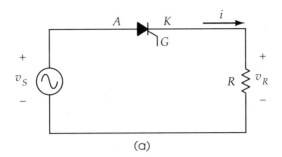

(a)

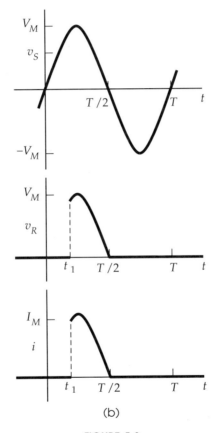

(b)

FIGURE 5.8

EXAMPLE 5.6

A half-wave, phase-controlled rectifier with resistive load—as shown in Figure 5.8(a)—has a load of 20 Ω and a source voltage of 240-V RMS, 60 Hz. The circuit operates with $\alpha = 40°$. Find:

(a) peak load voltage

(b) peak load current

(c) average load voltage

(d) average load current

(e) RMS load current

(f) power to the load.

Solution

(a) $\quad$ Peak load voltage $= V_m = 1.414 V_{RMS} = (1.414)(240)$
$$= 339.4 \text{ V}$$

(b) $\quad$ Peak load current $= \dfrac{V_m}{R} = \dfrac{339.4}{20} = 16.97 \text{ A}$

(c) $\quad$ Average load voltage $= \left(\dfrac{V_m}{2\pi}\right)(1 + \cos \alpha)$

$$= \left(\dfrac{339.4}{2\pi}\right)(1 + \cos 40°) = 95.4 \text{ V}$$

(d) $\quad$ Average load current $= \left(\dfrac{I_m}{2\pi}\right)(1 + \cos \alpha)$

$$= \left(\dfrac{16.97}{2\pi}\right)(1 + \cos 40°) = 4.77 \text{ A}$$

(e) $\quad$ RMS load current as determined from Equation 5.33:

$$I_{RMS} = \left(\dfrac{I_m}{2}\right)\left[1 - \left(\dfrac{\alpha}{\pi}\right) + \left(\dfrac{\sin 2\alpha}{2\pi}\right)\right]^{0.5}$$

$$I_{RMS} = \left(\dfrac{16.97}{2}\right)\left[1 - \left(\dfrac{40}{180}\right) + \left(\dfrac{\sin 80°}{2\pi}\right)\right]^{0.5}$$

$$I_{RMS} = 8.20 \text{ A}$$

(f) $\quad$ Power to load $= (I_{RMS})^2(R) = (8.20)^2(20) = 1345 \text{ W}.$ $\quad$ ■

Phase Control: Full-Wave, Resistive

In the circuit in Figure 5.5(a), the diodes have been replaced by SCRs and the circuit is shown in Figure 5.9. Phase control of a full-wave type now is possible.

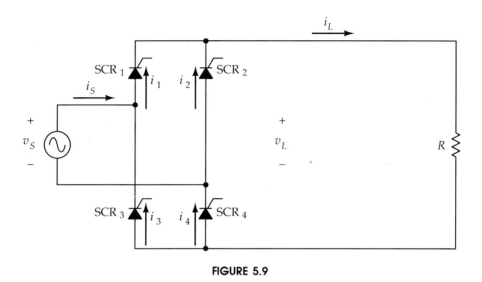

FIGURE 5.9

The SCRs are controlled and gated in pairs again with a phase delay of α. The current and voltage waveforms become full-wave as shown in Figure 5.10, where $t_1 = \alpha/\omega$ and $t_2 = t_1 + T/2$.

The average values of current and voltage can be obtained by inspection because the area under the full-wave curves is twice the area of the half-wave case. Thus, from Equations 5.30 and 5.31,

$$I_{avg} = \left(\frac{I_m}{\pi}\right)(1 + \cos\alpha) \tag{5.34}$$

$$I_{avg} = \left(\frac{V_m}{\pi R}\right)(1 + \cos\alpha) \tag{5.35}$$

and

$$V_{avg} = \left(\frac{V_m}{\pi}\right)(1 + \cos\alpha). \tag{5.36}$$

The load current's RMS value is obtained by modifying Equation 5.33 for the half-wave case. There are now two pulses per cycle as compared to the half-wave case. The RMS value is $(2)^{0.5}$ times as large as in Equation 5.33. The resulting RMS value is given by Equation 5.37:

$$I_{RMS} = \left[\frac{I_m}{(2)^{0.5}}\right]\left[1 - \left(\frac{\alpha}{\pi}\right) + \left(\frac{\sin 2\alpha}{2\pi}\right)\right]^{0.5}. \tag{5.37}$$

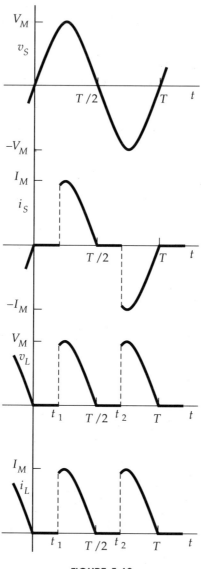

FIGURE 5.10

EXAMPLE 5.7

A full-wave, phase-controlled rectifier with resistive load—as shown in Figure 5.9—has a load of 20 Ω and a source voltage of 240-V RMS, 60 Hz. The circuit operates with $\alpha = 40°$. Find:

(a) peak load voltage

(b) peak load current

(c) average load voltage

(d) average load current

(e) RMS load current

(f) power to the load.

Solution

(a) Peak load voltage $= V_m = 1.414V_{RMS} = (1.414)(240)$
$$= 339.4 \text{ V}$$

(b) Peak load current $= \dfrac{V_m}{R} = \dfrac{339.4}{20} = 16.97 \text{ A}$

(c) Average load voltage $= \left(\dfrac{V_m}{\pi}\right)(1 + \cos \alpha)$

$$= \left(\dfrac{339.4}{\pi}\right)(1 + \cos 40°) = 190.8 \text{ V}$$

(d) Average load current $= \left(\dfrac{I_m}{\pi}\right)(1 + \cos \alpha)$

$$= \left(\dfrac{16.97}{\pi}\right)(1 + \cos 40°) = 9.54 \text{ A}$$

(e) RMS load current using Equation 5.37:

$$I_{RMS} = \left[\dfrac{I_m}{(2)^{0.5}}\right]\left[1 - \left(\dfrac{\alpha}{\pi}\right) + \left(\dfrac{\sin 2\alpha}{2\pi}\right)\right]^{0.5}$$

$$I_{RMS} = \left[\dfrac{16.97}{(2)^{0.5}}\right]\left[1 - \left(\dfrac{40}{180}\right) + \left(\dfrac{\sin 80°}{2\pi}\right)\right]^{0.5}$$

$$I_{RMS} = 11.60 \text{ A}$$

(f) Power to load $= (I_{RMS})^2(R) = (11.60)^2(20) = 2690 \text{ W.}$ ∎

Phase Control: Full-Wave, Inductive Load

Once again the load inductance is assumed to be large enough that the load current has negligible ripple. Figure 5.6 is redrawn here as Figure 5.11, with the diodes replaced by SCRs.

Consider an instant at which $v_S > 0$ and SCR_1 and SCR_4 are conducting. At this time $i_S > 0$. If a voltage equation is written around the loop of v_S, SCR_1, and SCR_2, the following equation is obtained:

$$v_S = v_{AK_1} - v_{AK_2}. \tag{5.38}$$

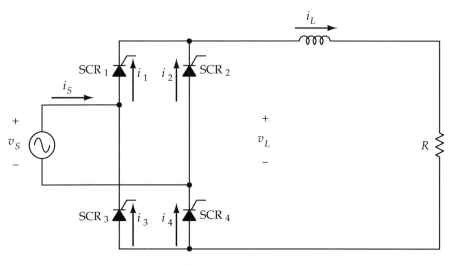

FIGURE 5.11

But because SCR_1 is conducting, $v_{AK_1} = 0$, and therefore

$$v_{AK_2} = (-v_S) < 0, \qquad (5.39)$$

which means that SCR_2 is reverse-biased.

A voltage equation around the loop of v_S, SCR_1, the load, and SCR_4 gives the equation

$$v_S = v_{AK_1} + v_L + v_{AK_4}. \qquad (5.40)$$

Once again, the conducting SCRs have zero anode-to-cathode voltage. Therefore,

$$v_L = v_S. \qquad (5.41)$$

Now, as v_S changes to a negative value, the above equations do not change form, although some of the quantities change sign. Recall that no change in the current path can occur because SCR_2 and SCR_3 have not yet been gated on. Because $v_S < 0$, v_{AK_2} is > 0, and thus SCR_2 is ready to turn on but has not yet received a gate signal. Likewise, SCR_3 is ready to turn on. The load voltage is now negative because $v_S < 0$.

The result of these statements is shown in the graph in Figure 5.12. The time during which these conditions occur is from t_1 to t_2. During the interval from t_1 to $T/2$, the load voltage is positive and SCR_2 is reverse-biased. From $T/2$ to t_2, the load voltage is negative, and SCR_2 is forward-biased but has not yet been provided a turn-on signal.

Now at $t = t_2$, with $v_S < 0$, SCR_2 and SCR_3 are provided gate signals to turn on. Note that both SCRs have positive anode-to-cathode voltages at this

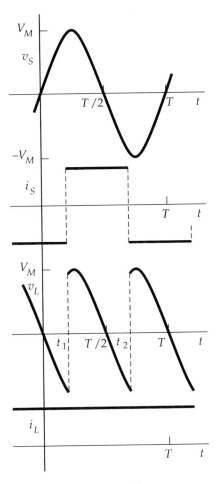

FIGURE 5.12

time. If in Equation 5.38 the value of v_{AK_2} is set equal to zero, because SCR$_2$ has just been turned on, then v_{AK_1} must be negative. This means that SCR$_1$ is reverse-biased and therefore is in the OFF state. In a similar manner, SCR$_4$ also is turned off.

At this point, the load is connected to the source by way of SCR$_2$ and SCR$_3$ so that the load voltage becomes the negative of v_S. Ideally, there is a discontinuity of v_L as shown in Figure 5.12 at time t_2.

The effect of phase control has been to delay the transfer of the current path from the natural point in time to a later time; the result is that the load voltage has intervals during which its instantaneous value is negative. This is in contrast to the diode case in which the transfer occurs at $v_S = 0$.

The average value of this output voltage is a function of α. The integration is best done over a half-period from t_1 to t_2:

$$V_{avg} = \frac{2}{T} \int_{t_1}^{t_2} V_m \sin \omega t \, dt \qquad (5.42)$$

$$V_{avg} = \left(\frac{2}{\pi}\right) V_m \cos \alpha. \qquad (5.43)$$

Average current still is V_{avg}/R, so

$$I_{avg} = \left(\frac{2}{\pi}\right)\left(\frac{V_m}{R}\right) \cos \alpha. \qquad (5.44)$$

It may be noted that for $\alpha = 0$ (no intentional phase control), the above expressions reduce to those for the diode case.

EXAMPLE 5.8

A full-wave, phase-controlled rectifier with an inductive load as shown in Figure 5.11 has the resistive part of the load equal to 20 Ω and a source voltage of 240-V RMS, 60 Hz. The phase control angle is 40°. Find:

(a) peak load voltage

(b) average load voltage

(c) average load current

(d) peak load current

(e) RMS load current

(f) power to the load

(g) average current in each SCR.

Solution

(a)   Peak load voltage $= V_m = 1.414 V_{RMS} = (1.414)(240)$
$$= 339.4 \text{ V}$$

(b)   Average load voltage $= \left(\frac{2}{\pi}\right) V_m \cos \alpha$

$$= \left(\frac{2}{\pi}\right)(339.4)(\cos 40°) = 165.5 \text{ V}$$

(c)   Average load current $= \dfrac{V_{avg}}{R} = \dfrac{165.5}{20} = 8.28 \text{ A}$

(d)   Peak load current $=$ average load current $= 8.28$ A

(e)   RMS load current $=$ average load current $= 8.28$ A

(f) Power to load $= (I_{RMS})^2(R) = (8.28)^2(20) = 1370$ W

(g) SCR average current $= \dfrac{1}{2} I_{avg} = \dfrac{8.28}{2} = 4.14$ A.

The $\frac{1}{2}$ factor in item (g) results from the fact that the SCRs in the bridge conduct on alternate half-cycles. ■

Addition of Freewheeling Diode

The circuit in Figure 5.11 now is modified by the addition of a freewheeling diode (FWD) as shown in Figure 5.13. The added element provides an additional path for the load current so that three paths are possible: SCR_1 with SCR_4, SCR_2 with SCR_3, and, finally, the path of the freewheeling diode D_1. Furthermore, the presence of D_1 prevents negative values of v_L from occurring. Negative values of v_L correspond to forward bias on D_1, and the model for diodes requires zero voltage for forward current.

The portions in Figure 5.12 where $v_L < 0$ now are replaced by $v_L = 0$ as shown in Figure 5.14. During these intervals, the load current occurs in D_1; both the SCR currents and i_S are zero. To demonstrate this current commutation (or transfer from one path to another), consider the equation around the path that includes v_S, SCR_1, v_L, and SCR_4:

$$v_S = v_{AK_1} + v_L + v_{AK_4}. \tag{5.45}$$

Now, with $v_S < 0$ and $v_L = 0$ by reason of the FWD, it is true that

$$v_{AK_1} + v_{AK_4} < 0. \tag{5.46}$$

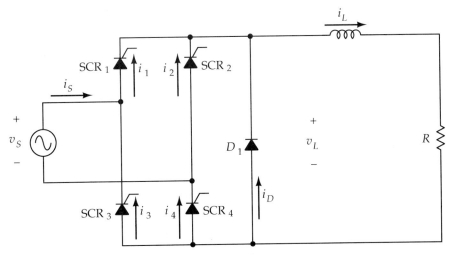

FIGURE 5.13

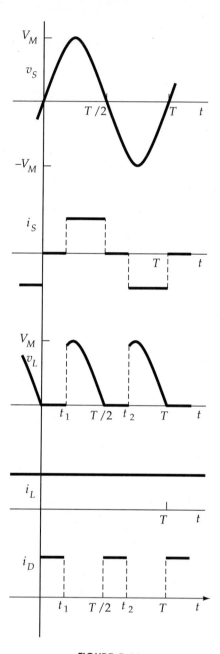

FIGURE 5.14

Thus, the two SCRs in series are reverse-biased and turn off. This is consistent with the transfer of the load current to the freewheeling diode.

A new equation for average load voltage is not necessary because the load voltage waveform is the same as that for the resistive load case. The average load voltage is the same as in Equation 5.36:

$$V_{avg} = \left(\frac{V_m}{\pi}\right)(1 + \cos \alpha). \tag{5.47}$$

One additional current exists as compared to the case without the FWD. The current in the FWD is the same as the load current in the interval from $t = 0$ to $t = \alpha/\omega$ and for a similar interval in the second half-cycle. The current is zero for the remaining time. The average and the peak currents are needed to select this circuit element. The FWD's peak current is the same as the load current. Average current in the FWD is given by Equation 5.48:

$$I_{D_{avg}} = I_L\left[\frac{t_1}{T/2}\right] = I_L\left(\frac{\alpha}{\pi}\right). \tag{5.48}$$

EXAMPLE 5.9

A full-wave, phase-controlled rectifier with a freewheeling diode supplies an inductive load as shown in Figure 5.13. The resistive part of the load equals 20 Ω. Source voltage is 240-V RMS, 60 Hz, and $\alpha = 40°$. Find:

(a) peak load voltage

(b) average load voltage

(c) average load current

(d) peak load current

(e) RMS load current

(f) power to the load

(g) average current in each SCR

(h) FWD average current.

Solution

(a)   Peak load voltage $= V_m = 1.414V_{RMS} = (1.414)(240)$
$= 339.4$ V

(b)   Average load voltage $= \left(\frac{V_m}{\pi}\right)(1 + \cos \alpha)$

$= \left(\frac{339.4}{\pi}\right)(1 + \cos 40°) = 190.8$ V

(c) $\qquad$ Average load current $= \dfrac{V_{\text{avg}}}{R} = \dfrac{190.8}{20} = 9.54$ A

(d) $\qquad$ Peak load current $=$ average load current $= 9.54$ A

(e) $\qquad$ RMS load current $=$ average load current $= 9.54$ A

(f) $\qquad$ Power to load $= (I_{\text{RMS}})^2(R) = (9.54)^2(20) = 1820$ W

(g) $\qquad$ SCR average current $= \left(\dfrac{140}{360}\right)(9.54) = 3.71$ A.

The factor in item (g) results from the fact that the SCRs in the bridge conduct on alternate half-cycles for 140°.

(h) From Equation 5.48,

$$I_{D_{\text{avg}}} = \frac{(9.54)(40)}{180} = 2.12 \text{ A.} \qquad\qquad \blacksquare$$

Triggering in Phase-Control Circuits

The SCR gate pulses for phase-controlled rectifiers must be delayed with respect to the zero crossing of the AC-source voltage. Some synchronizing means must be used to ensure that the gate pulses do not occur randomly with respect to that zero crossing. If a capacitor is charged and then discharged to generate such pulses, synchronization can be ensured by completely discharging the capacitor at the end of each half-cycle of the voltage source. Thus, there is a known and repeatable starting point for the capacitor-charging interval.

Several three-terminal semiconductor switching devices can perform this gate-triggering function. One such device, a programmable unijunction transistor (PUT), is used to illustrate the use of such devices, especially in SCR turn on under phase-control conditions. The device symbol with bias source and a graph of v_{AK} versus i_A are both shown in Figure 5.15.

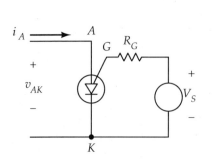
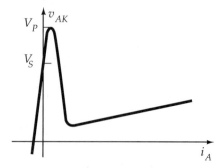

FIGURE 5.15

To have appreciable anode current, the anode voltage must exceed V_S by a small threshold, typically less than one volt. If this occurs, the device switches into a conducting state and provides appreciable current conduction. The voltage level at which the switching occurs is programmable through its dependence on V_S. The desired value of V_S typically is obtained by means of a voltage-divider circuit; its Thévenin equivalent is represented by R_G and V_S in Figure 5.15.

The use of the PUT is similar to that of the DIAC element used in Chapter 3. It discharges a capacitor into the gate lead of an SCR. The switching voltage depends on V_S and this is used to provide the required synchronization of capacitor charging.

The circuit in Figure 5.16 illustrates the use of a PUT to trigger an SCR in a half-wave resistive circuit. The zener diode provides a nearly constant voltage for V_S during the half-cycle that the source voltage is positive. At PUT turn on, the capacitor is discharged rapidly into the parallel combination of the resistor R_K and SCR gate circuit. At the end of the positive portion of each source voltage cycle, V_S becomes zero, and because the anode-to-cathode voltage peak value can be only a fraction of a volt greater than V_S, the rapidly falling value of V_S causes the capacitor to discharge at the end of each positive half-cycle. The graphs in Figure 5.17 illustrate the manner in which the capacitor is discharged at the end of this half-cycle interval.

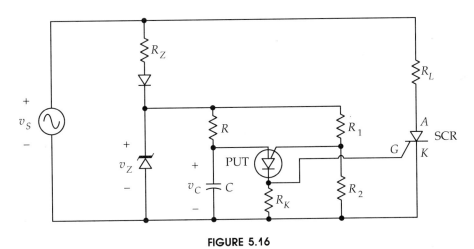

FIGURE 5.16

In Figure 5.17, the capacitor charges to a voltage slightly higher than the value determined by R_1, R_2, and the clipping level of the zener diode. The capacitor then discharges through the PUT, R_K, and the SCR's gate. After this initial discharge, the capacitor begins one or more additional charge–discharge cycles. These additional cycles have no effect because the SCR already is in the conducting state.

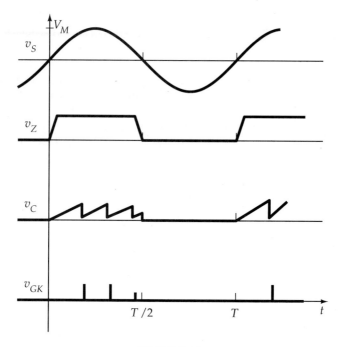

FIGURE 5.17

A model of the PUT in the conducting state is similar to the piecewise linear model of the DIAC in Chapter 3. The circuit in Figure 5.18 can be used to represent a portion of the circuit in Figure 5.16 during the PUT's conduction interval. This circuit ignores certain second-order effects such as the PUT's turn-on time and additional charging of the capacitor during the discharge time.

In Figure 5.18 the E_S and R_S values, which represent the PUT as a switch, can be determined from the device datasheet. A piecewise linear model is an approximation but remains a useful means of circuit analysis.

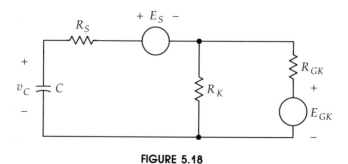

FIGURE 5.18

E X A M P L E   5 . 1 0

In the circuit in Figure 5.16, certain values are given. Remaining values are to be determined to meet the required condition that α be variable from $30°$ to $150°$ and that the SCR be provided sufficient gate current for reliable turn on. The zener diode shown may be modeled as ideal; when conducting in the reverse direction, its voltage is 20 V. For reliable turn on, the SCR requires a gate current greater than 0.1 A for 3 μs.

$$V_S = 120\text{-V RMS, 60 Hz} \qquad R_K = 50 \ \Omega \qquad R_Z = 4 \ k\Omega$$

$$\text{SCR gate model:} \quad E_{GK} = 1.2 \text{ V} \qquad R_{GK} = 15 \ \Omega$$

$$\text{PUT Model for 2N6028 when conducting:} \quad E_S = 1.0 \text{ V} \qquad R_S = 0.5 \ \Omega.$$

Find:

(a) values for R_1 and R_2

(b) a C value that provides adequate gate current

(c) the range of R required for the extremes of α.

Solution

(a) A wide range of values can be used for these two resistors. A reasonable choice is to make them equal and of such value that R_G in Figure 5.15 is 100 Ω. This is midway between datasheet values for which performance is specified. It is a compromise between a large value that results in a small peak anode current before turn on and a small value that yields a small offset in peak capacitor voltage relative to gate-source voltage, V_S. If these choices are made, $R_1 = R_2 = 200 \ k\Omega$.

(b) The circuit model to determine C is the PUT conducting model together with the SCR gate-to-cathode conducting model as shown in Figure 5.19. The initial v_C value is essentially 10 V as provided by the voltage-divider action of R_1 and R_2. A Thévenin equivalent of Figure 5.19 (shown

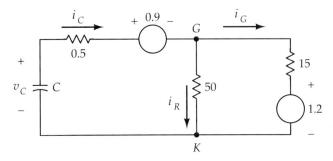

FIGURE 5.19

in Figure 5.20) is used for analysis:

$$i_C = \left(\frac{10 - 0.9 - 0.923}{11.54 + 0.5}\right) e^{-t/\tau}$$

$$= 0.679\, e^{-t/\tau}$$

$$\tau = (11.54 + 0.5)C$$

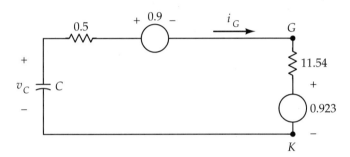

FIGURE 5.20

The capacitor current can be found by further circuit analysis:

$$v_{GK} = 0.923 + 11.54 i_C$$

$$v_{GK} = 0.923 + 7.837\, e^{-t/\tau}$$

$$i_R = \frac{v_{GK}}{R_K} = 0.018 + 0.157\, e^{-t/\tau}$$

$$i_G = i_C - i_R = -0.018 + 0.522\, e^{-t/\tau}.$$

At $t = 3\ \mu s$, i_G is required to be 0.10 A. Solving the above equation gives the value of τ:

$$\tau = 2.02\ \mu s = 12.04\ C$$

$$C = 0.168\ \mu F.$$

(c) For this calculation, we neglect that the initial part of the voltage across the zener diode is less than 20 V. It has a small effect on the resistance value, especially for small values of α. For $\alpha = 30°$, the capacitor must charge to 10 V from a 20-V source in 1.39 ms:

$$10 = 20(1 - e^{-t/\tau})$$

$$\tau = 2.00\ ms$$

with $C = 0.168\ \mu F$ and $R = 11.94\ k\Omega$.

For $\alpha = 150°$, the capacitor must charge in 6.94 ms, and the corresponding resistor value is 59.65 kΩ.

■

5.4
POWER FACTOR

The power factor of a rectifier and load as presented to the AC source has economic importance in two cases. Large loads on a utility system frequently are charged for a low power factor as well as for the actual energy consumed. In general, rectifier loads present a power factor less than unity and, in some cases, appreciably less. In addition, the power factor affects the transformer size required to serve a given load. An analysis of some of the common single-phase, full-wave cases follows. Generally, half-wave rectifier loads are small and do not have an appreciable power cost; they are not considered here.

Resistive Load with Phase Control

The AC-source current waveform in Figure 5.10 for a bridge rectifier has an RMS value that is the same as that for the load current given by Equation 5.37. The RMS value is a squared function and independent of the sign of a particular current. The currents on both the AC and DC sides of the bridge have the same RMS value.

Power factor is defined as the ratio of power delivered to the volt-ampere product of RMS voltage and RMS current. This definition yields a power factor less than unity for a resistive load with phase control.

Using the result from Equation 5.37 for RMS current, the power factor is determined as follows: S is defined as the volt-ampere product of AC-source RMS current and RMS voltage; on the DC side of the bridge, the power is found using Equation 5.49. Using the definition of power factor, additional equations can be written for the AC side of the bridge rectifier:

$$P = (I_{RMS})^2 R \tag{5.49}$$

$$S = V_{RMS}I_{RMS} = \left(\frac{V_m}{1.414}\right)(I_{RMS}) \tag{5.50}$$

$$\text{Power factor} = \frac{P}{S} = \frac{1.414RI_{RMS}}{V_m}. \tag{5.51}$$

Because V_m, I_m, and R are related, the result of Equation 5.51 can be rearranged to give Equation 5.52 using Equation 5.37:

$$\text{Power factor} = \left(1 - \frac{\alpha}{\pi} + \frac{\sin 2\alpha}{2\pi}\right)^{0.5}. \tag{5.52}$$

For the case of no phase control with $\alpha = 0$, the power factor becomes unity, as expected.

Figure 5.21 shows the circuit for a single-phase, full-wave rectifier that uses a transformer with a center-tapped secondary. Each half of the secondary has a unidirectional component of current. The magnetic flux in the transformer core does not have a unidirectional component because of the opposing effect of these components in the two halves of the secondary winding. The load current, voltage, and primary current are the same as corresponding currents for the bridge rectifier shown in Figure 5.9. The major difference is that alternate half-cycles of rectified load current exist in each half of the secondary and its corresponding SCR. The graph in Figure 5.22 is similar to Figure 5.10 except for these differences.

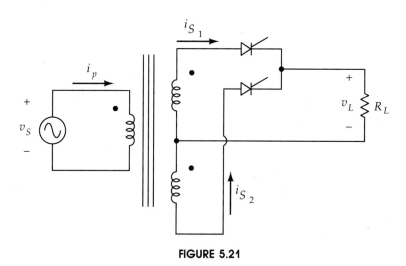

FIGURE 5.21

We can analyze the relation of primary current to secondary current by assuming an ideal transformer. For this analysis, the number of turns on each of the three windings is N. An ampere-turn equation provides the necessary relation. Because the turn ratio is unity, the peak value of load voltage is the same as that of the source voltage. The following relations demonstrate that the primary current is alternating and in the same way as the case of the bridge rectifier:

$$Ni_p - Ni_{s_1} + Ni_{s_2} = 0 \tag{5.53}$$

$$i_p = i_{s_1} - i_{s_2}. \tag{5.54}$$

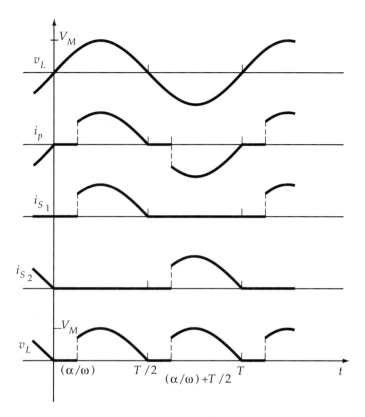

FIGURE 5.22

The volt-ampere rating of the primary and secondary windings is not the same because of the DC component of current in the secondary windings. The power factor for the secondary side therefore differs from that for the primary side, which has the same result as that for the bridge rectifier given in Equation 5.52.

For the secondary side, the RMS value of each secondary current can be computed from Equation 5.33 because the waveform is the same in the two cases. The following equations express the calculations needed. Note that the total secondary volt-ampere product is twice that of one winding:

$$S = (2)\left(\frac{V_m}{1.414}\right) I_{\text{RMS}}. \tag{5.55}$$

In Equation 5.55, I_{RMS} is the RMS current in one secondary winding. The RMS value of load current is 1.414 times as large as that in one secondary winding, so the load power may be expressed as shown in Equation 5.56:

$$P = (1.414 I_{RMS})^2 R \qquad (5.56)$$

$$\text{Power factor} = \frac{P}{S} = \left(\frac{1 - \dfrac{\alpha}{\pi} + \dfrac{\sin 2\alpha}{2\pi}}{2} \right)^{0.5} . \qquad (5.57)$$

The secondary power factor is less than that for the primary winding by a factor of 0.707. The transformer must necessarily be larger than would be the case for a transformer supplying a bridge rectifier.

EXAMPLE 5.11

A resistive load is to be supplied from a phase-controlled rectifier. A step-down transformer connects the 480-V RMS, 60 Hz, source to the rectifier. Peak secondary voltage to the load is required to be 100 V. The load resistance is 10 Ω. The value of the phase control angle is 45°.

(a) For a bridge rectifier connected to the secondary winding, find the primary and secondary power factors.

(b) For the case of a center-tapped transformer, find the volt-ampere rating of the transformer primary and secondary windings.

(c) Find the secondary power factor.

Solution

(a) From Equation 5.52, the power factor may be obtained:

$$\text{Power factor} = \left(1 - \frac{45°}{180°} + \frac{\sin 90°}{2\pi} \right)^{0.5} = 0.9535.$$

(b) Each secondary current has an RMS value obtained from Equation 5.33:

$$I_m = \frac{100}{10} = 10 \text{ A}$$

$$I_{RMS} = \left(\frac{10}{2} \right) \left(1 - \frac{45°}{180°} + \frac{\sin 90°}{2\pi} \right)^{0.5}$$

$$= 4.767 \text{ A}.$$

Using Equation 5.55 for the secondary windings,

$$S_2 = (2) \left(\frac{100}{1.414} \right) (4.767) = 674 \text{ V-A}.$$

Using Equation 5.37, the primary winding RMS value of current is found. The value of I_m in the primary must be adjusted for the turn ratio:

$$I_m = (10)\left[\frac{100}{(480)(1.414)}\right] = 1.473 \text{ A}$$

$$I_{\text{RMS}} = \left(\frac{1.473}{1.414}\right)(0.9535) = 0.993 \text{ A}$$

$$S_1 = (480)(0.993) = 477 \text{ V-A.}$$

(c) The secondary power factor is found from Equation 5.57:

$$\text{Power factor} = \left(\frac{1 - \dfrac{45°}{180°} + \dfrac{\sin 90°}{2\pi}}{2}\right)^{0.5}$$

$$= 0.674. \qquad\blacksquare$$

Inductive Load with Phase Control

The load on the rectifier is changed to include a large inductance so that the load current is constant throughout each cycle. For the case of a bridge rectifier such as that shown in Figure 5.11, the power factor can be determined as follows (the constant value of the rectified current is noted as I_L):

$$P = I_L^2 R \tag{5.58}$$

$$S = \left(\frac{V_m}{1.414}\right)(I_L) \tag{5.59}$$

$$I_L = \left(\frac{2V_m}{\pi R}\right)\cos\alpha. \tag{5.60}$$

Combining the three previous relations gives the result in Equation 5.61:

$$\text{Power factor} = \frac{P}{S} = 0.900\cos\alpha. \tag{5.61}$$

Note that even without phase control using a diode rectifier, the power factor is less than unity when the load is inductive.

If a transformer serves the bridge rectifier, both primary and secondary conditions of current and voltage have the same relationship as expressed in the preceding equations. Both primary and secondary power factors therefore are expressed by Equation 5.61. The transformer volt-ampere rating must be greater than the rectifier power output for any value of α.

If the rectifier is served by a transformer with a center-tapped secondary, the secondary power factor is less than that for the primary. Once again, I_L is the DC load current and V_m is the peak value of the voltage for one of the two secondary windings. The RMS value of current for one of the secondary windings can be calculated by noting that this current equals I_L for one-half the period and is zero for the other half. Equation 5.62 expresses this relation:

$$I_{RMS} = \frac{I_L}{1.414} \tag{5.62}$$

$$S_2 = 2\left(\frac{V_m}{1.414}\right)(I_{RMS}) = V_m I_L. \tag{5.63}$$

Using the expression from Equation 5.58 for load power and Equation 5.60 for I_L, the power factor can be found:

$$\text{Power factor} = \frac{P}{S_2} = \left(\frac{2}{\pi}\right)\cos \alpha. \tag{5.64}$$

The primary power factor remains the same as it is for the bridge rectifier case.

EXAMPLE 5.12

The circuit in Example 5.11 is changed to include a large inductance in series with the load resistance. Repeat the solution.

Solution

(a) From Equation 5.61,

$$\text{Power factor} = 0.900 \cos 45° = 0.6364.$$

(b)
$$I_L = \left(\frac{2}{\pi}\right)(100)\left(\frac{\cos 45°}{10}\right) = 4.50 \text{ A.}$$

From Equation 5.63 for the secondary windings,

$$S_2 = V_m I_L = (100)(4.50) = 450 \text{ V-A.}$$

The primary current is alternating with a constant value in each half-cycle. The value is related to I_L and the turn ratio:

$$I_P = I_L\left(\frac{N_2}{N_1}\right) = (4.50)\left[\frac{100}{(480)(1.414)}\right] = 0.663 \text{ A.}$$

For the primary winding,

$$S_1 = (480)(0.663) = 318.2 \text{ V-A.}$$

(c) Secondary power factor can be found by using the power factor definition:

$$P = I_L^2 R = (4.50)^2(10) = 202.5 \text{ W}$$

$$\text{Power factor} = \frac{P}{S_2} = \frac{202.5}{450} = 0.450. \qquad \blacksquare$$

5.5

HARMONICS

The various phase-controlled rectifiers produce distorted currents in the AC source. Such harmonic components may have unwanted effects on the AC system or cause interference with adjacent equipment. The value of these harmonic currents can be calculated for each of the possible rectifier circuits to determine their effects.

To reduce such harmonic current effects, several measures are possible. A circuit arrangement that is inherently better may be selected, or a low-pass filter can be inserted between the AC source and the rectifier. For very large values of rectifier power, the cost of such a filter may not be justified. For these situations, a polyphase rectifier with an increased number of phases and inherently lower harmonic generation may be justified. Such polyphase rectifiers will be considered in Section 5.8.

Resistive Loads

Only full-wave rectifiers are used with large loads that are likely to cause harmonic-generation problems. The AC source current with phase control has a waveform that is independent of the use of either a bridge rectifier or one with a center-tapped transformer. The graph of current versus time in Figure 5.23 is used for the Fourier series analysis of harmonic current components. The Fourier series coefficients are calculated in the usual manner. From the graph in Figure 5.23, it is evident that A_0 is zero:

$$A_n = \left(\frac{4}{T}\right) \int_{\alpha/\omega}^{T/2} I_m \sin \omega t \cos n\omega t \, dt \qquad (5.65)$$

$$B_n = \left(\frac{4}{T}\right) \int_{\alpha/\omega}^{T/2} I_m \sin \omega t \sin n\omega t \, dt. \qquad (5.66)$$

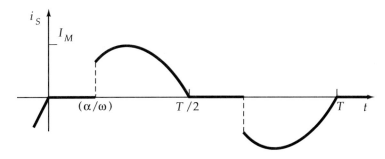

FIGURE 5.23

Evaluating these two integrals gives the following results (in the case of the general coefficients, n is odd and equal to 3 or more):

$$A_1 = \left(\frac{I_m}{2\pi}\right)[(\cos 2\alpha) - 1] \tag{5.67}$$

$$B_1 = \left(\frac{I_m}{2\pi}\right)(2\pi - 2\alpha + \sin 2\alpha) \tag{5.68}$$

$$A_n = \left(\frac{I_m}{\pi}\right)\left(\frac{2}{n^2 - 1}\right)(1 - n \sin n\alpha \sin \alpha - \cos n\alpha \cos \alpha) \tag{5.69}$$

$$B_n = \left(\frac{I_m}{\pi}\right)\left[\frac{2}{n^2 - 1}\right](n \cos n\alpha \sin \alpha - \sin n\alpha \cos \alpha). \tag{5.70}$$

The magnitude of the harmonic coefficients as a function of α for several values of n are graphed in Figure 5.24. All currents are normalized to the value of the fundamental current for $\alpha = 0$.

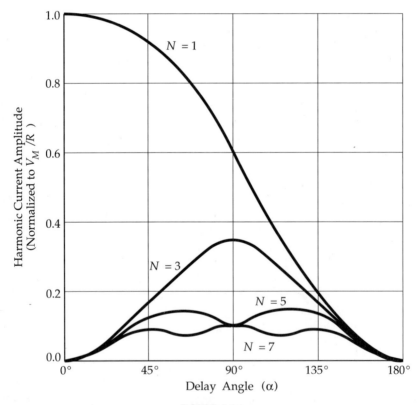

FIGURE 5.24

Inductive Loads

For the case of a full-wave rectifier with a large inductance component of the load, the AC source current has an alternating rectangular wave. If there is no FWD, each conduction period is 180° for each polarity; if an FWD *is* present, then the conduction of each polarity exists for an interval of $(T/2 - \alpha/\omega)$. The graph in Figure 5.25 is used to determine the harmonic currents; the time origin has been shifted so that the AC source current is an even function of time.

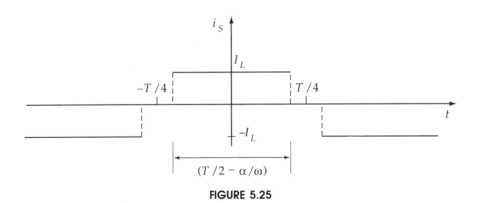

FIGURE 5.25

For the case using an FWD, both the pulse width and amplitude depend on α; without the FWD, only the amplitude depends on α. The analysis for the Fourier coefficients using the graph in Figure 5.25 applies to the case using an FWD. For this case, the A_n coefficients are found by the integration indicated in Equation 5.71:

$$A_n = \left(\frac{8}{T}\right)\int_0^{(T/4 - \alpha/2\omega)} I_L \cos n\omega t \, dt \qquad (5.71)$$

$$A_n = \left(\frac{4I_L}{n\pi}\right)\sin\left[\left(\frac{n}{2}\right)(\pi - \alpha)\right]. \qquad (5.72)$$

The value of I_L may be expressed using the previous result from Equation 5.35, which yields the result in Equation 5.73:

$$A_n = \left(\frac{V_m}{R}\right)\left(\frac{4(1 + \cos\alpha)}{n\pi^2}\right)\left\{\sin\left[\left(\frac{n}{2}\right)(\pi - \alpha)\right]\right\}. \qquad (5.73)$$

For the case without an FWD, the pulse width does not vary with α, although the value I_L does vary. In Equation 5.72, the value of I_L is replaced by the value from Equation 5.44, and the α in the argument of the sinusoidal term is removed. For this case, A_n is given by the result in Equation 5.74:

$$A_n = \left(\frac{V_m}{R}\right)\left(\frac{8}{n\pi^2}\right)(\cos\alpha)\left[\sin\left(\frac{n\pi}{2}\right)\right]. \qquad (5.74)$$

The variation of these harmonics is shown for the case with the FWD in Figure 5.26 and without the FWD in Figure 5.27. Note that for given values of V_m and R with $\alpha = 0$, the fundamental current amplitude is less than it is for the resistive case. In these two graphs, all currents are normalized with respect to V_m/R.

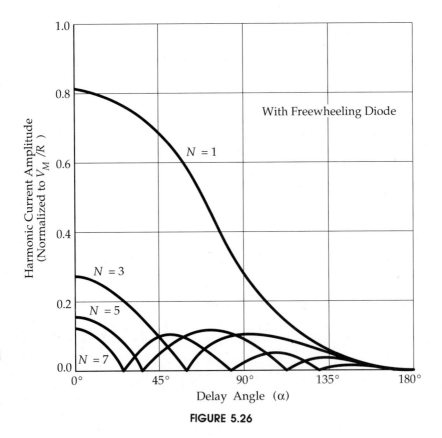

FIGURE 5.26

EXAMPLE 5.13

A full-wave bridge rectifier supplies power to an inductive load from a 240-V, 60-Hz source. The output voltage ranges from 200 V to 80 V. There is no FWD. Load resistance is 4 Ω. Find the third- and fifth-order source harmonic currents at each extreme of output voltage.

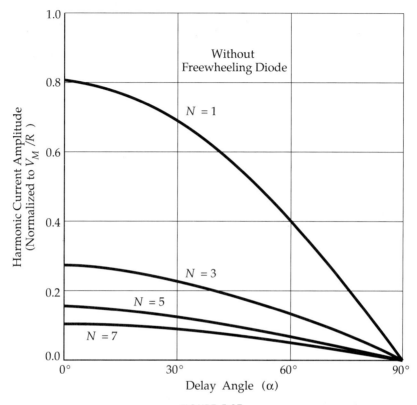

FIGURE 5.27

Solution   For $V_L = 200$ V,

$$200 = \frac{(240)(1.414)(2)(\cos \alpha)}{\pi}$$

$$\alpha = 22.2^{\circ}$$

$$\frac{V_m}{R} = \frac{(240)(1.414)}{4} = 84.85 \text{ A.}$$

From Equation 5.74,

$$|A_3| = 84.85\left(\frac{8}{3\pi^2}\right)\cos 22.2^{\circ} = 21.22 \text{ A}$$

$$|A_5| = 84.85\left(\frac{8}{5\pi^2}\right)\cos 22.2^{\circ} = 12.74 \text{ A.}$$

For $V_L = 80$ V, $\alpha = 68.3°$;

$$|A_3| = 84.85\left(\frac{8}{3\pi^2}\right)\cos 68.3° = 8.47 \text{ A}$$

$$|A_5| = 84.85\left(\frac{8}{5\pi^2}\right)\cos 68.3° = 5.09 \text{ A}.$$ ∎

5.6
DC LOAD VOLTAGE

Some circuit arrangements effectively place a DC voltage in the circuit as part of the load. This might result from capacitor voltage where the capacitor has been added as part of a smoothing filter. Another source may be the back electromotive force (EMF) of a DC motor. Figure 5.28 models this situation. As shown, if the inductor is ideal (no resistance), then the circuit equations impose the constraint that $V_{L_{avg}} = E$. For the capacitive case, it means the capacitor charges to a level that is consistent with the average value of the rectifier output voltage. In the case of a DC-motor load, it means that the back EMF, and hence the motor speed, must adjust to the average value of the rectifier output voltage. If the inductance also must be modeled by adding a resistance element, then the above statements need modification.

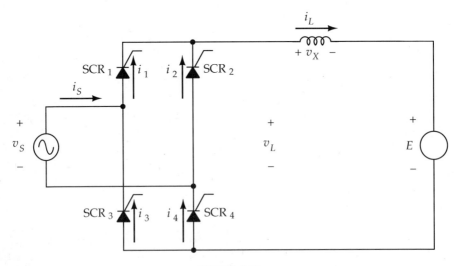

FIGURE 5.28

Large Inductance

The first case we will consider is that of large inductance and no resistance; this is shown in Figure 5.28. Here there are no special problems such as occur in the following section on critical inductance; as stated above, E will have to adjust to fit the average value of v_L. The average value of $i_L(t)$ is indeterminate, and other circuit conditions must be considered to determine its value. Just what arrangement is being modeled by the voltage source E? If it is as shown in Figure 5.29, then the average value of $i_L(t)$ is found easily. In that figure, the current relation of Equation 5.75 holds for instantaneous values and the relation of Equation 5.76 holds for average values:

$$i_L(t) = i_C + i_R \qquad (5.75)$$

$$I_L = I_C + I_R. \qquad (5.76)$$

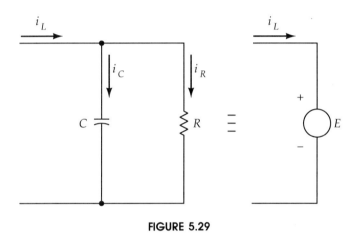

FIGURE 5.29

The average value of the capacitor current is zero for steady periodic operation, the average inductor current is the same as the average resistor current, and this in turn is given by Equation 5.77:

$$I_L = I_R = \frac{E}{R}. \qquad (5.77)$$

Critical Inductance

Certain circuit configurations, however, cause a marked departure from the previous equations if the load inductance is smaller than some critical value. Then the average load voltage is significantly different from the values predicted by the previous equations. If the circuit has a DC-voltage source present in the load, then a critical inductance value determines whether there is continuous inductor current. If there is, then the output voltage of the rectifier (and hence input to the load) is defined at all times and the previous equations apply. If the inductor current is not continuous, then a different analysis is required. In previous equations, the average load voltage has been independent of the load resistance. For the discontinuous current mode, the average load voltage becomes dependent upon the load resistance.

Determination of Critical Inductance

A critical inductance value can be calculated for the circuit arrangement in Figure 5.28. If v_L is given by a full-wave, phase-controlled waveform, then the graph in Figure 5.30 applies for the case of the source voltage greater than E at time t_1. In the figure, the L and R values are so related that the operation is on the boundary between continuous and discontinuous modes of operation. This condition is used to calculate the critical inductance relation. Furthermore,

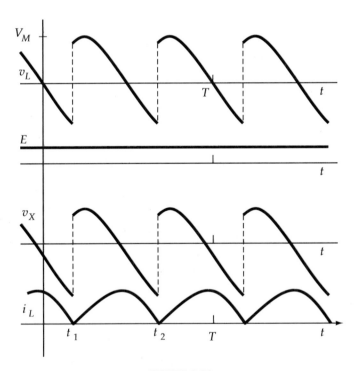

FIGURE 5.30

minimum current occurs at SCR switching time, which is not true for all values of α.

Because v_X is the voltage across the inductance, this is used as the starting point to obtain $i_L(t)$:

$$\frac{di_L}{dt} = \frac{v_X}{L} = \frac{v_L - E}{L} \tag{5.78}$$

$$i_L(t) = \int_{t_1}^{t} \left(\frac{v_L - E}{L}\right) dt = \int_{t_1}^{t} \left(\frac{V_m \sin \omega t - E}{L}\right) dt \tag{5.79}$$

$$i_L(t) = \left(\frac{V_m}{\omega L}\right)(\cos \omega t_1 - \cos \omega t) - \left(\frac{E}{L}\right)(t - t_1). \tag{5.80}$$

Because $i_L(t) = 0$ at $t = t_1$, it is evident from the graph that for periodic operation $i_L(t)$ must again be zero at $t = t_2$.

We must meet the condition that the average value of $i_L(t)$ be the proper value, namely the value of E/R. Furthermore, because operation is at the boundary of continuous current operation, the relation between V_m and the average rectifier voltage, E, still holds. The average value of $i_L(t)$ is determined by integration:

$$I_{avg} = \frac{2}{T} \int_{t_1}^{t_2} i_L(t) \, dt \tag{5.81}$$

where $(t_2 - t_1) = T/2$.

Using the equation for $i_L(t)$ and performing the integration yields the result in Equation 5.82:

$$I_{avg} = \left(\frac{V_m}{\omega L}\right)\left[\cos \alpha + \left(\frac{2}{\pi}\right)\sin \alpha\right] - \left[\frac{(E)\left(\frac{\pi}{2}\right)}{\omega L}\right]. \tag{5.82}$$

Then, using $I_{avg} = E/R$ and the relation $E = (2/\pi)V_m \cos \alpha$, the result in Equation 5.83 is obtained:

$$L = \left(\frac{R}{\omega}\right)\tan \alpha. \tag{5.83}$$

This critical value separates the continuous and discontinuous modes of operation. There still remains the requirement of obtaining the relation between V_m, α, and E for L less than the critical value. This will be done in the forthcoming section on discontinuous inductor current.

The preceding analysis was for the case in which minimum current occurs at the switching point. For this to happen, the current must increase for $t > t_1$ and thus $v_L > E$ at the switching point. The limit occurs for $v_L = E$ at time t_1.

Using the two relations that apply, a boundary condition is obtained:

$$E = \left(\frac{2}{\pi}\right) V_m \cos \alpha \tag{5.84}$$

and

$$v_L = V_m \sin \alpha, \tag{5.85}$$

where $\alpha = \omega t_1$. Equating v_L and E gives

$$\left(\frac{2}{\pi}\right) V_m \cos \alpha = V_m \sin \alpha \tag{5.86}$$

$$\tan \alpha = \frac{2}{\pi} \tag{5.87}$$

$$\alpha = 32.48°. \tag{5.88}$$

EXAMPLE 5.14

A full-wave rectifier of a 60-Hz, 240-V RMS AC source operates to supply a variable voltage to a 20-Ω resistive load with the arrangement shown in Figure 5.31. The load voltage is required to be adjustable from 100 V to 180 V. Find:

(a) the required range of α

(b) the smallest L value that ensures continuous inductor current for all values of α.

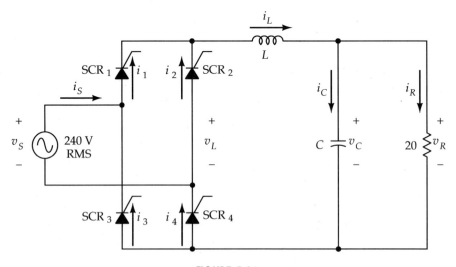

FIGURE 5.31

Solution

(a) Assuming continuous inductor current for $V_L = 100$ V:

$$100 = \left(\frac{2}{\pi}\right) V_m \cos \alpha = \left(\frac{2}{\pi}\right) 339.4 \cos \alpha$$

$$\alpha = 62.43°.$$

For $V_L = 180$ V:

$$180 = \left(\frac{2}{\pi}\right) V_m \cos \alpha = \left(\frac{2}{\pi}\right) 339.4 \cos \alpha$$

$$\alpha = 32.58°.$$

(b) The range of α meets the conditions of Equation 5.88. The larger value of α from part (a) requires the larger value of L. Therefore, from Equation 5.83:

$$L = \left(\frac{20}{120\pi}\right) \tan 62.43°$$

$$L = 0.102 \text{ H}.$$

This value of L is more than sufficient to maintain continuous current at the smaller of the two α values.   ■

α Less than 32.48°

For control in which $\alpha < 32.48°$, the value of v_L is less than E at the switching point, so the current continues to decrease beyond the switching point. Let θ be the angle corresponding to t_3 in Figure 5.32 where minimum current occurs.

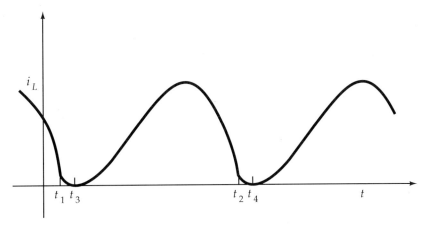

FIGURE 5.32

This value is found by noting that minimum current occurs at

$$v_L = E = V_m \sin \theta \tag{5.89}$$

and

$$E = \left(\frac{2}{\pi}\right) V_m \cos \alpha. \tag{5.90}$$

Combining Equations 5.89 and 5.90 gives

$$\theta = \sin^{-1}\left[\left(\frac{2}{\pi}\right)\cos \alpha\right] \qquad \alpha < 32.48°. \tag{5.91}$$

Note that for $\alpha = 32.48°$, $\theta = 32.48°$. Again this shows the boundary between the two modes of operation.

The critical inductance for this case is found in a manner similar to that in the preceding section. Again, the starting point to find the current is

$$\frac{di_L}{dt} = \frac{v_X}{L} = \frac{v_L - E}{L}. \tag{5.92}$$

Because $i_L(t) = 0$ at $t = t_3$,

$$i_L(t) = \int_{t_3}^{t} \frac{v_L - E}{L} \, dt = \int_{t_3}^{t} \frac{V_m \sin \omega t - E}{L} \, dt \tag{5.93}$$

$$i_L(t) = \left(\frac{V_m}{\omega L}\right)(\cos \omega t_3 - \cos \omega t) - \left(\frac{E}{L}\right)(t - t_3). \tag{5.94}$$

The last equation applies for the interval between the switching points of t_1 and t_2. The average of $i_L(t)$ over this interval is given by Equation 5.95:

$$I_{avg} = \frac{2}{T} \int_{t_1}^{t_2} i_L(t) \, dt = \frac{2}{T} \int_{\alpha/\omega}^{(\alpha+\pi)/\omega} i_L(t) \, dt. \tag{5.95}$$

By performing the indicated operations, we obtain the following result:

$$I_{avg} = \left(\frac{V_m}{\omega L}\right)\left[\cos \theta + \left(\frac{2}{\pi}\right)(\cos \alpha)\left(\theta - \alpha - \frac{\pi}{2}\right) + \left(\frac{2}{\pi}\right)\sin \alpha\right]. \tag{5.96}$$

The above mathematical operations recognized that

$$E = \left(\frac{2}{\pi}\right) V_m \cos \alpha. \tag{5.97}$$

The average current is related to the load resistance, so again

$$I_{avg} = \frac{E}{R} = \left(\frac{2}{\pi}\right)\left(\frac{V_m}{R}\right)\cos \alpha. \tag{5.98}$$

Equating these two relations gives

$$L = \frac{R}{4f \cos \alpha} \left[\cos \theta + \left(\frac{2}{\pi} \right) \left(\theta - \alpha - \frac{\pi}{2} \right) (\cos \alpha) + \left(\frac{2}{\pi} \right) \sin \alpha \right]. \qquad (5.99)$$

Recognizing that θ is a function of α, as expressed in Equation 5.91, the above equation expresses the critical inductance as a function of α. It would be unwieldy if we expressed the function this way, so we leave it in its present form.

If we investigate the entire range of α to be used, we can find a value of L that ensures continuous inductor current over the whole range. Figure 5.33 shows how the critical inductance, which is required to maintain continuous current, varies with α. As α approaches $90°$, it becomes increasingly difficult to have sufficient inductance to maintain continuous inductor current. The graph in Figure 5.33 combines the two ranges of α involved in Equations 5.83 and 5.99.

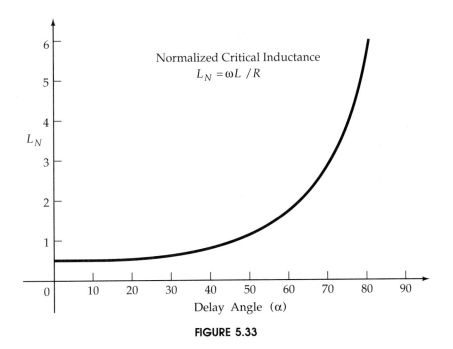

FIGURE 5.33

EXAMPLE 5.15

A full-wave, phase-controlled rectifier supplies 10 A at an average 205 V to a load represented by the circuit arrangement in Figure 5.31. The source is 240-V RMS, 60 Hz. Find:

(a) the α value required

(b) the critical inductance.

Solution

(a)
$$E = V_{L_{avg}} = \left(\frac{2}{\pi}\right) V_m \cos \alpha$$

$$205 = \left(\frac{2}{\pi}\right)(339.4) \cos \alpha$$

$$\alpha = 18.42°.$$

(b) $\alpha < 32.48°$, so Equation 5.91 is used to find θ:

$$\theta = \sin^{-1}\left[\left(\frac{2}{\pi}\right)\cos 18.42°\right] = 37.16°$$

$$R = \frac{E}{I_{avg}} = \frac{205}{10} = 20.5\ \Omega.$$

Substituting values of α, θ, R, and the frequency in Equation 5.99 gives a value of $L = 0.0222$ H for the critical inductance.

An alternate solution is to use the graph in Figure 5.33. The value of L_N at $\alpha = 18.42°$ is 0.43. Using this value,

$$L = \frac{L_N R}{\omega} = \frac{(0.43)(20.5)}{377} = 0.023\ \text{H}. \qquad \blacksquare$$

Discontinuous Inductor Current

With less than the critical inductance, the average load voltage becomes dependent upon the load resistance, and new voltage relations are required. The graphs in Figure 5.34 show that inductor current begins at $t = t_1$, at which time the rectifier SCRs also begin conduction. Inductor current increases to a maximum and then returns to zero at $t = t_3$. The time, t_3, is less than a half-period later than t_1. During the interval from t_3 to t_2, inductor current is zero and all SCRs are nonconducting; consequently, v_L is equal to the capacitor voltage rather than being defined by the AC-source voltage. This action must be accounted for in finding the average load voltage. Again, the filter capacitor is assumed large enough that v_C has negligible ripple.

To find the inductor current, the corresponding differential equation is solved. First, the voltage equation is written for the interval from t_1 to t_3 using the circuit in Figure 5.28:

$$v_S = v_X + E \qquad\qquad\qquad\qquad\qquad\qquad \textbf{(5.100)}$$

$$V_m \sin \omega t = L\left(\frac{di_L}{dt}\right) + E \qquad\qquad\qquad\qquad \textbf{(5.101)}$$

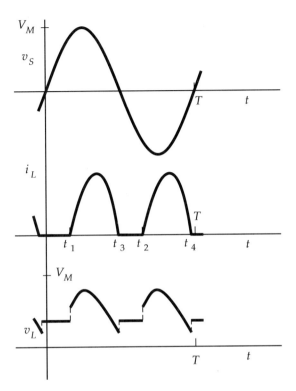

FIGURE 5.34

$$\frac{di_L}{dt} = \frac{V_m \sin \omega t - E}{L} \tag{5.102}$$

$$i_L(t) = \int_{t_1}^{t} \left(\frac{V_m \sin \omega t - E}{L} \right) dt \tag{5.103}$$

$$i_L(t) = \left(\frac{V_m}{\omega L} \right) (-\cos \omega t + \cos \omega t_1) - \left(\frac{E}{L} \right) (t - t_1). \tag{5.104}$$

At $t = t_3$, $i_L(t)$ goes to zero. The current in Equation 5.104 is set equal to zero, and an expression for t_3 is found:

$$0 = \left(\frac{V_m}{\omega L} \right) (-\cos \omega t_3 + \cos \omega t_1) - \left(\frac{E}{L} \right) (t_3 - t_1) \tag{5.105}$$

or

$$\omega t_3 - \omega t_1 = \left(\frac{V_m}{E} \right) (\cos \omega t_1 - \cos \omega t_3). \tag{5.106}$$

The value of ωt_1 is the angle α. The value of ωt_3 is set to the angle β, with the result given in Equation 5.107:

$$\beta - \alpha = \left(\frac{V_m}{E}\right)(\cos \alpha - \cos \beta). \qquad (5.107)$$

For further simplification, set $(\beta - \alpha) = \gamma$ and, for the purpose of normalization, let $\dfrac{E}{V_m} = m$:

$$\gamma = \frac{\cos \alpha - \cos \beta}{m}. \qquad (5.108)$$

The transcendental relation in Equation 5.108 can be solved numerically. The results are presented in Figure 5.35, with the various possible operating conditions graphed.

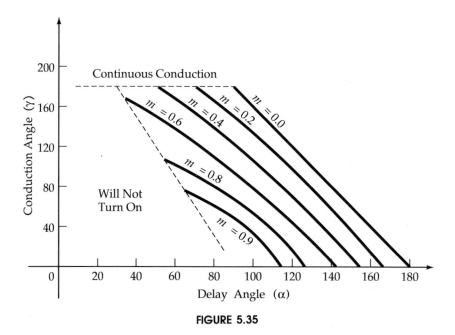

FIGURE 5.35

The average current required by the load determines whether the mode is of discontinuous or continuous current. Once the γ value is known, the value of t_3 is known and average inductor current can be found:

$$I_{L_{avg}} = \left(\frac{2}{T}\right)\int_{t_1}^{t_3} i_L(t)\, dt \qquad (5.109)$$

$$I_{L_{avg}} = \left(\frac{2}{T}\right) \int_{t_1}^{t_3} \left(\frac{V_m}{\omega L}\right)(\cos \omega t_1 - \cos \omega t)\, dt$$

$$+ \left(\frac{2}{T}\right) \int_{t_1}^{t_3} \left(\frac{E}{L}\right)(t_1 - t)\, dt \qquad (5.110)$$

$$I_{L_{avg}} = \left(\frac{2}{T}\right) \left\{ \begin{array}{l} \left(\dfrac{V_m}{\omega L}\right)\left[(t)(\cos \omega t_1) - \dfrac{\sin \omega t}{\omega}\right] \Big|^{t_3} \\[2ex] + \left(\dfrac{E}{L}\right)\left[(t)(t_1) - \dfrac{t^2}{2}\right] \end{array} \right\}_{t_1} \qquad (5.111)$$

$$I_{L_{avg}} = \left(\frac{V_m}{\pi L}\right)\left[(t_3 - t_1)\cos \omega t_1 - \left(\frac{\sin \omega t_3 - \sin \omega t_1}{\omega}\right)\right]$$

$$- \left(\frac{E}{TL}\right)(t_3 - t_1)^2. \qquad (5.112)$$

Equation 5.112 can be normalized by dividing by the factor $(V_m/\omega L)$. The result is in Equation 5.113:

$$I_{LN} = \left(\frac{\gamma}{\pi}\right)(\cos \alpha) - \left(\frac{1}{\pi}\right)(\sin \beta - \sin \alpha) - \left(\frac{m\gamma^2}{2\pi}\right). \qquad (5.113)$$

The function of Equation 5.113 is presented graphically in Figure 5.36.

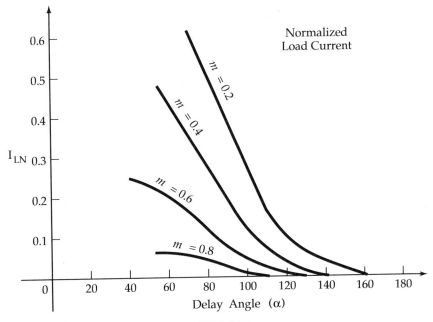

FIGURE 5.36

Note by examining Figures 5.35 and 5.36 that certain regions of the graphs do not represent possible operating conditions. Two examples are immediately evident. For a given α to be possible, the instantaneous source voltage at that α must be greater than E; otherwise, the SCR is reverse-biased. The second situation is that for each value of L and for other given circuit parameters, there is a certain average inductor current (normalized). For a load current greater than that given by these graphical relations, inductor current is no longer discontinuous and this analysis does not apply; then the continuous current analysis of earlier sections applies.

EXAMPLE 5.16

In Figure 5.37, the phase-controlled rectifier operates to produce an average load voltage of 90 V from a source whose peak value is 150 V. The capacitor is large enough that negligible ripple occurs. The phase control angle is 50°. The load resistance is 20 Ω. Find:

(a) the circuit mode (continuous or discontinuous current)

(b) the rectifier conduction interval

(c) the inductance of L.

Solution

(a) If the circuit is in continuous mode, then from Equation 5.90,

$$E = V_L = \left(\frac{2}{\pi}\right) V_m \cos 50° = 61.38 \text{ V}.$$

Because $E > 61.38$ V, the mode is discontinuous.

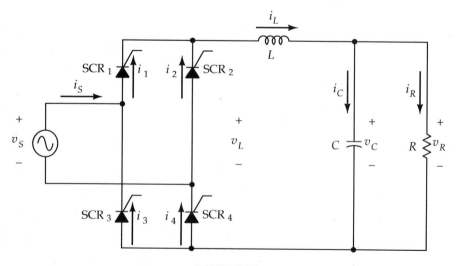

FIGURE 5.37

(b)
$$m = \frac{E}{V_m} = \frac{90}{150} = 0.6.$$

From Figure 5.35, the conduction angle is read as $150°$.

(c) The normalized load current, I_{LN}, is read from Figure 5.36 to be 0.233;

$$I_{avg} = \frac{E}{R} = \frac{90}{20} = 4.5 \text{ A}$$

$$I_{LN} = \frac{I_{avg}}{V_m/\omega L} = 0.233$$

$$\frac{4.5}{150/377L} = 0.233$$

$$L = 0.0206 \text{ H.} \qquad \blacksquare$$

EXAMPLE 5.17

A DC motor is represented by the circuit shown in Figure 5.38. The motor's back EMF is modeled by the source voltage, E, which is proportional to motor speed. Given data:

$E = 90$ V	$f = 60$ Hz
$V_m = 150$ V	Motor constant $K = 1.1$ V-s
$\alpha = 45°$	$= 1.1$ N-m/A
$L = 0.01$ H	Negligible motor resistance

Find:

(a) motor average current

(b) rectifier conduction angle

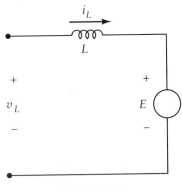

FIGURE 5.38

(c) motor average torque

(d) motor speed.

Solution

(a)
$$\frac{V_m}{\omega L} = \frac{150}{(377)(0.01)} = 39.79 \text{ A}$$

$$m = \frac{E}{V_m} = \frac{90}{150} = 0.6$$

$$I_{LN} = 0.243 \text{ (from Figure 5.36)}$$

$$I_{L\text{avg}} = (0.243)(39.79) = 9.67 \text{ A}.$$

(b) $\gamma = 156°$ (from Figure 5.35).

(c)
$$\text{Average torque} = KI_{L\text{avg}} = (1.1)(9.67) = 10.64 \text{ N-m}.$$

(d)
$$\text{Motor speed} = \frac{E}{K} = \frac{90}{1.1} = 81.82 \text{ rad/s}$$

$$= 781 \text{ rpm}. \qquad \blacksquare$$

5.7

NONIDEAL ASPECTS

Many nonideal characteristics could be considered as part of the circuit analysis. Two are considered in this section.

Transformer Leakage Inductance

If the full-wave rectifier function is obtained by using a transformer, all of our previous developments apply, provided that the transformer can be modeled as an ideal transformer. Actual transformers do not have ideal coupling from primary to secondary, and this characteristic is modeled with a leakage inductance added to the ideal transformer model.

As a starting point for the analysis, we will use a situation in which an ideal transformer uses a center-tapped secondary. In Figure 5.39, the load inductance is large enough that negligible ripple occurs in the load current. The graphs in Figure 5.40 show circuit operation. With a phase control angle of α, SCR$_1$ conducts the load current from angle α to $(\alpha + \pi)$. The current equation for the transformer equates primary and total secondary ampere-turns as given

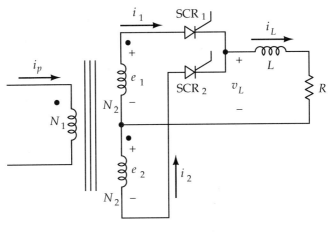

FIGURE 5.39

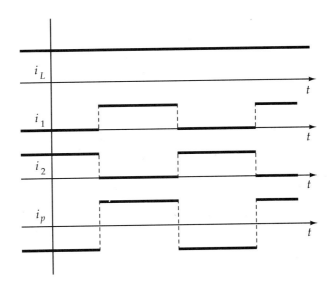

FIGURE 5.40

below in two equations that apply to instantaneous values:

$$N_1 i_p = N_2 i_1 - N_2 i_2 \qquad (5.114)$$

$$i_p = \left(\frac{N_2}{N_1}\right)(i_1 - i_2). \qquad (5.115)$$

From the difference between i_1 and i_2, it is evident that the result is alternating. Thus, the primary current is alternating with a rectangular waveform.

All these results are the same as for the SCR bridge rectifier, except for the amplitude change introduced by the transformer turn ratio.

Now the transformer is made less than ideal by adding an inductance, L_1, in series with each secondary winding. This inductance represents the less-than-ideal coupling between transformer windings. Because the transformer actually is a three-winding transformer, a minimum of two inductances is required. By reason of symmetry, the two values are equal. Figure 5.41 shows the modified circuit.

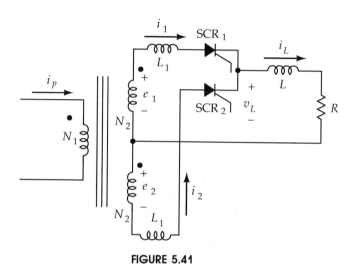

FIGURE 5.41

Adding this leakage inductance means that at SCR turn on it is no longer possible for the other SCR current to commutate to zero instantaneously. Now as SCR_1 turns on, i_2 is reduced to zero gradually as i_1 increases from zero to the value of the load current. Instead of a zero commutation interval of time, the time is nonzero although still relatively short. The graphs in Figure 5.40 are modified as shown in Figure 5.42.

The circuit analysis of the commutation assumes a short commutation period for which the source voltages of the transformer secondaries remain constant. Further, the load current is assumed constant during this interval. For Figure 5.41, Equation 5.116 can be written at the time of commutation. In the equation, V_m is the peak voltage of each of the two secondary windings:

$$e_1 = e_2 = V_m \sin \alpha. \tag{5.116}$$

A voltage equation can be written around the loop of the two secondary windings and the two leakage inductances. SCR_2 has been ON, is still ON because $i_2 > 0$, and SCR_1 has just been turned on. Therefore, for a short time both SCRs are conducting.

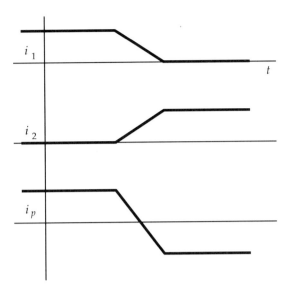

FIGURE 5.42

$$e_1 + e_2 - L_l\left(\frac{di_1}{dt}\right) + L_l\left(\frac{di_2}{dt}\right) = 0 \qquad (5.117)$$

$$i_1 + i_2 = i_L = \text{a constant} \qquad (5.118)$$

$$\left(\frac{di_1}{dt}\right) + \left(\frac{di_2}{dt}\right) = 0 \qquad (5.119)$$

$$\frac{di_1}{dt} = -\frac{di_2}{dt} \qquad (5.120)$$

$$V_m \sin \alpha + V_m \sin \alpha + L_l\left(\frac{di_2}{dt}\right) + L_l\left(\frac{di_2}{dt}\right) = 0 \qquad (5.121)$$

$$\frac{di_2}{dt} = -\left(\frac{V_m}{L_l}\right)\sin \alpha \qquad (5.122)$$

$$\frac{di_1}{dt} = \left(\frac{V_m}{L_l}\right)\sin \alpha. \qquad (5.123)$$

The two currents thus change at the same rate, one increasing and the other decreasing. During the commutation interval, the load voltage is zero. This is observed by another voltage equation:

$$e_1 - L_l\left(\frac{di_1}{dt}\right) - v_L = 0. \qquad (5.124)$$

Upon substituting the value of di_1/dt, v_L is found to be zero while the currents are changing. The time interval during which this change occurs depends on the load current at the commutation time and is given by Equation 5.125:

$$\Delta t = \frac{I_L}{di_1/dt} \tag{5.125}$$

$$\Delta t = \frac{I_L L_l}{V_m \sin \alpha} \tag{5.126}$$

The net result is that a portion of the area under the curve of v_L versus time is lost, and the average load voltage is reduced. The graph in Figure 5.43 shows this effect, although exaggerated for clarity. The shaded area is the lost area. Its net reduction is given by Equation 5.127:

$$\Delta A = (V_m \sin \alpha)(\Delta t) = I_L L_l. \tag{5.127}$$

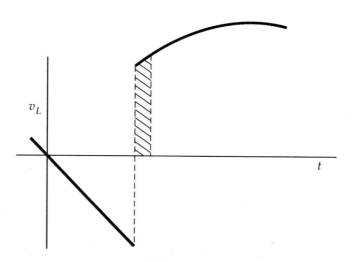

FIGURE 5.43

The reduction in average voltage for the full-wave case is given by Equation 5.129:

$$\Delta V_L = \frac{\Delta A}{T/2} \tag{5.128}$$

$$\Delta V_L = 2\left(\frac{I_L L_l}{T}\right). \tag{5.129}$$

The result depends on load current, so the average voltage has a drooping output characteristic. This is the same effect as from a source resistance, even though no resistance has been included in the circuit model.

A similar effect occurs in the case of a two-winding transformer supplying a full-wave bridge rectifier. Equation 5.129 also applies in this case, with L_l being the leakage reactance between primary and secondary windings.

EXAMPLE 5.18

A full-wave center-tap rectifier delivers 20 A to an inductive load at $\alpha = 40°$ from a 60-Hz source. Transformer leakage inductance in each secondary is 1 mH. The peak load voltage from the rectifier is 205 V. Find:

(a) the reduction in output voltage resulting from the transformer leakage inductance

(b) the output voltage.

Solution

(a)

$$\Delta V_L = \frac{(2)(I_L)(L_l)}{T}$$

$$= \frac{(2)(20)(0.001)}{0.01667}$$

$$= 2.4 \text{ V}.$$

(b) Ideally,

$$V_L = \left(\frac{2}{\pi}\right)(205)(\cos 40°) = 100 \text{ V}.$$

With the effect of part (a) included,

$$V_L = 100 - 2.4 = 97.6 \text{ V}.$$

Therefore, instead of the ideal 100 V supplied to the load, the actual load voltage is only 97.6 V. This could be corrected in a closed-loop system by a slight reduction in the value of α. ∎

Inductor Resistance

In all previous analyses, the inductor has either been considered ideal or in series with a load resistance, which could include the inductor resistance. In the interest of high efficiency, inductors usually are designed to have small resistance and hence small losses. In this section, we will examine the effect of this resistance.

Figure 5.44 shows the circuit to be analyzed. Only the continuous current mode is considered. The instantaneous voltage equation can be written for this circuit as shown in Equation 5.130:

$$v_L = v_R + v_X + E. \tag{5.130}$$

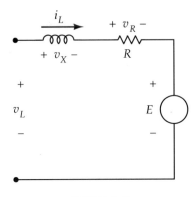

FIGURE 5.44

Using average values, Equation 5.130 is rewritten as

$$V_L = V_R + E. \tag{5.131}$$

Again, the average voltage across the inductor for periodic operation is zero. The voltage V_R for the resistor is just average load current multiplied by the resistance. The equation becomes

$$V_L = (I_L)(R) + E. \tag{5.132}$$

Considering average values, then, the effect of inductor resistance is simply to cause a difference between the average input voltage to the load and the net value of E. A small effect is seen on the current wave shape versus time and also on the conditions for continuous inductor current.

E X A M P L E 5 . 1 9

A full-wave controlled rectifier supplies power to a DC motor in a continuous current mode. Under the condition that the motor average torque requires a current of 10 A and with an α of 30°, find the motor speed. The motor speed constant K is 1.10 V-s.

$$V_m = 170 \text{ V} \qquad R_L = 0.35 \ \Omega$$

Solution

$$V_L = \left(\frac{2}{\pi}\right) V_m \cos \alpha = \left(\frac{2}{\pi}\right)(170) \cos 30° = 93.7 \text{ V}$$

$$E = V_L - (I_L)(R_L) = 93.7 - (10)(0.35) = 90.2 \text{ V}$$

$$\text{Motor speed} = \frac{E}{K} = \frac{90.2}{1.1} = 82 \text{ rad/s} = 783 \text{ rpm.}' \qquad \blacksquare$$

5.8
POLYPHASE RECTIFIERS

All of the preceding single-phase rectifier circuits have corresponding polyphase versions. These polyphase rectifiers, both controlled and noncontrolled, provide a smoother output with higher ripple frequency than their corresponding single-phase versions. The output filtering thus is done more easily. In large power rectifiers, the filter components become large and costly, so a reduction or elimination of filters is important. Thus, the higher the output power, the more likely a polyphase arrangement will be used. Because three-phase sources are so widely used, only polyphase systems with three-phase sources will be studied.

Half-Wave, Three-Phase Diode Rectifier

A basic three-phase, half-wave rectifier is shown in Figure 5.45. As is evident from the circuit diagram, each source may have only unidirectional current. The three sources shown constitute a balanced, three-phase, alternating source. The diodes shown are ideal.

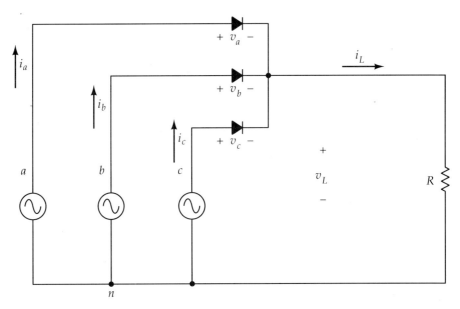

FIGURE 5.45

Only one current may be greater than zero at any one instant. This one current is determined by which of the three sources is most positive at that instant. In Figure 5.46, at time t_3, $v_{an} > v_{bn}$ and $v_{an} > v_{cn}$, so $i_a > 0$, and the other

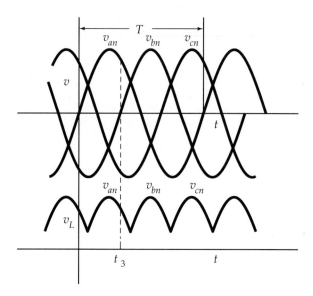

FIGURE 5.46

currents are zero. When $i_a > 0$, voltage v_a is zero, so therefore at that time $v_L = v_{an}$ by the circuit voltage equation. At the same instant, another circuit voltage equation can be used to get v_b and v_c:

$$v_{an} - v_a + v_b - v_{bn} = 0 \tag{5.133}$$

and

$$v_{an} - v_a + v_c - v_{cn} = 0. \tag{5.134}$$

Because $v_a = 0$, the result for diode voltages is given by

$$v_b = v_{bn} - v_{an} \tag{5.135}$$

$$v_c = v_{cn} - v_{an'} \tag{5.136}$$

and because at this instant v_{an} is greater than either v_{bn} or v_{cn}, both diodes for Phases B and C are reverse-biased. As a result, the load voltage is "piecewise" equal to the largest of the three source voltages. This also is shown in Figure 5.46.

Thus, during each period of the source voltage, the load voltage consists of three identical sections, each of which is one-third of the period of the source sinusoid. These sections are taken in turn from one of the three phases of the source voltage.

Because the load is resistive, the load current has the same waveform as the load voltage. The individual diode currents equal the load current whenever a particular diode conducts for its 120° interval. Each diode current is then zero for a 240° interval. Currents are shown in Figure 5.47. An expression for the

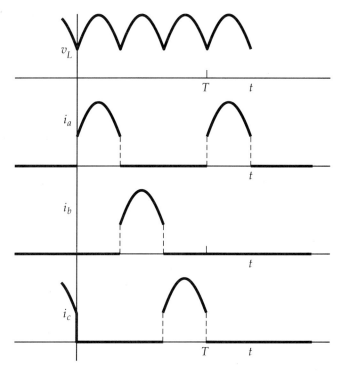

FIGURE 5.47

average load voltage is found by integrating the load voltage. Inspection of the waveform shows that this can be found by integrating over one-third of the basic period. This means, of course, that the load-voltage ripple frequency is three times that of the AC source frequency:

$$V_{avg} = \frac{3}{T} \int_{t_1}^{t_2} V_m \sin \omega t \, dt, \tag{5.137}$$

where t_1 and t_2 correspond to 30° and 150° on the sinusoid for v_{an}. Thus,

$$t_1 = \frac{\pi}{6\omega} \tag{5.138}$$

and

$$t_2 = \frac{5\pi}{6\omega}. \tag{5.139}$$

Evaluation of Equation 5.137 gives Equation 5.140:

$$V_{avg} = \frac{(3)(3)^{0.5}(V_m)}{2\pi} = 0.827V_m. \tag{5.140}$$

Average load current is given by Equation 5.141:

$$I_{avg} = \frac{V_{avg}}{R} \qquad \text{(5.141)}$$

$$I_{avg} = \frac{(3)(3)^{0.5}(V_m)}{(2\pi)(R)} = \frac{0.827 V_m}{R}. \qquad \text{(5.142)}$$

The average current in one of the diodes is only one-third the load current. Peak load current and peak diode current are obviously the same, and because the load is resistive,

$$I_m = \frac{V_m}{R}. \qquad \text{(5.143)}$$

If the load now is changed to include an appreciable inductance in series with its resistance, the load current will have negligible ripple. The currents then become as shown in Figure 5.48. There is no change in the waveform of load

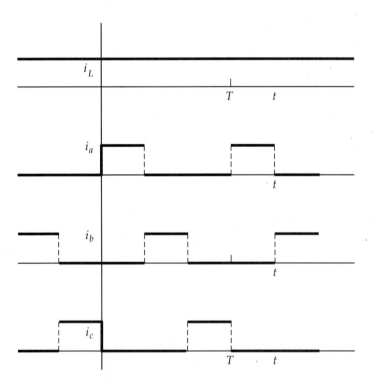

FIGURE 5.48

voltage because there is no change in the circuit voltage equations. The same expression for average load voltage applies because the waveform has not changed. Average load current likewise does not change because the average load voltage is the same. Peak load and diode currents, however, *do* change and these are the same as average load current.

EXAMPLE 5.20

A three-phase diode rectifier is supplied by a four-wire, 480-V RMS, 60-Hz source as shown in Figure 5.45. The load is a 25-Ω resistance. Find:

(a) peak load voltage
(b) average load voltage
(c) peak load current
(d) average load current
(e) peak diode current
(f) peak reverse diode voltage
(g) average diode current.

Solution

(a) $\qquad V_m =$ peak $L-N$ voltage $= \dfrac{(1.414)(480)}{1.732} = 391.9$ V

(b) $\qquad$ Average load voltage $= 0.827 V_m = (0.827)(391.9) = 324.1$ V

(c) $\qquad$ Peak load current $= I_m = \dfrac{V_m}{R} = \dfrac{391.9}{25} = 15.68$ A

(d) $\qquad$ Average load current $= I_{avg} = \dfrac{V_{avg}}{R} = \dfrac{324.1}{25} = 12.96$ A

(e) $\qquad$ Peak diode current $= I_m = 15.68$ A.

(f) Peak diode reverse voltage occurs when one diode is conducting and peak line-to-line voltage occurs between the conducting phase and the phase for which the reverse voltage is being calculated:

$$\text{Peak reverse voltage} = (480)(1.414) = 678.8 \text{ V.}$$

The diode requires a reverse voltage rating in excess of this value. In consideration of standard values, this must be at least 800 V.

(g) $\qquad\qquad$ Average diode current $= \dfrac{I_{avg}}{3} = 4.32$ A. $\qquad$ ∎

EXAMPLE 5.21

The load in Example 5.20 now has sufficient inductance added so that load current ripple is negligible. Find:

(a) peak load voltage
(b) average load voltage
(c) peak load current
(d) average load current
(e) peak diode current
(f) peak reverse diode voltage
(g) average diode current.

Solution

(a) Same as in Example 5.20: 391.9 V
(b) Same as in Example 5.20: 324.1 V
(c) Same as the average current because there is no ripple: 12.96 A
(d) Same as in Example 5.20: 12.96 A
(e) Same as the average current: 12.96 A
(f) Same as in Example 5.20: 678.8 V
(g) Same as in Example 5.20: 4.32 A.   ∎

A comment on Examples 5.20 and 5.21: The only effect on circuit design of the load being inductive is that the diode peak current is reduced somewhat by the inductance. Because average current is the primary element in diode-rectifier selection, the inductance has essentially no effect on the choice of a rectifier diode. The exact circuit inductance, whether large or small or even of unknown value, thus has practically no effect on circuit design.

EXAMPLE 5.22

For this example, find how much inductance is required for negligible ripple in the load current. Use the data from Example 5.20.

Solution   This is not an exact solution, but it does provide a result useful in design. If the reactance part of the load impedance (at the lowest ripple frequency) is made large compared to the load resistance, then there is negligible ripple current. A reasonable choice is to make the reactance 10 times the resistance. The lowest ripple frequency is 180 Hz, so therefore

$$(2\pi)(180)L = (10)(25\ \Omega) \qquad L = 0.221\ \text{H}.$$

A Fourier analysis of the actual load-voltage waveform yields a value of $0.207V_m$ for the magnitude of the lowest ripple frequency. This frequency's peak current can be found by

$$|I_3| = \frac{|V_3|}{|Z_3|} = \frac{(0.207)(391.9)}{|25 + j(3)(60)(2\pi)(0.221)|}$$

$$|I_3| = \frac{81.12}{251.2} = 0.323 \text{ A}.$$

The DC part, or the average current, is 12.96 A, so the peak ripple is 2.5% of the average. The ripple is not zero, but it is relatively small. ∎

Half-Wave, Three-Phase Controlled Rectifiers

The diode rectifiers in Figure 5.45 are replaced by SCRs. The cases considered here are similar to the single-phase cases. The first is the resistive load. Each SCR is delayed in turn on beyond the normal time. The situation is slightly more involved than the single-phase case. If the delay angle $\alpha < 30°$, then the Phase A SCR continues to conduct until the Phase B SCR is turned on. The load voltage and load current do not go to zero at any time. The average load voltage is reduced compared to the $\alpha = 0$ case. The graph in Figure 5.49 shows voltage and current as a function of time.

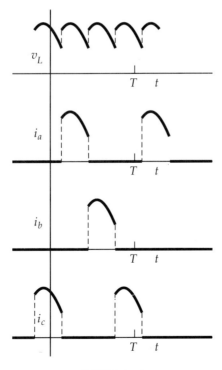

FIGURE 5.49

Again, the average load voltage is found by an integration:

$$V_{avg} = \frac{3}{T} \int_{t_1}^{t_2} V_m \sin \omega t \, dt \tag{5.144}$$

where the times t_1 and t_2 correspond to $(30° + \alpha)$ and $(150° + \alpha)$, respectively:

$$t_1 = \frac{\left[\left(\frac{\pi}{6}\right) + \alpha\right]}{\omega} \tag{5.145}$$

$$t_2 = \frac{\left[\left(\frac{5\pi}{6}\right) + \alpha\right]}{\omega}. \tag{5.146}$$

Upon substituting Equations 5.145 and 5.146 into Equation 5.144, the average voltage equation becomes

$$V_{avg} = \frac{3}{T} \int_{(\pi/6 + \alpha)/\omega}^{(5\pi/6 + \alpha)/\omega} V_m \sin \omega t \, dt \tag{5.147}$$

$$V_{avg} = 0.827 V_m \cos \alpha. \tag{5.148}$$

Note that the effect of phase control is to add the term $(\cos \alpha)$ rather than the result in Equation 5.140.

EXAMPLE 5.23

In Example 5.20, the resistive load now is served by a controlled rectifier using three SCRs in a half-wave circuit. The delay angle is 25°. Find:

(a) peak load voltage
(b) average load voltage
(c) peak load current
(d) average load current
(e) peak SCR current
(f) peak reverse SCR voltage
(g) average SCR current.

Solution

(a) $\qquad V_m = \dfrac{(1.414)(480)}{1.732} = 391.9 \text{ V}$

(b) $\qquad V_{avg} = 0.827 V_m \cos \alpha = (0.827)(391.9)(\cos 25°) = 293.7 \text{ V}$

(c) $$I_m = \frac{V_m}{R} = \frac{391.9}{25} = 15.68 \text{ A}$$

(d) $$I_{avg} = \frac{V_{avg}}{R} = \frac{293.7}{25} = 11.75 \text{ A}$$

(e)   Peak SCR current $= I_m = 15.68$ A

(f)   Peak SCR reverse voltage $= (480)(1.414) = 678.8$ V

(g)   SCR average current $= \dfrac{I_{avg}}{3} = \dfrac{11.75}{3} = 3.92$ A. ∎

If α is permitted values greater than $30°$, the load current will go to zero at one instant and then seek to become negative. This cannot occur, and with a resistive load, the load current and voltage both are zero until the next SCR begins conduction. Appropriate waveforms are shown in Figure 5.50. Again, the average load voltage is found by integration from t_1 to t_2, but now the load voltage is zero from t_4 to t_2. During this latter interval, the load is disconnected from all three source voltages:

$$V_{avg} = \frac{3}{T} \int_{t_1}^{t_2} v_L \, dt \tag{5.149}$$

$$V_{avg} = \frac{3}{T} \int_{t_1}^{t_4} V_m \sin \omega t \, dt + \frac{3}{T} \int_{t_4}^{t_2} (0) \, dt \tag{5.150}$$

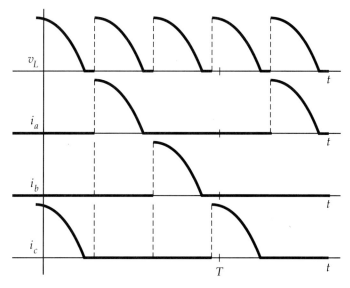

FIGURE 5.50

where t_1 continues to correspond to $(30° + \alpha)$ and t_4 corresponds to $180°$;

$$V_{avg} = \frac{3}{2\pi} \int_{(\pi/6+\alpha)/\omega}^{\pi/\omega} V_m \sin \omega t \, dt \tag{5.151}$$

$$V_{avg} = \left(\frac{3V_m}{2\pi}\right)(1 + 0.866 \cos \alpha - 0.5 \sin \alpha) \tag{5.152}$$

Equation 5.152 is valid for α in the range from $30°$ to $150°$.

EXAMPLE 5.24

In Example 5.23, the delay angle is changed to $80°$. Because the load remains resistive, this delay angle requires a change in the voltage equations. Find:

(a) peak load voltage

(b) average load voltage

(c) peak load current

(d) average load current

(e) peak SCR current

(f) peak reverse SCR voltage

(g) average SCR current.

Solution

(a) Because SCR turn on occurs after the peak of the source voltage, peak load voltage is less than V_m:

$$\text{Peak load voltage} = V_m \sin(\alpha + 30°)$$
$$= (391.9)(\sin 110°) = 368.3 \text{ V}.$$

(b) From Equation 5.152:

$$V_{avg} = \left(\frac{3V_m}{2\pi}\right)(1 + 0.866 \cos 80° - 0.5 \sin 80°)$$
$$= 0.314 V_m = (0.314)(391.9) = 123.1 \text{ V}.$$

(c)
$$\text{Peak load current} = \frac{\text{Peak load voltage}}{R}$$
$$= \frac{391.9 \sin(30° + 80°)}{R}$$
$$= \frac{368.3}{25}$$
$$= 14.73 \text{ A}.$$

(d) $$I_{avg} = \frac{V_{avg}}{R} = \frac{123.1}{25} = 4.92 \text{ A.}$$

(e)   Peak SCR current = Peak load current = 14.73 A.

(f)   Peak SCR reverse voltage = $(480)(1.414) = 678.8$ V.

(g)   SCR average current $= \dfrac{I_{avg}}{3} = \dfrac{4.92}{3} = 1.64$ A.   ∎

The next case is that of an inductive load without a freewheeling diode. We assume that the inductance is large enough that load current is not only continuous but also essentially constant. The load voltage now may be negative for some values of α. For $\alpha < 30°$, the load voltage is always positive, and the average voltage is the same as that of the resistive case. But for $\alpha > 30°$, the situation changes, and the load voltage becomes negative for part of each cycle. The situation is shown in Figure 5.51 for $\alpha = 60°$.

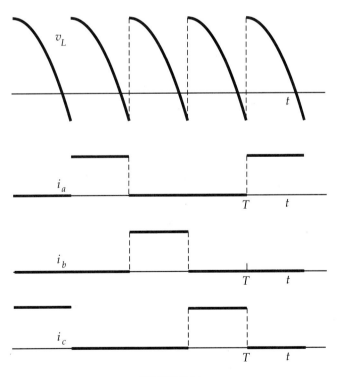

FIGURE 5.51

The average load voltage again is found by integration from t_1 to t_2, where t_1 corresponds to $(\alpha + \pi/6)$ and t_2 corresponds to $(\alpha + 5\pi/6)$:

$$V_{avg} = \frac{3}{T} \int_{t_1}^{t_2} V_m \sin \omega t \, dt \qquad (5.153)$$

$$V_{avg} = \left[\frac{(3)(3)^{0.5}}{2\pi} \right] V_m \cos \alpha = 0.827 V_m \cos \alpha. \qquad (5.154)$$

The result is familiar: It is the same as the resistive case although no longer restricted to $\alpha < 30°$. The previous restriction resulted from the load voltage changing shape for $\alpha > 30°$ with a resistive load. The load voltage now continues along the same segment of a sinusoid for $\alpha > 30°$. Except for the leading numerical value, the variation with α is the same as for the corresponding single-phase case.

EXAMPLE 5.25

A highly inductive load is provided a rectified voltage from a 480-V, three-phase, four-wire source by a three-SCR, half-wave, controlled rectifier. There is no freewheeling diode. The delay angle is 50° and $R = 25\ \Omega$. Find:

(a) peak load voltage
(b) average load voltage
(c) peak load current
(d) average load current
(e) peak SCR current
(f) peak reverse SCR voltage
(g) average SCR current.

Solution

(a) Because SCR turn on occurs before the peak of the source voltage, peak load voltage is V_m;

$$V_m = 391.9.$$

(b) $V_{avg} = 0.827 V_m \cos \alpha = (0.827)(391.9)(\cos 50°) = 208.3$ V.

(c)   Peak load current = average load current $= \dfrac{V_{avg}}{R}$

$$= \frac{208.3}{25} = 8.33 \text{ A.}$$

(d) $I_{avg} = \dfrac{V_{avg}}{R} = \dfrac{208.3}{25} = 8.33$ A.

(e)   Peak SCR current = peak load current = 8.33 A.

(f)   Peak SCR reverse voltage = (480)(1.414) = 678.8 V.

(g)   SCR average current $= \dfrac{I_{avg}}{3} = \dfrac{8.33}{3} = 2.78$ A.   ∎

The final case is an inductive load with a freewheeling diode present. Once again, negative load voltage values may not exist, and the result for average load voltage is the same as for the resistive case. For $\alpha < 30°$, the FWD has no effect and Equation 5.154 applies. For greater values of α, the average load voltage is given by Equation 5.152 for $30° < \alpha < 150°$. For this range of the phase-control angle, the FWD conducts load current during three intervals in each cycle. For Phase A, an SCR conducts from $\omega t = (\alpha + 30°)$ to $180°$. The FWD conducts from $180°$ to the time of next SCR conduction at $\omega t = (\alpha + 150°)$. The total time of conduction for the SCR and one FWD period is $120°$ as shown in Figure 5.52 for the case of $\alpha = 75°$.

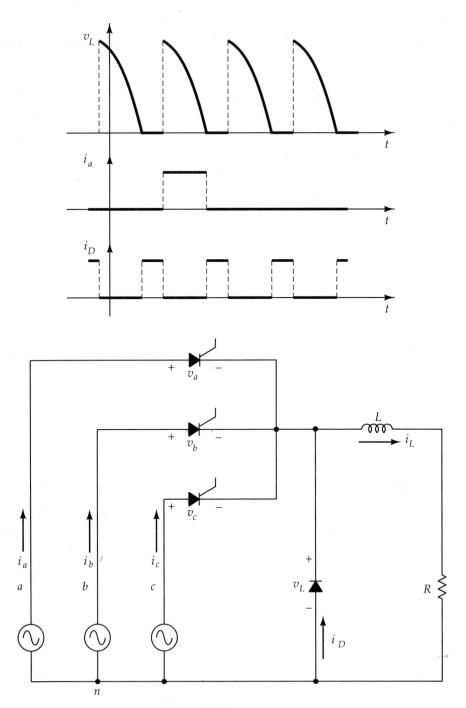

FIGURE 5.52

Three-Phase Diode Bridge

The preceding half-wave circuits served as an introduction to polyphase rectifier circuits. Such half-wave circuits are not used widely because the unidirectional source currents may adversely affect the AC source. A bridge rectifier
overcomes this problem and also provides an output that has lower ripple amplitude with higher ripple frequency. The diode bridge rectifier in Figure 5.53
therefore is widely used. In addition, the bridge circuit requires only a three-wire
connection to the AC source.

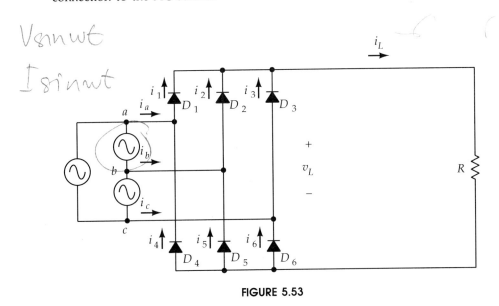

$V_{an} \, \omega t$

$I \sin \omega t$

FIGURE 5.53

With the diode bridge, there is little difference whether the load is inductive or resistive. The load voltage is always the most positive of the six values
of the line-to-line voltages of the source. The number 6 is used because v_{ba} is
considered as well as the more usual v_{ab}. In the earlier treatment of the single-
phase bridge, the corresponding number was 2. The load voltage is as shown in
Figure 5.54. The wave shape of the voltage in this figure leads to this arrangement sometimes being referred to as a "six-pulse rectifier" because there are six
segments to the voltage waveform in one period.

At time t_3, the most positive voltage is v_{ac}, and therefore $v_L = v_{ac}$. At
this instant, Diodes 1 and 6 conduct, while Diodes 2, 3, 4, and 5 are reverse-
biased and do not conduct. In Equations 5.155 and 5.156, v_1, v_2, and v_3 are
voltages of Diodes 1, 2, and 3, with the plus reference at the anode. A voltage
equation around one loop is as follows:

$$v_{ab} - v_1 + v_2 = 0. \tag{5.155}$$

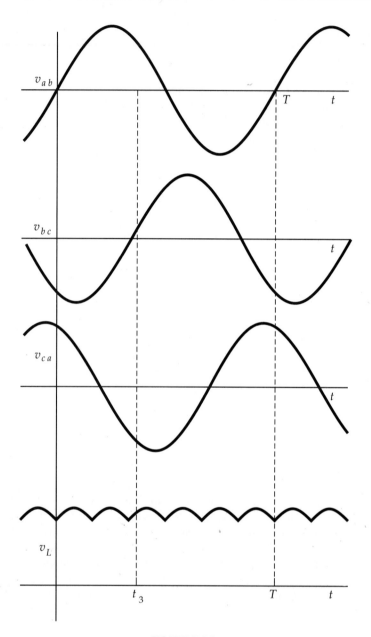

FIGURE 5.54

Because Diode 1 is conducting, $v_1 = 0$, and thus $v_2 = -v_{ab}$. At this instant, $v_{ab} > 0$ and thus $v_2 < 0$, which means that Diode 2 is reverse-biased. A voltage equation written around another loop gives

$$v_{ac} - v_1 + v_3 = 0. \tag{5.156}$$

Again, $v_1 = 0$ and $v_3 = -v_{ac}$, and because $v_{ac} > 0$, Diode 3 is reverse-biased. Further examination of the circuit and graphs reveals the cyclic pattern of diode conduction and turnoff.

During one interval, Diodes 1 and 5 conduct; at the end of this interval, 5 turns off and 6 turns on, so that 1 and 6 begin to conduct. This change occurs at $t = t_2$ in Figure 5.55. The conduction pattern is as shown, with changes occurring at 60° intervals. Each diode conducts one-third of the time, or 120° of the 360° cycle.

If the load is inductive, the load current will have reduced ripple current. The graph in Figure 5.55 shows the case in which there is negligible load current ripple. The inductance required is not large, because the ripple in the load voltage is relatively small. The graph for the three line currents is found by using a current equation at each of the bridge's three input nodes. For line current i_a, this is Equation 5.157:

$$i_a = i_1 - i_4. \tag{5.157}$$

The graph for i_a thus is easily found from that for i_1 and i_4. The large amount of cyclic symmetry in the various quantities should be noted.

The average load voltage is found by integrating over a 60° interval of one of the line-to-line voltages. In this illustration, v_{ab} is used in the interval from 60° to 120°:

$$V_{avg} = \left(\frac{6}{2\pi}\right) \int_{\pi/3}^{2\pi/3} V_m \sin \theta \, d\theta \tag{5.158}$$

$$V_{avg} = \left(\frac{6}{2\pi}\right) V_m = 0.955 V_m. \tag{5.159}$$

Note that this integration used an angle variable rather than the time variable.

EXAMPLE 5.26

A three-phase, 460-V, 60-Hz system supplies a diode bridge rectifier. The load is a 100-Ω resistor. Find:

(a) average load voltage

(b) average load current ✓

(c) average current that each diode must conduct

(d) peak reverse voltage to which each diode is subjected

(e) average load power.

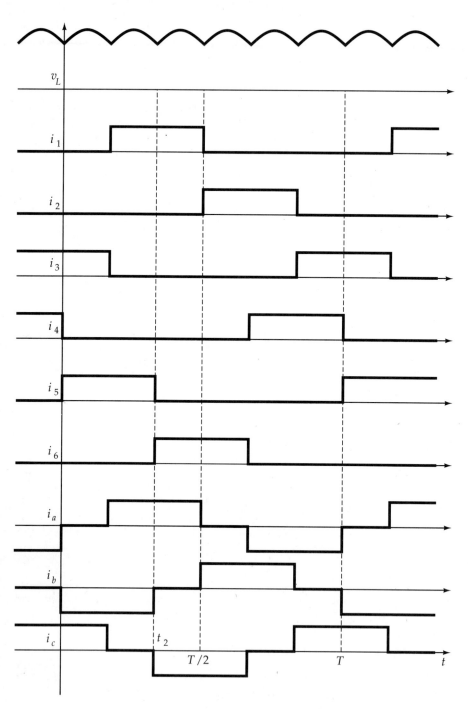

FIGURE 5.55

Solution

(a)

$$V_{L_{avg}} = 0.955 V_m$$

$$\sqrt{2} = 1.414$$

$$V_m = (1.414)(460) = 650 \text{ V rms}$$

$$V_{L_{avg}} = (0.955)(650) = 621 \text{ V}.$$

(b)

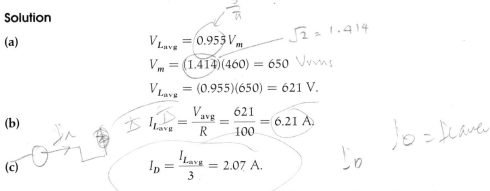

$$I_{L_{avg}} = \frac{V_{avg}}{R} = \frac{621}{100} = 6.21 \text{ A}$$

$$b = \text{Leave}$$

(c)

$$I_D = \frac{I_{L_{avg}}}{3} = 2.07 \text{ A}.$$

$$b$$

(d) Peak reverse voltage occurs with one diode conducting, such as 1. The peak value of v_{ab} then is applied to Diode 2. Thus, each diode is subjected to a reverse voltage of 650 V. To allow for transient peaks on the power system, the diodes must have a rating greater than this value. Depending on the system's protective features and the severity of surges, the diode rating should be at least 800 V.

(e) Average load power is found by using the RMS value of the load current:

$$(I_{L_{RMS}})^2 = \left(\frac{6}{2\pi}\right) \int_{\pi/3}^{2\pi/3} (I_m \sin \theta)^2 \, d\theta$$

$$I_{L_{RMS}} = 0.956 I_m = (0.956)(6.5) = 6.212.$$

Thus, it is evident that the current has such a small ripple that there is little difference between the average and RMS values:

$$\text{Average load power} = (I_{L_{RMS}})^2(R) = (6.212)^2(100) = 3860 \text{ W}. \quad \blacksquare$$

Phase-Controlled Bridge, $\alpha < 60°$

The bridge rectifier now is constructed with SCRs instead of diode elements. The SCR conduction now may be delayed from the normal point where conduction would begin if the elements were diodes. The angle α is measured from this normal point of commutation. For $\alpha < 60°$, the instantaneous load voltage is positive, load current always exists, and, insofar as load voltage is concerned, it does not matter whether the load is inductive or a freewheeling diode is present. The graph of load voltage for $\alpha = 30°$ is shown in Figure 5.56.

Note that each element begins conducting 30° later than if the elements were diodes. Each element conducts for a 60° interval as would be the case with no phase control. Thus, the average load voltage is found by integrating over an appropriate 60° interval. The only change in the average voltage equation, as compared to the diode case, results from a shift in the limits of integration.

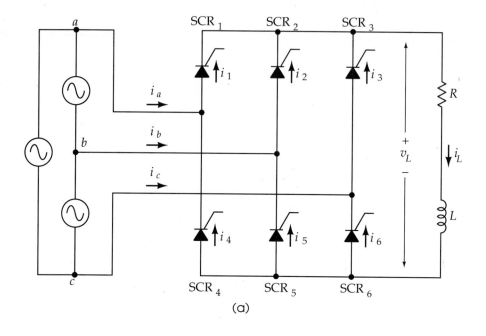

(a)

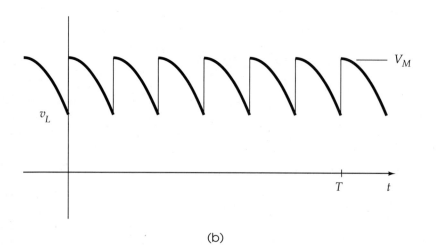

(b)

FIGURE 5.56

This is similar to Equation 5.158, except for the limits:

$$V_{avg} = \left(\frac{6}{2\pi}\right) \int_{(\pi/3+\alpha)}^{(2\pi/3+\alpha)} V_m \sin\theta \, d\theta \tag{5.160}$$

$$V_{avg} = \left(\frac{6}{2\pi}\right) V_m \cos\alpha = 0.955\, V_m \cos\alpha. \tag{5.161}$$

Average load current is found by dividing average load voltage by the load resistance.

The SCRs follow the same conduction pattern as in the diode bridge case. If the load is inductive, the SCR currents are identical in wave shape to the diode currents in Figure 5.55 although shifted to the right by the angle α. Remember that the amplitude of the load current is changed because of the $(\cos\alpha)$ term for average voltage; the wave shape is not changed except as noted above.

E X A M P L E 5 . 2 7

The circuit in Example 5.26 now includes an inductive load and the bridge diodes are replaced by SCRs. The delay angle is $45°$. Find:

(a) average load voltage
(b) average load current
(c) average current that each SCR must conduct
(d) peak reverse voltage to which each SCR is subjected
(e) average load power.

Solution

(a) V_m from the previous example is 650 V. From Equation 5.161,

$$V_{avg} = 0.955\, V_m \cos\alpha = (0.955)(650)(\cos 45°) = 439 \text{ V}.$$

(b) $$I_{avg} = \frac{V_{avg}}{R} = \frac{439}{100} = 4.39 \text{ A} = I_{RMS}.$$

(c) $$\text{SCR average current} = \frac{I_{avg}}{3} = \frac{4.39}{3} = 1.46 \text{ A}.$$

(d) $$\text{Peak reverse voltage} = V_m = 650 \text{ V}.$$

(e) $$\text{Average load power} = (I_{RMS})^2(R) = (4.39)^2(100) = 1930 \text{ W}. \qquad \blacksquare$$

Phase-Controlled Bridge, $\alpha > 60°$

As α is increased to a value greater than $60°$, the instantaneous load voltage becomes negative in parts of the cycle. If there is no freewheeling diode, Equation 5.161 for average voltage still applies, as do other equations for SCR current and line current. Only in the case of a freewheeling diode does the average voltage equation change form to accommodate the interval during which the instantaneous load voltage is zero. The graph in Figure 5.57 shows waveforms for $\alpha = 90°$.

Average load voltage is found in a manner similar to the previous cases. The upper limit for the integration is π, because this limits the instantaneous load voltage to zero or positive values:

$$V_{avg} = \left(\frac{6}{2\pi}\right) \int_{(\pi/3 + \alpha)}^{\pi} V_m \sin \theta \, d\theta \tag{5.162}$$

$$V_{avg} = \left[\left(\frac{3}{\pi}\right) V_m\right] \left\{1 + \cos\left[\left(\frac{\pi}{3}\right) + \alpha\right]\right\}. \tag{5.163}$$

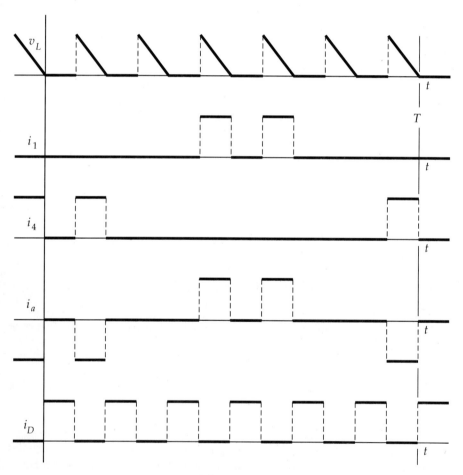

FIGURE 5.57

Bridge and FWD Currents

Values of currents in both the SCRs and the three lines are of interest for circuit design. If I_L is the average load current (assuming negligible ripple current in the load), then average SCR current is calculated as follows. For the case without an FWD, the SCR average current is given in Equation 5.164:

$$I_{SCR_{avg}} = \frac{I_L}{3}. \tag{5.164}$$

But if $\alpha > 60°$ and there is an FWD, the FWD conducts the load current for the angle $(\alpha - 60°)$ twice in each $120°$ interval. The SCR thus conducts for the interval $[120° - 2(\alpha - 60°)]$ or for the interval $(240° - 2\alpha)$ if $\alpha > \pi/3$. The average SCR current is given in Equation 5.165:

$$I_{SCR_{avg}} = \left(\frac{240 - 2\alpha}{360}\right)(I_L) \tag{5.165}$$

$$I_{SCR_{avg}} = \left(\frac{120 - \alpha}{180}\right)(I_L). \tag{5.166}$$

The freewheeling diode's average current is found by

$$I_{FWD_{avg}} = \left[\frac{(3)(2)(\alpha - 60)}{360}\right](I_L) = \left(\frac{\alpha - 60}{60}\right)(I_L). \tag{5.167}$$

Note in Equation 5.167 that the factor of 3 comes from the freewheeling diode's conduction during all periods of freewheeling action; similarly, the factor of 2 comes from the FWD's conduction twice per cycle for each phase.

The AC line current is best described by its RMS value, because it determines not only the required wire and fuse sizes, but also the current rating of the source. This probably would be the current rating of transformers serving as the source to the rectifier.

For either $\alpha < 60°$ or no FWD present, the line current consists of a positive value equal to the load current for $120°$ duration and an equal but negative value for $120°$ duration. There are two $60°$ intervals of zero value. The RMS value is given in Equation 5.168:

$$I_{RMS} = \left[\left(\frac{120}{180}\right)(I_L)^2\right]^{0.5} = 0.816I_L. \tag{5.168}$$

For the case in which $\alpha > 60°$ and an FWD is present, each cycle of line current consists of two positive segments, both of $(120° - \alpha)$ duration. There are two similar negative segments. The remaining intervals are of zero value. The RMS value is determined by Equation 5.169:

$$I_{RMS} = \left[\left(\frac{120 - \alpha}{90}\right)(I_L)^2\right]^{0.5}. \tag{5.169}$$

EXAMPLE 5.28

A three-phase bridge rectifier with six SCRs supplies an inductive load with a variable voltage. The average voltage must be variable from 100 V to 600 V. A freewheeling diode is used; $R_L = 10 \, \Omega$ and $V_S = 460$-V RMS. Find:

(a) necessary range of α

(b) load current range

(c) SCR average current rating

(d) SCR voltage rating

(e) maximum load power

(f) FWD average current rating.

Solution

(a) For $V_L = 600$ V, from Equation 5.161:

$$600 = (1.414)(460)(0.955) \cos \alpha$$
$$\alpha = 15.0°.$$

For $V_L = 100$ V, from Equation 5.163:

$$100 = \left(\frac{3}{\pi}\right)(1.414)(460)[1 + \cos(\alpha + 60°)]$$
$$\alpha = 87.0°.$$

Note that $\alpha > 60°$, which validates the use of Equation 5.163.

(b) For $V_L = 600$ V:

$$I_L = \frac{600}{10} = 60 \text{ A}$$

For $V_L = 100$ V:

$$I_L = \frac{100}{10} = 10 \text{ A}.$$

(c) The largest SCR current occurs at the largest load voltage. From Equation 5.164:

$$I_{SCR_{avg}} = \frac{60}{3} = 20 \text{ A}.$$

(d) The SCRs must withstand system peak voltage or greater:

$$V_m = (1.414)(460) = 650.5 \text{ V}.$$

The next highest available SCR rating is 800 V, the absolute minimum acceptable value.

(e) At $\alpha = 15°$ and an inductive load, the load current is constant at 60 A:

$$P_{load} = (60)^2(10) = 36,000 \text{ W.}$$

(f) FWD current is determined from Equation 5.167. The largest value of this current is not obvious because I_L is also a function of α. An iterative process provides a result that is maximum at $\alpha = 75.2°$. For this value of α:

$$V_L = \left(\frac{3}{\pi}\right)(1.414)(460)[1 + \cos(75.2 + 60)]$$

$$V_L = 180.4 \text{ V}$$

$$I_L = \frac{V_L}{R_L} = 18.04 \text{ A}$$

$$I_{\text{FWD}_{avg}} = \left(\frac{\alpha - 60}{60}\right)I_L$$

$$= \left(\frac{75.2 - 60}{60}\right)(18.04) = 4.57 \text{ A.}$$

The FWD selection should be based on this average current and the need to block the peak system voltage. ∎

Continuous Inductor Current

The circuit arrangement in Figure 5.58 occurs in many situations. The voltage source can represent the back EMF of a DC motor or a filter capacitor used as part of an LC filter arrangement. If the inductance value is too small, then the

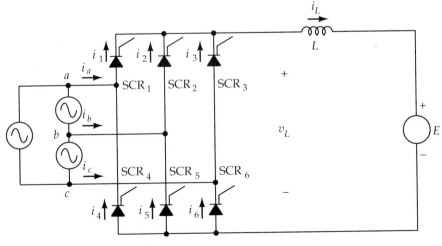

FIGURE 5.58

inductor current is discontinuous. This is similar to the single-phase situation in Section 5.6.

   If the inductor current is discontinuous, then the average value of v_L is changed from that for the continuous conduction case assumed in earlier parts of Section 5.8. Good design of a controlled rectifier requires a known operating condition and a known value of output voltage as a function of α. To provide continuous inductor current, the critical inductance must be determined.

   For a diode bridge rectifier or for a controlled rectifier with zero turn-on delay, the output voltage ripple is small and relatively little inductance is required to maintain continuous inductor current. But as the value of α is increased, the load voltage ripple increases and additional inductance is necessary.

   The graph in Figure 5.59(a) shows certain relations in a phase-controlled, three-phase rectifier in which the inductor current becomes zero at the end of each SCR conduction interval. In the graph, the source voltage at the time of

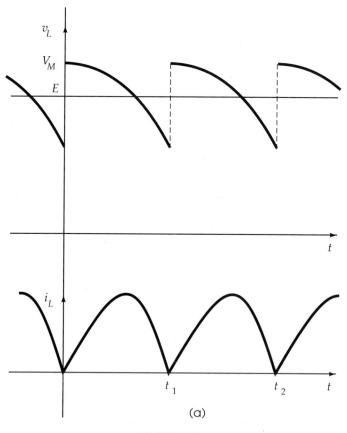

(a)

FIGURE 5.59

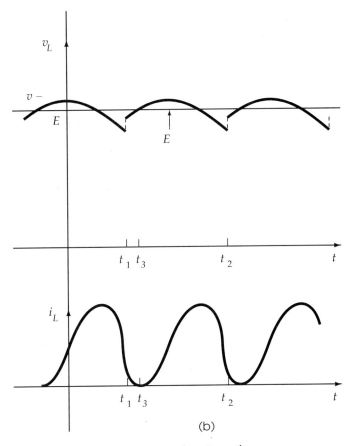

(b)

FIGURE 5.59 (continued)

switching is greater than the average output voltage, E. For the conditions shown, i_L increases for $\omega t > \alpha$, and the minimum value of i_L occurs at the switching point.

A second possibility is that the source voltage at the switching point is less than the average output voltage, E. In this case, i_L decreases for a short time beyond the switching time as shown in Figure 5.59(b). The minimum value of i_L does not occur at the switching point, t_1, but instead later, at t_3.

The value of α, the boundary between these two cases, must be determined. The circuit and graph in Figure 5.60 are the basis of the analysis. In the graph, the period of interest is $\dfrac{\pi}{3}$ radians of the original three-phase system voltage. The value of v_S is the same as E at the instant of turn on. This relation is noted in Equation 5.170. The point of turn on occurs at time t_1, which is α/ω later than

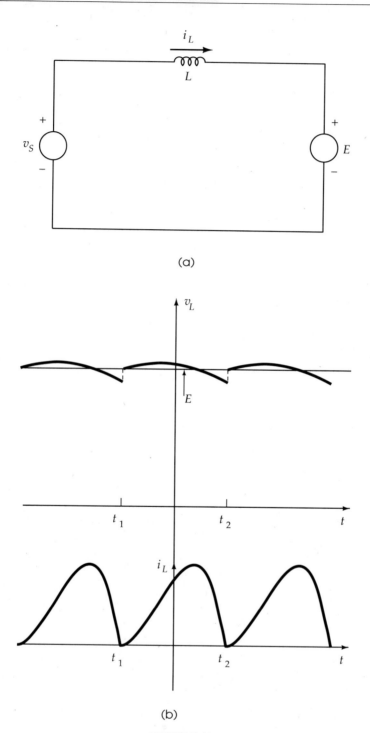

(a)

(b)

FIGURE 5.60

the earliest point of possible turn on:

$$V_m \cos \omega t_1 = E = \left(\frac{3}{\pi}\right) V_m \cos \alpha \qquad (5.170)$$

or

$$\cos\left(\alpha - \frac{\pi}{6}\right) = \left(\frac{3}{\pi}\right) \cos \alpha. \qquad (5.171)$$

Solving Equation 5.171 yields a value of $10.08°$ for α.

A solution valid for $\alpha > 10.08°$ starts by writing an equation for i_L during conduction:

$$\frac{di_L}{dt} = \frac{V_m \cos \omega t - E}{L}. \qquad (5.172)$$

The value of i_L is zero at the switching point as shown in Figure 5.59(a). The relation of Equation 5.172 can be solved for i_L as given in Equation 5.174:

$$i_L = \int_{t_1}^{t} \frac{V_m \cos \omega t - E}{L} dt \qquad (5.173)$$

$$i_L = \left(\frac{1}{\omega L}\right)[V_m(\sin \omega t - \sin \omega t_1) - E(\omega t - \omega t_1)]. \qquad (5.174)$$

If Equation 5.161 is used for E, then Equation 5.175 results:

$$i_L = \left(\frac{V_m}{\omega L}\right)[\sin \omega t - \sin \omega t_1 - \left(\frac{3}{\pi}\right)(\cos \alpha)(\omega t - \omega t_1)]. \qquad (5.175)$$

The value of i_L must be zero at t_2, which is $T/6$ later than t_1. Substitution of $t = (t_1 + T/6)$ verifies this condition.

The average value of i_L over the interval from $t_1 = (\alpha - \pi/6)/\omega$ to $t_2 = (\alpha + \pi/6)/\omega$ is found by integrating Equation 5.175:

$$I_L = \left(\frac{6}{T}\right) \int_{t_1}^{t_2} \frac{V_m}{\omega L} \left[\sin \omega t - \sin \omega t_1 - \left(\frac{3}{\pi}\right)(\cos \alpha)(\omega t - \omega t_1) \right] dt \qquad (5.176)$$

$$I_L = \left(\frac{3V_m}{\pi \omega L}\right) \left\{ \left[1 - \frac{\pi}{2(3)^{0.5}} \right] \sin \alpha \right\}. \qquad (5.177)$$

The average value of inductor current depends on the load resistance or some equivalent element that determines load current:

$$I_L = \frac{E}{R} = \frac{\left(\frac{3}{\pi}\right) V_m (\cos \alpha)}{R}. \qquad (5.178)$$

Using Equations 5.177 and 5.178 gives the normalized result for critical inductance:

$$\frac{\omega L}{R} = 0.0931 \tan \alpha. \qquad (5.179)$$

Comparing Equations 5.179 and 5.83 for the single-phase case demonstrates the value of using a polyphase rectifier. A much smaller inductance value is required to maintain continuous current for the polyphase case. The inductance value to maintain any degree of current smoothing also is smaller for the three-phase bridge in comparison to the value required for the single-phase case.

For the case in which $\alpha < 10.08°$, a slightly different analysis is required. The time at which i_L becomes zero is not at the switching point as shown in Figure 5.59(b). Equation 5.175 is rewritten as Equation 5.180 and with a starting point of t_3 to reflect this fact:

$$i_L = \left(\frac{V_m}{\omega L}\right)\left[\sin \omega t - \sin \omega t_3 - \left(\frac{3}{\pi}\right)(\cos \alpha)(\omega t - \omega t_3)\right]. \qquad (5.180)$$

The average value of i_L is found over the same interval as in Equation 5.176. The result is shown in Equation 5.181:

$$i_L = \left(\frac{6}{T}\right)\int_{t_1}^{t_2} \frac{V_m}{\omega L}\left[\sin \omega t - \sin \omega t_3 - \left(\frac{3}{\pi}\right)(\cos \alpha)(\omega t - \omega t_3)\right]dt \qquad (5.181)$$

$$I_L = \frac{3V_m}{\pi \omega L}\left[\sin \alpha - \left(\frac{\pi}{3}\right)(\sin \theta) + (\theta - \alpha)\cos \alpha\right], \qquad (5.182)$$

where $\theta = \omega t_3$. The requirement of Equation 5.178 still applies. Combining Equations 5.178 and 5.182 yields

$$\frac{\omega L}{R} = \tan \alpha - \left(\frac{\pi \sin \theta}{3 \cos \alpha}\right) + \theta - \alpha. \qquad (5.183)$$

Note in Equation 5.183 that θ has a negative value. In the graph in Figure 5.59(b), the source voltage is represented by a cosine function, and t_3 necessarily must occur for a negative time value. At t_3, the following equations apply:

$$V_m \cos \omega t = V_m \cos \theta = \left(\frac{3}{\pi}\right)V_m \cos \alpha \qquad (5.184)$$

$$\theta = \cos^{-1}\left[\left(\frac{3}{\pi}\right)\cos \alpha\right]. \qquad (5.185)$$

In Equation 5.185 the negative value must be selected for the double-valued inverse cosine function.

EXAMPLE 5.29

A three-phase bridge rectifier supplies power to a DC motor with negligible armature resistance. The source is 240-V RMS, 60 Hz. The average load voltage must vary from 150 V to 300 V. The minimum average load current at any load voltage is 10 A. Continuous load current is a requirement. Find:

(a) required range for α

(b) minimum value of inductance necessary for continuous motor current.

Solution

(a) From Equation 5.161 for $V_L = 100$ V:

$$100 = \left(\frac{3}{\pi}\right)(240)(2)^{0.5}\cos \alpha$$

$$\alpha = 72.0° = 1.257 \text{ rad.}$$

For $V_L = 300$ V:

$$300 = \left(\frac{3}{\pi}\right)(240)(2)^{0.5}\cos \alpha$$

$$\alpha = 22.24° = 0.388 \text{ rad.}$$

(b) For both ends of the control range, Equation 5.177 applies. The minimum value of I_L can be used to determine the inductance required.

For $V_L = 100$ V:

$$10 = \left[\frac{(3)(339.4)}{(\pi)(377)(L)}\right]\left\{\left[1 - \frac{\pi}{2(3)^{0.5}}\right]\sin 72.0°\right\}$$

$$L = 0.00761 \text{ H.}$$

For $V_L = 300$ V:

$$10 = \left[\frac{(3)(339.4)}{(\pi)(377)(L)}\right]\left\{\left[1 - \frac{\pi}{2(3)^{0.5}}\right]\sin 22.24°\right\}$$

$$L = 0.00303 \text{ H.}$$

The larger of the two values is selected so that continuous current exists over the entire control range. ∎

Power Factor

In most cases of large rectifier loads with polyphase sources, the rectifier is a bridge arrangement. The load frequently is inductive and thus the DC current may be considered constant for analysis purposes. In this section, a bridge rectifier supplying such a load is analyzed for its power factor with respect to the AC system.

The graphs in Figure 5.61 show the line current and two of the source voltages for a three-phase bridge rectifier. The line current is drawn for a phase-control angle α for a rectifier without an FWD.

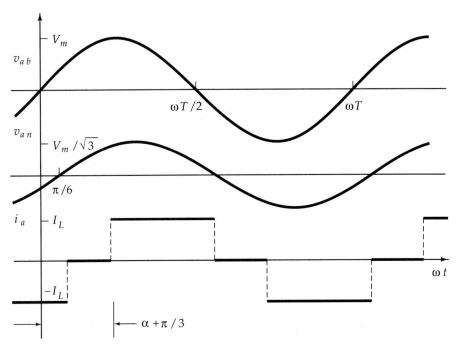

FIGURE 5.61

In the graph in Figure 5.61, the line current for Phase A would begin $\pi/6$ radians later than the voltage zero for v_{an}, if the phase-control angle α is zero. For the general case, the current for Phase A is shown phase-delayed by the additional angle α.

Analysis for the power factor can be done on a per-phase basis. The average power per phase is determined by an integration, with the limits chosen to recognize that the current is zero during part of each half-cycle. The integration also uses an angle variable rather than time as the variable:

$$P_{avg} = \left(\frac{1}{\pi}\right) \int_{\alpha+\pi/3}^{\alpha+\pi} I_L \left(\frac{V_m}{1.732}\right) \sin\left(\theta - \frac{\pi}{6}\right) d\theta \qquad (5.186)$$

$$P_{avg} = \left(\frac{V_m I_L}{\pi}\right) \cos\alpha. \qquad (5.187)$$

The RMS value of the line current for Phase A is determined easily because in each half-cycle the current is constant and is zero the remaining portion of the half-cycle. The RMS value of the L–N voltage recognizes the fact that V_m is the peak value of the L–L voltage:

$$I_{RMS} = \left(\frac{2}{3}\right)^{0.5} I_L = 0.8165 I_L \tag{5.188}$$

$$V_{RMS} = \frac{V_m}{6^{0.5}} \tag{5.189}$$

$$S/\text{phase} = V_{RMS} I_{RMS} \tag{5.190}$$

$$\text{Power factor} = \frac{P_{avg}}{S} = \left(\frac{3}{\pi}\right) \cos \alpha. \tag{5.191}$$

Because the AC line current is not a sinusoid, the power factor of the rectifier and its load cannot be unity even for $\alpha = 0$.

For the case with an FWD present, there is no change for α less than or equal to 60°. For $\alpha > 60°$, the FWD conducts some of the load current, and the line current changes wave shape as shown in Figure 5.57. The changes that reflect this in Figure 5.61 are shown in Figure 5.62.

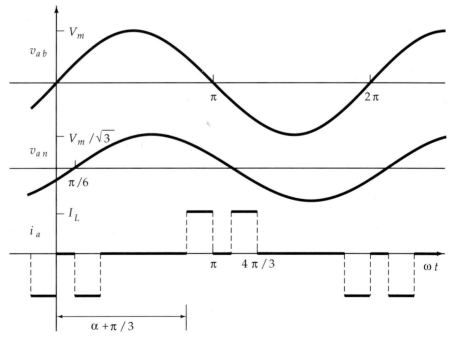

FIGURE 5.62

With the FWD present, the instantaneous load voltage cannot be negative. Line A current becomes zero at the time v_{ab} goes to zero at $\omega t = \pi$ in Figure 5.62. The Phase A current again is nonzero starting at $\omega t = 2\pi/3 + \alpha$. This current also becomes zero when a source voltage, V_{ca}, becomes zero at $\omega t = 4\pi/3$. The average power is evaluated by the summation of two integrals over the intervals that the current is nonzero:

$$P_{avg} = \left(\frac{I_L}{\pi}\right)\left[\frac{V_m}{(3)^{0.5}}\right]\left[\int_{\alpha+\pi/3}^{\pi} \sin\left(\theta - \frac{\pi}{6}\right)d\theta + \int_{\alpha+2\pi/3}^{4\pi/3} \sin\left(\theta - \frac{\pi}{6}\right)d\theta\right]$$

(5.192)

$$P_{avg} = \left(\frac{V_m I_L}{\pi}\right)\left[1 + \cos\left(\alpha + \frac{\pi}{3}\right)\right] \qquad \alpha > \frac{\pi}{3}.$$ (5.193)

The conduction interval for the two pulses of line current in each half-cycle have a total duration of $\left[\left(\frac{4\pi}{3}\right) - 2\alpha\right]$ radians. The RMS value can be found as shown by Equation 5.194:

$$I_{RMS} = \left\{\frac{\left[\left(\frac{4\pi}{3}\right) - 2\alpha\right]}{\pi}\right\}^{0.5} I_L.$$ (5.194)

The RMS value of the L–N voltage is the same as in Equation 5.189. The value of S and the power factor now may be determined by combining several of the preceding equations:

$$\text{Power factor} = \left[\frac{(6)^{0.5}}{\pi}\right]\left[1 + \cos\left(\alpha + \frac{\pi}{3}\right)\right]\left[\frac{\left(\frac{4\pi}{3} - 2\alpha\right)}{\pi}\right]^{-0.5}.$$ (5.195)

EXAMPLE 5.30

A three-phase bridge rectifier supplies variable power to a highly inductive load. An FWD is used. The average value of the load voltage is variable from 600 V to 200 V; $V_S = 480$ V, 60 Hz, L–L; and $R_L = 10\ \Omega$. Find:

(a) the range of α that is required

(b) the power factor for $V_L = 600$ V

(c) the power factor for $V_L = 200$ V.

Solution

(a) $V_m = (480)(1.414) = 678.8$ V.

For $V_L = 600$ V, using Equation 5.161:

$$600 = \left(\frac{3}{\pi}\right)(678.8)\cos\alpha$$

$$\alpha = 22.24°.$$

For $V_L = 200$ V, using Equation 5.163:

$$200 = \left(\frac{3}{\pi}\right)(678.8)\left[1 + \cos\left(\alpha + \frac{\pi}{3}\right)\right]$$

$$\alpha = 73.75°.$$

(b) For $\alpha = 22.24°$, using Equation 5.191:

$$\text{Power factor} = \left(\frac{3}{\pi}\right)\cos 22.24° = 0.884.$$

(c) For $\alpha = 73.75°$, using Equation 5.195:

$$\text{Power factor} = \left(\frac{2.45}{\pi}\right)(1 + \cos 133.75°)\left[\frac{(240 - 147.5)}{180}\right]^{-0.5}$$

$$\text{Power factor} = 0.336.$$ ∎

Harmonics

The AC line currents to polyphase-controlled rectifiers contain harmonics of the source frequency. Knowing the size of the various harmonics is helpful in determining possible adverse effects from these harmonic currents on other equipment or on the AC power system.

In this section we will compute the harmonics for the case of a controlled rectifier with an inductive load. The current waveform in Figure 5.61 applies if there is no FWD or if α is less than or equal to 60°. If the origin in this figure is shifted to a proper location, the graph of line current can be made an even function, as shown in Figure 5.63. Only the A_n terms, where n is an odd integer,

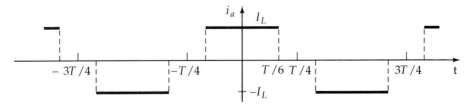

FIGURE 5.63

exist for this function. The coefficients can be determined as shown in Equation 5.196:

$$A_n = \left(\frac{8}{T}\right) \int_0^{T/6} I_L \cos n\omega t \, dt \qquad (5.196)$$

$$A_n = \left(\frac{4I_L}{n\pi}\right) \sin\left(\frac{n\pi}{3}\right). \qquad (5.197)$$

Values of n that are multiples of 3 in Equation 5.197 cause A_n to become zero. No multiples of a third harmonic current may exist in such a three-phase system with a three-wire connection of source to load.

For values of $\alpha > 60°$, the AC line currents take on a different form, if an FWD is used. The graph in Figure 5.62 is redrawn as Figure 5.64 so that the line current becomes an even function of time. For this waveform, the A_n coefficients can be evaluated by the integral in Equation 5.198:

$$A_n = \left(\frac{4}{\pi}\right) \int_{(\alpha-\pi/3)/2}^{(\pi-\alpha)/2} I_L \cos n\theta \, dt \qquad (5.198)$$

$$A_n = \left(\frac{4I_L}{n\pi}\right) \left\{ \left[\sin\left(\frac{n\pi}{2}\right)\right]\left[\cos\left(\frac{n\alpha}{2}\right)\right] + \left[\sin n\left(\frac{\pi}{6}-\frac{\alpha}{2}\right)\right]\right\} \qquad \alpha > \frac{\pi}{3}. \qquad (5.199)$$

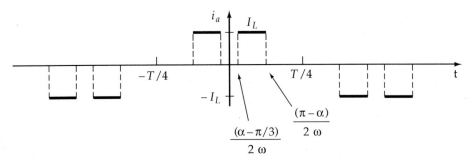

FIGURE 5.64

E X A M P L E   5 . 3 1

A three-phase, controlled bridge rectifier is supplied by a 240-V RMS, 60-Hz source. The load is highly inductive and an FWD is used. For a phase-control angle of 30°, the average load power is 20 kW. Find:

(a) the load resistance

(b) the AC line current fundamental and fifth-order harmonic current

(c) the fundamental and fifth-order harmonic current if α is increased to $75°$.

Solution

(a) For $\alpha = 30°$, the FWD does not conduct:

$$V_L = \left(\frac{3}{\pi}\right)(240)(1.414)\cos 30° = 280.7 \text{ V}.$$

Because the load is highly inductive, the load power may be found by the product of load average voltage and current:

$$I_L = \frac{20,000}{280.7} = 71.25 \text{ A}$$

$$R_L = \frac{280.7}{71.25} = 3.940 \ \Omega.$$

(b) The FWD does not conduct, so Equation 5.197 applies:

$$A_1 = \left[\frac{(4)(71.25)}{\pi}\right]\left(\sin\frac{\pi}{3}\right) = 78.56 \text{ A}$$

$$A_5 = \left[\frac{(4)(71.25)}{(5)(\pi)}\right]\sin\left(\frac{5\pi}{3}\right) = -15.71 \text{ A}.$$

(c) For $\alpha = 75°$, the FWD does conduct. From Equation 5.163:

$$V_{L_{avg}} = \left[\left(\frac{3}{\pi}\right)(240)(1.414)\right][1 + \cos(60° + 75°)]$$

$$= 94.93 \text{ V}$$

$$I_L = \frac{V_{L_{avg}}}{R_L} = \frac{94.93}{3.94} = 24.09 \text{ A}.$$

From Equation 5.199:

$$A_1 = \left[\frac{(4)(24.09)}{\pi}\right]\left\{\left[(\sin 90°)\cos\left(\frac{75°}{2}\right)\right] + \left[\sin\left(30° - \frac{75°}{2}\right)\right]\right\}$$

$$= 20.33 \text{ A}$$

$$A_5 = \left[\frac{(4)(24.09)}{5\pi}\right]\left\{[\sin(5)(90°)]\left[\cos(5)\left(\frac{75°}{2}\right)\right] + \left[\sin 5\left(30° - \frac{75°}{2}\right)\right]\right\}$$

$$= -9.82 \text{ A}.$$

Increased Pulse Number

In very large polyphase rectifiers, economics may dictate increasing pulse number from 6 to 12. This means an effective increase in the number of phases from the initial three-phase system. The benefits of such increased-pulse-number systems include a reduced ripple voltage in the DC output and an increased frequency for the lowest ripple voltage. Less load inductance then is required to maintain a given ripple content in the load current. A further benefit of increased pulse number is a reduction in the AC system's harmonic currents and an improvement in the power factor.

Several circuit arrangements can be used to accomplish the above objectives. For the limited purpose of this section, the circuit arrangement in Figure 5.65 serves to illustrate the method. The circuit arrangement is relatively simple to understand. The system consists of two bridge rectifiers connected so that the DC outputs are in series and the two voltages add. The AC inputs to the two bridges are isolated by two transformers that are connected wye–delta and delta–delta, respectively. The transformers are connected to take advantage of the differing phase shifts of the two connections.

In Figure 5.65, the two load voltages, which combine to give the total load voltage, each have the same waveform as that for a usual six-pulse bridge

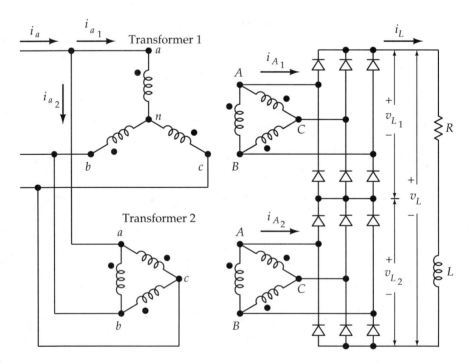

FIGURE 5.65

rectifier. Each voltage contains a DC component and harmonics that are multiples of six times the AC source frequency. The input AC voltages to the two bridges are arranged to differ by $30°$ in phase as a result of the transformer connections. The resulting sixth-order harmonics in the output voltage of the two bridges therefore differ by $(6)(30°)$ or $180°$, and thus add to zero in the total output voltage. Only harmonics of the 12th, 24th, and higher orders appear in the rectified output. In addition to being of higher frequency, the 12th-order harmonic is lower in amplitude than the 6th-order harmonic. The size of load inductance required to maintain constant load current therefore is reduced appreciably.

In Figure 5.65, the transformers have turn ratios that make the secondary line-to-line voltages equal to each other. Therefore, Transformer 1 has 0.577 times as many turns on one of its wye-connected primary windings as the number of turns on the primary windings of delta-connected Transformer 2. This fact must be used in obtaining the amplitudes shown in the graphs in Figure 5.66.

On the primary side of each transformer, the two line currents that add to give a total line current are in phase for the fundamental component. The fifth-order harmonic currents to each of the two transformers are $180°$ out of phase, so the total line current does not contain such a component. This also is true for the seventh harmonic. The lowest-order harmonic that is present is the 11th.

In Figure 5.66, inspection of the waveforms shows that the total primary line current contains smaller harmonic currents than do the primary currents of either transformer. This results from the partial cancellation of the harmonic currents upon addition of the harmonics in the two primary windings. The equations soon to follow provide quantitative results for the harmonics.

On the secondary side of the transformers, i_{A_1} and i_{A_2} differ by $30°$ in phase. These currents have the same Fourier series except for this difference. In Figure 5.66, the graph for i_{A_1} is an even function and can be expressed by a Fourier series with coefficients that are given by Equation 5.197. The coefficients for i_{A_2} are the same except for the phase shift.

When reflected to the primary side as line currents, the turn ratios give the same harmonic component magnitudes in the primary side line currents for each transformer. The difference that occurs is in the phase shifts for the two transformer arrangements. Transformer 2 is delta–delta and its primary currents and all harmonics have no phase shift between primary and secondary currents. The primary line current for Transformer 2 has the same wave shape as its secondary current.

Transformer 1, which is wye–delta connected, does have a phase shift from secondary to primary, which is different for the various harmonic current components. An analysis of the phase shift for the reference directions shown in Figure 5.65 shows that the fundamental component of i_{a_1} is $30°$ ahead of the

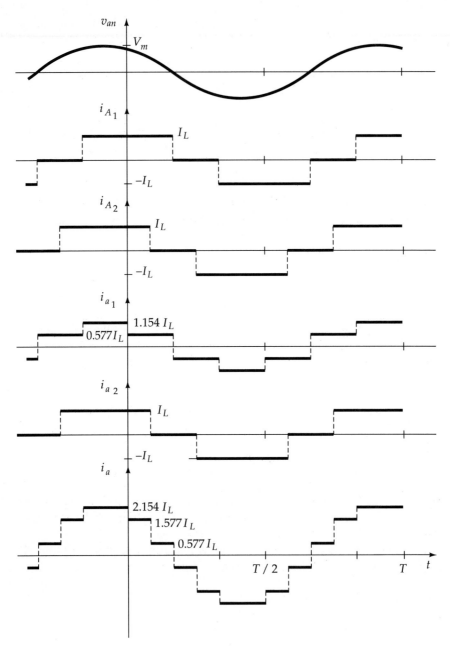

FIGURE 5.66

fundamental component of i_{A_1}. The fifth harmonic for the primary is 30° behind; the seventh harmonic is 30° ahead. The pattern continues for higher-order harmonics. Using this information enables equations to be written for the primary line currents.

We can use Equation 5.197 to write an expression for the various currents:

$$i_{A_1} = A_1 \cos \omega t + A_5 \cos 5\omega t + A_7 \cos 7\omega t + A_{11} \cos 11\omega t$$
$$+ A_{13} \cos 13\omega t + \cdots \tag{5.200}$$

$$i_{A_2} = A_1 \cos\left(\omega t + \frac{\pi}{6}\right) + A_5 \cos 5\left(\omega t + \frac{\pi}{6}\right) + A_7 \cos 7\left(\omega t + \frac{\pi}{6}\right)$$
$$+ A_{11} \cos 11\left(\omega t + \frac{\pi}{6}\right) + A_{13} \cos 13\left(\omega t + \frac{\pi}{6}\right) + \cdots . \tag{5.201}$$

With a transformer line-to-line turn ratio of unity, the primary currents can be expressed in terms of the secondary currents:

$$i_{a_1} = A_1 \cos\left(\omega t + \frac{\pi}{6}\right) + A_5 \cos\left(5\omega t - \frac{\pi}{6}\right) + A_7 \cos\left(7\omega t + \frac{\pi}{6}\right)$$
$$+ A_{11} \cos\left(11\omega t - \frac{\pi}{6}\right) + A_{13} \cos\left(13\omega t + \frac{\pi}{6}\right) + \cdots \tag{5.202}$$

$$i_{a_2} = A_1 \cos\left(\omega t + \frac{\pi}{6}\right) + A_5 \cos\left(5\omega t + \frac{5\pi}{6}\right) + A_7 \cos\left(7\omega t + \frac{7\pi}{6}\right)$$
$$+ A_{11} \cos\left(11\omega t - \frac{\pi}{6}\right) + A_{13} \cos\left(13\omega t + \frac{\pi}{6}\right) + \cdots . \tag{5.203}$$

The total line current is obtained from the sum of the transformer line currents:

$$i_a = 2A_1 \cos\left(\omega t + \frac{\pi}{6}\right) + 2A_{11} \cos\left(11\omega t - \frac{\pi}{6}\right)$$
$$+ 2A_{13} \cos\left(13\omega t + \frac{\pi}{6}\right) + \cdots . \tag{5.204}$$

The fifth and seventh harmonics in the total line current are zero. The lowest-order harmonic present is the 11th; it is smaller in amplitude than would be the amplitude of the fifth-order harmonic if a six-pulse rectifier were used.

The fact that the AC line current is more nearly sinusoidal has reduced the RMS value of this current as compared to the six-pulse rectifier. This reduction means an improvement in the power factor.

EXAMPLE 5.32

A rectifier constructed as in Figure 5.65 supplies power to an inductive load with $R_L = 5\ \Omega$. The supply is 240-V RMS, 60-Hz. The transformers may be considered ideal, and each three-phase transformer has a 1:1 turn ratio with respect to line-to-line voltages. Find:

(a) average load voltage

(b) load power

(c) amplitude of the lowest-order harmonic line current

(d) RMS value of line current

(e) power factor presented to the AC system.

Solution

(a) Each bridge rectifier contributes one-half of the total voltage:

$$V_{L_1} = V_{L_2} = \left(\frac{3}{\pi}\right)(240)(1.414) = 324\ \text{V}$$

$$V_L = 648\ \text{V}.$$

(b)
$$I_L = \frac{V_L}{R_L} = \frac{648}{5} = 129.6\ \text{A}$$

$$P = V_L I_L = 84\ \text{kW}.$$

(c) From Equation 5.197:

$$A_{11} = \left[\frac{(4)(129.6)}{11\pi}\right]\sin\left(\frac{11\pi}{3}\right)$$

$$= -12.99\ \text{A}.$$

The primary line current magnitude for this harmonic is 12.99 A for each transformer, and these currents are in phase in the two transformers. The total magnitude is twice that for one transformer and is 25.98 A.

(d) The RMS line current can be determined from an integration of the waveform for the total line current shown in Figure 5.66. The integration is performed over an interval of $T/4$. Because the current is constant in each interval, the integration is replaced by a multiplication.

$$I_{\text{RMS}} = I_L\{(\tfrac{1}{3})[(2.155)^2 + (1.577)^2 + (0.577)^2]\}^{0.5}$$
$$= 1.577 I_L = (1.577)(129.6) = 204.4\ \text{A}.$$

(e)
$$S = (1.732)(240)(204.4) = 84{,}980\ \text{V-A}$$

$$\text{Power factor} = \frac{P}{S} = \frac{84{,}000}{84{,}980} = 0.988. \qquad\blacksquare$$

5.9
PROBLEMS

5.1 In the circuit in Figure 5.2(a), V_S is 240-V RMS, 60-Hz, and R is 40 Ω. Find:

(a) peak diode current

(b) peak diode reverse voltage

(c) load average power.

5.2 In the circuit in Figure 5.2(a), an inductor is added in series with the load resistor. V_S is a sinusoid of 120-V RMS, 60-Hz; $R = 10\ \Omega$ and $L = 0.1$ H.

(a) Find an expression for i as a function of time.

(b) How long after the beginning of each cycle does the current become zero?

(c) Is there a value of L that causes the current to be greater than zero for the entire cycle?

5.3 (a) In Figure 5.67, find the average value of the load voltage.

(b) Find the average load current.

(c) Find the diode current and voltage ratings.

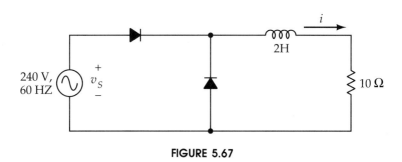

FIGURE 5.67

5.4 In a circuit like that in Figure 5.5(a), V_S is a 480-V RMS, 60-Hz source. $R = 20\ \Omega$. Find:

(a) peak load current   (b) average load current

(c) RMS load current   (d) average load power

(e) average diode current   (f) peak diode reverse voltage.

5.5 The circuit in Figure 5.6 is used to rectify a 240-V RMS, 60-Hz source. Load inductance is large. Required load power is 6 kW. Find:

(a) average load current (b) peak load current

(c) average diode current (d) peak diode reverse voltage.

5.6 A half-wave phase-control circuit like that in Figure 5.8(a) is used to control the power to a load of 25 Ω from a 240-V RMS, 60-Hz source. The phase-control angle can be varied from 10° to 125°. Find:

(a) the range of load power

(b) the peak SCR current

(c) the peak reverse SCR voltage

(d) the largest value of SCR average current over the range of α.

5.7 A full-wave circuit like that in Figure 5.9 supplies an average current of 20 A from a 460-V RMS, 60-Hz source at α = 50°. Find:

(a) load average power (b) load resistance

(c) SCR average current rating (d) SCR peak current

(e) SCR peak reverse voltage.

5.8 In a circuit like that in Figure 5.9, the load is supplied from a 230-V RMS, 60-Hz source. The load power must be variable from 1.5 kW to 8 kW. The smallest possible value of α is 10°. Find:

(a) a suitable range for α

(b) a corresponding value of R

(c) SCR current and voltage ratings.

5.9 In the circuit in Figure 5.11, the source is a 460-V RMS, 60-Hz sinusoid. R = 20 Ω, and the range of α is from 15° to 70°. The inductance is large. Find:

(a) load average power for each extreme of α

(b) SCR average current rating

(c) SCR voltage rating.

5.10 The circuit in Figure 5.11 supplies 40 A to a load from a 230-V RMS, 60-Hz source at α = 15°. Find:

(a) average load power for α = 70°

(b) SCR average current at α = 15°.

5.11 A full-wave phase-control circuit such as that in Figure 5.11 supplies an average voltage ranging from 50 V to 200 V to a load of 5 Ω. The source voltage is 240-V RMS, 60-Hz.

(a) determine the required range of α

(b) find the SCR ratings

(c) find the range of average power to the load.

5.12 In the circuit in Figure 5.13, V_S is a source of 460-V RMS, 60-Hz, and R is 20 Ω. The value of $\alpha = 100°$. Find:

(a) average load current

(b) SCR average current

(c) FWD average current

(d) peak SCR forward and reverse voltage.

5.13 Use the circuit in Figure 5.13 to supply a variable voltage to a load of $R = 5$ Ω. The source is 120-V RMS, 60-Hz. The load power has a maximum value of 2100 W and a minimum of 500 W. Find:

(a) the required range of α

(b) the SCR average current requirement

(c) the current rating of the FWD.

5.14 A full-wave bridge rectifier with phase control supplies power to a resistive load of 10 Ω; $V_S = 230$-V RMS, 60-Hz; and $\alpha = 75°$. Find:

(a) the load average power

(b) the power factor of the rectifier and its load.

5.15 In Problem 5.14, the load now has an added inductive element so that load current is constant. Solve the problem again.

5.16 In the circuit in Figure 5.21, the source voltage is 480-V RMS, 60-Hz, and the load resistance is 20 Ω. The ratio of primary turns to the turns of one secondary is 3:1; $\alpha = 40°$. Find:

(a) the RMS value of the primary current

(b) the power factor for the primary winding

(c) the required volt-ampere rating for the transformer's primary and secondary windings.

5.17 Repeat Problem 5.16 for an inductive load.

5.18 A bridge rectifier using phase control is supplied by a 240-V RMS, 60-Hz, single-phase source. The DC load is resistive; $R_L = 10$ Ω and $\alpha = 40°$. Find the amplitude of the fundamental and third harmonic currents in the AC source.

5.19 In Problem 5.18, the load is changed to an inductive one. Solve the problem again.

5.20   A bridge rectifier with phase control supplies an inductive load. An FWD is used; $\alpha = 36°$, $R_L = 15\ \Omega$, and $V_S = 460\text{-V}$ RMS, 60-Hz. Find the amplitude of the third- and fifth-order harmonic components of the source current.

5.21   A bridge rectifier without an FWD supplies power to an inductive load. Find the amplitude of the third- and fifth-order harmonic components of the AC source current. $V_S = 230\text{-V}$ RMS, 60-Hz; $R_L = 10\ \Omega$; and $\alpha = 50°$.

5.22   In the circuit in Figure 5.31, the source voltage is 460-V RMS, 60-Hz, and the load resistance is $15\ \Omega$. For an output voltage of 300 V, find the minimum value of L needed to maintain continuous inductor current.

5.23   In Problem 5.22, the load voltage is variable from 200 V to 400 V. Find the minimum value of L needed to maintain continuous inductor current for all conditions.

5.24   In the circuit in Figure 5.31, the inductance is just sufficient to maintain continuous current. $V_S = 240$ V-RMS, 60-Hz; $R = 10\ \Omega$; and $\alpha = 40°$. The capacitor is large enough that the load ripple voltage is negligible but nonzero. As an approximation for part (b), the inductor current may be represented by a Fourier series with a DC term and one AC term. The DC term is the average inductor current, and the AC term is such that the total current varies from zero to twice the DC value. Find:

   (a) the inductor current as a function of time

   (b) the amplitude of the second harmonic component of i_L using the above approximation

   (c) the value of C that limits the ripple in the load voltage to 5-V peak value.

5.25   In a circuit such as that in Figure 5.31, the source voltage is 240-V RMS, 60-Hz. The average load power is required to be variable from 3 kW to 6 kW. The value of α may not be smaller than 10°. Inductor current is just continuous at one extreme value of α. Find:

   (a) the required range of α

   (b) the required value of L

   (c) the current rating of the bridge SCRs.

5.26   In the circuit in Figure 5.37, the source is 230-V RMS, 60-Hz, and the load voltage average value is 130 V. $R_L = 20\ \Omega$ and $\alpha = 75°$. Find:

   (a) rectifier conduction interval   **(b)** the inductance L.

5.27   A full-wave, center-tap rectifier circuit like that in Figure 5.41 supplies a load current of 40 A with an α value of 40°. The transformer primary voltage is 480-V RMS, 60-Hz, and N_1/N_2 is 3.5. The leakage inductance is 4 mH. The value of L is large. Find:

(a) the idealized average value of V_L

(b) the reduction in V_L resulting from the leakage inductance

(c) the time duration in each half-cycle during which commutation occurs.

5.28 Repeat Problem 5.27 with a source voltage of 240-V RMS, 60-Hz, and a turn ratio of 1.5. The leakage inductance is 5 mH.

5.29 In Problem 5.27, the primary winding has a resistance of 0.20 Ω, and each secondary winding has a resistance of 0.023 Ω. Other conditions remain the same. Find the average value of the load voltage.

5.30 A rectifier like that in Figure 5.45 supplies a resistive load of 15 Ω from a 460-V RMS, 60-Hz source. Find:

(a) average load current   (b) peak load current

(c) diode current rating   (d) diode reverse voltage rating.

5.31 Repeat Problem 5.30 with the load changed to include a large inductance in series with the load resistance.

5.32 The diodes in Figure 5.45 are replaced by SCRs to control the power to a resistive load. The source and the load are the same as those in Problem 5.30. The value of α is 70°. Find:

(a) average load voltage   (b) peak load current

(c) average load current   (d) average SCR current

(e) peak SCR forward voltage   (f) peak SCR reverse voltage.

5.33 The circuit in Figure 5.45 has the diodes replaced by SCRs and a load with a large inductance component; $V_S = 240$-V RMS, 60-Hz; $R = 20$ Ω; the range of α is 20° to 75°. Find:

(a) the range of average load voltage

(b) the range of average load power

(c) the SCR current rating required.

5.34 In the circuit in Figure 5.45, the source is 460-V RMS, 60-Hz, and the load power varies from 3 kW to 1 kW. The diodes are replaced by SCRs. The load has a large inductance component. The phase-control angle cannot be less than 10°. Find:

(a) the required range of α

(b) peak SCR current

(c) average SCR current

(d) peak SCR forward or reverse voltage.

5.35 In the circuit in Figure 5.53, the source is 460-V RMS, 60-Hz, and R is 25 Ω. There is no load inductance. Find:

(a) average load voltage

(b) average load current

(c) average load power

(d) average diode current

(e) peak diode reverse voltage.

5.36 In Figure 5.53, the load has an added inductor so that the load current does not vary with time; V_S = 230-V RMS, 60-Hz, and R = 20 Ω. Find the RMS value of the line current.

5.37 In Figure 5.56(a), the value of the phase-control angle, α, is 50°. The load is resistive. V_S = 460-V RMS, 60-Hz, and R = 20 Ω. Find:

(a) the average load voltage

(b) the average SCR current

(c) the average load power.

5.38 In Problem 5.37, the load now is inductive, so the load current does not vary with time. Find:

(a) the average SCR current

(b) the average load power

(c) the RMS value of the AC line currents

(d) peak SCR voltages.

5.39 In Figure 5.56(a), the load is inductive and has an added FWD. The load power is variable from 4.5 kW to 1.2 kW. V_S = 230-V RMS, 60-Hz, and R = 10 Ω. Find:

(a) the range of α required

(b) the largest SCR average current

(c) the largest value of FWD average current.

5.40 In Figure 5.58, E represents a load resistor and a large capacitor in parallel. A load current of 20 A is supplied at α = 25° from a 230-V RMS, 60-Hz source. Find the value of L required to maintain continuous inductor current.

5.41 In Figure 5.58, the source voltage E represents a DC motor with variable speed. The minimum motor current is 5 A average. For $0° < \alpha < 60°$, continuous inductor current is to be maintained. The source voltage is 460-V RMS, 60-Hz. Find the value of L needed for each extreme value of α.

5.42 In Problem 5.40, estimate the value of C required to maintain the ripple voltage at the load to 2% of the average load voltage. (For the purpose of this problem, the inductor current may be represented by a DC component and the first AC term of a Fourier series. The inductor current thus varies from zero to twice the DC component.)

5.43 A three-phase bridge rectifier supplies power to an inductive load. Find the power factor presented to the AC source; $V_S = 480$-V RMS, L–L, 60-Hz; $R_L = 20 \ \Omega$; and $P = 15$ kW.

5.44 In Problem 5.43, an FWD is used and $\alpha = 75°$. Find the power factor.

5.45 Now in Problem 5.43, the value of α is changed to 40°. Find the magnitude of the fifth- and seventh-order harmonic AC line currents. Compare the magnitudes to the fundamental AC line current.

5.46 A bridge rectifier with an inductive load supplies power from a 240-V RMS, 60-Hz, three-phase source to a load resistance of 20 Ω. An FWD is used. For $\alpha = 75°$, find the fifth harmonic component of the AC line current.

5.47 A 12-pulse diode rectifier like that in Figure 5.65 supplies rectified power to an inductive load. The transformers have a step-down ratio of 2:1 for L–L voltages. The AC source is 480-V RMS, L–L, 60-Hz, and the DC load power is 100 kW. Find:

(a) the volt-ampere ratings of the transformers

(b) the ratio of the 11th-order harmonic line current to the fundamental line current.

5.48 In Problem 5.47, the diodes are changed to SCRs, which are operated at $\alpha = 45°$. Find:

(a) the DC load voltage

(b) the load power

(c) the power factor presented to the AC source.

CHAPTER · 6

AC–AC Phase Control

When the load power is to be controlled without altering the fundamental frequency, an AC switch can be used to control load power. This switch can be either a TRIAC or two SCRs connected in an inverse parallel arrangement as shown in Figure 6.1. Although there are a few exceptions, for most purposes the control result is independent of the switch implementation. Practical limitations of available TRIAC ratings limit the very high power applications for which TRIACs might otherwise be used.

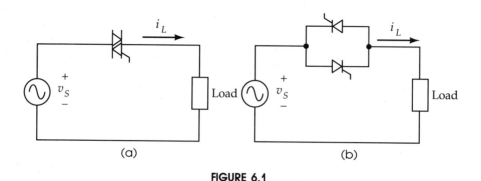

(a)   (b)

FIGURE 6.1

6.1

INTRODUCTION

Two basic methods can be used to control the load power. The first initiates and allows conduction for a certain number of full cycles. Conduction then is inhibited for some other number of cycles. The relation of ON to OFF intervals is arranged so that the average power delivered to the load meets some objective. Figure 6.2 shows a typical pattern of use.

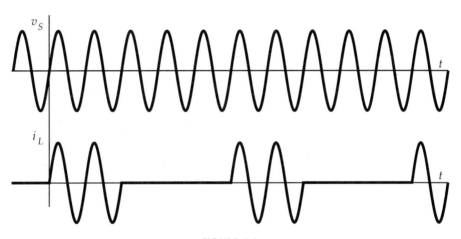

FIGURE 6.2

The time constant for load response should be relatively long so that the load responds to average power. Generally, response time should be in seconds, not in fractions of a second. Two suitable applications are (1) heating a liquid in a tank to maintain a certain temperature and (2) heating air in a duct by using a heater placed in the airstream. Either application can be part of a closed-loop system in which the switch on–off intervals are controlled to produce the desired temperature.

For those applications in which the preceding process is not suitable, phase control can be used for each of the half-cycles of a period. The graphs in Figure 6.3 represent situations in which the load is resistive. This process produces a phase-controlled alternating output that is suitable for some applications. Two possible applications are lamp dimming and motor-speed control. The motor-speed control method is suitable only for variable torque loads, such as fans and pumps in which the torque varies as the square of the speed.

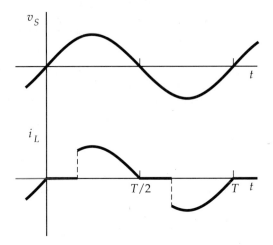

FIGURE 6.3

6.2

INTEGRAL CYCLE CONTROL

If the load is turned on and off in the manner shown in Figure 6.2, the average power to the load can be varied. The ratio of ON time to total cycle time, during which the conduction pattern repeats, controls the average load power. In Figure 6.2, k is the number of cycles for which the load is energized and n is the number of cycles for the full period of operation. During k cycles, the switch is on and the load power is maximum. During the remaining $(n - k)$ cycles, the switch is off and the load power is zero. The average load power is given by Equation 6.1 for the case of a resistive load:

$$P_{avg} = \left(\frac{V_S^2}{R_L}\right)\left(\frac{k}{n}\right). \qquad (6.1)$$

Because k can be varied only as an integer, the average value of the load power can take on only discrete values. The number of available steps in regulating the average power depends on the total number of cycles included in the repeat pattern.

A closed-loop control system can be used to vary the value of k to maintain some variable at or close to some set point. As mentioned earlier, such a system depends on sufficient energy storage in the controlled system to smooth variations that result from the on–off nature of the control. One advantage of this control method is that switching occurs only at zero voltage for resistive loads. The rate of change of load current is governed by the system frequency, and this rate of change may be small compared to the rate obtained by other control means. The resulting electrical noise thus may be smaller than with other methods.

EXAMPLE 6.1

A resistive load is controlled to produce complete cycles of load power. The source is 230-V RMS, 60-Hz. Load power must be varied from 2 kW to 10 kW. The maximum interval for repetition is 0.5 second. $R_L = 5.29\ \Omega$. Find:

(a) the switch current rating

(b) the fraction of time that the load is energized to produce maximum power

(c) the values of n and k to produce minimum power

(d) the smallest increment in power that is possible.

Solution

(a)
$$I_m = \frac{(230)(1.414)}{5.29} = 61.5 \text{ A peak value}$$

$$I_{L_{RMS}} = \frac{61.5}{1.414} = 43.5 \text{ A.}$$

(b) If the switch is always on,

$$P_{avg} = (230)(43.5) = 10{,}000 \text{ W.}$$

The switch must be on 100% of the time to achieve full power.

(c) For $P = 2000$ W,

$$\frac{k}{n} = \frac{2000}{10{,}000} = 0.2.$$

If $n = 30$ cycles is selected, then

$$k = (0.2)(30) = 6 \text{ cycles.}$$

(d) The smallest increment in power occurs for a unit change of k:

$$\Delta P = \left(\frac{1}{30}\right)(10{,}000) = 333 \text{ W.}$$

For a change in the output power of less than 333 W, the value of k would have to be varied between two integer values. ∎

6.3

PHASE CONTROL OF RESISTIVE LOADS

The basic circuit in Figure 6.1 can be used to control the power to a resistive load. The graphs in Figure 6.3 are similar to those in Figure 5.8 for the full-wave rectifier with a resistive load. The difference here is that each second half-cycle has negative current rather than a positive value. There is, however, no effect on the power because power is a squared function.

The delay in conduction in each half-cycle is the angle α, which is given by

$$\alpha = \omega t_1. \tag{6.2}$$

This is the phase-control angle given in Chapter 5. The equation for the RMS value of the load current also is the same as Equation 5.34. That equation is restated here for the AC phase-control situation with a resistive load, becoming Equation 6.3:

$$I_{L_{\text{RMS}}} = \left[\frac{I_m}{(2)^{0.5}}\right]\left[1 - \left(\frac{\alpha}{\pi}\right) + \left(\frac{\sin 2\alpha}{2\pi}\right)\right]^{0.5}. \tag{6.3}$$

Load power is given by Equation 6.4:

$$P_{\text{avg}} = (I_{L_{\text{RMS}}})^2(R_L). \tag{6.4}$$

The RMS value of load voltage is similar to the expression given in Equation 6.3 for the RMS value of I_L. Equation 6.3 is changed by multiplying by R_L, with Equation 6.5 resulting:

$$V_{L_{\text{RMS}}} = \left[\frac{V_m}{(2)^{0.5}}\right]\left[1 - \left(\frac{\alpha}{\pi}\right) + \left(\frac{\sin 2\alpha}{2\pi}\right)\right]^{0.5}. \tag{6.5}$$

Examination of Equations 6.3 and 6.4 shows that the load power can be varied by changing α over the full range from zero to $180°$. Suitable trigger circuits exist to allow conduction to be adjusted essentially over this entire range.

Because the current is nonsinusoidal, the power factor presented to the AC source is less than unity even though the load is resistive. By definition, the power factor is given in Equation 6.6:

$$\text{Power factor} = \frac{\text{average power}}{V_{\text{RMS}} I_{\text{RMS}}}. \tag{6.6}$$

This definition can be evaluated using the expressions of Equations 6.3 and 6.4. In Equation 6.6, the value of V_{RMS} is that of the sinusoidal source voltage. Several of these equations can be combined to produce Equation 6.7:

$$\text{Power factor} = \left[1 - \left(\frac{\alpha}{\pi}\right) + \left(\frac{\sin 2\alpha}{2\pi}\right)\right]^{0.5}. \tag{6.7}$$

The resulting power factor is unity only for the case where α is zero; it becomes progressively smaller as α increases.

The switch current becomes zero at the same time that the source voltage is zero, because the load is resistive. Therefore, when the switch begins blocking at the time of current zero, negligible source voltage is present. The problem of dv/dt being large at turnoff does not exist, and no snubber would be required to reduce the rate of voltage build-up across the device terminals.

Because the load is resistive, there is no delay in the increase of load current at turn on. Providing sufficient current for latching is not a problem if the switch is not required to turn on at $\alpha = 0$. This is not a particularly restrictive requirement. For a very small value of α, generally there is sufficient voltage and resulting current to cause the semiconductor switch to latch into the conducting state.

For a value of $\alpha > 90°$, the switch blocks the peak source voltage before switch turn on. The minimum switch voltage capability therefore is the peak value of the source voltage. This same blocking capability is necessary, of course, in both directions for either the SCR or TRIAC implementation of the switch.

E X A M P L E 6 . 2

In the circuit in Figure 6.1, the switch controls power to a resistive load from a 460-V RMS, 60-Hz source. The load resistance is 20 Ω and α is 35°. Find:

(a) peak load current
(b) average load power
(c) switch voltage rating
(d) circuit power factor.

Solution

(a)
$$I_m = \frac{V_m}{R} = \frac{(460)(1.414)}{20} = 32.53 \text{ A.}$$

(b) From Equation 6.3,

$$I_{LRMS} = \left(\frac{32.53}{1.414}\right)\left[1 - \left(\frac{35°}{180°}\right) + \left(\frac{\sin 70°}{2\pi}\right)\right]^{0.5}$$

$$= 22.48 \text{ A}$$

$$P = (I_{LRMS})^2 R = (22.48)^2 20 = 10{,}105 \text{ W.}$$

(c) The switch must block the peak source voltage of 650 V. Minimum switch rating therefore is at least 800 V.

(d) From Equation 6.7,

$$\text{Power factor} = \left(1 - \frac{35°}{180°} + \frac{\sin 70°}{2\pi}\right)^{0.5}$$

$$= 0.9773.$$ ∎

EXAMPLE 6.3

A resistive load of 10 Ω is connected to a 240-V RMS source by a phase-control switch. The load power needs to be varied between 5 kW and 2 kW. Find:

(a) the peak load current

(b) the RMS value of load current for each extreme of α

(c) the range of α required

(d) the RMS value of the TRIAC current if the switch is like that in Figure 6.1(a)

(e) the average current in each of the two SCRs if the switch is like that in Figure 6.1(b)

(f) the minimum switch-blocking voltage

(g) the power factor for the smaller power value.

Solution

(a)
$$V_m = (1.414)(240) = 339.4 \text{ V}$$

$$I_m = \frac{V_m}{R_L} = \frac{339.4}{10} = 33.94 \text{ A.}$$

(b) For $P = 5000$ W,

$$5000 = (I_{L\text{RMS}})^2(10)$$

$$I_{L\text{RMS}} = 22.36 \text{ A.}$$

For $P = 2000$ W,

$$2000 = (I_{L\text{RMS}})^2(10)$$

$$I_{L\text{RMS}} = 14.14 \text{ A.}$$

(c) For $P = 5000$ W, using Equation 6.3:

$$22.36 = \left(\frac{33.94}{1.414}\right)\left[1 - \left(\frac{\alpha}{\pi}\right) + \left(\frac{\sin 2\alpha}{2\pi}\right)\right]^{0.5}$$

$$\alpha = 51.6°.$$

For $P = 2000$ W, using Equation 6.3:

$$14.14 = \left(\frac{33.94}{1.414}\right)\left[1 - \left(\frac{\alpha}{\pi}\right) + \left(\frac{\sin 2\alpha}{2\pi}\right)\right]^{0.5}$$

$$\alpha = 104.0°.$$

(d) I_{RMS} is the same as the load current $= 22.36$ A.

(e) The average value of each SCR current can be found by using Equation 5.27:

$$I_{avg} = \left(\frac{I_m}{2\pi}\right)(1 + \cos \alpha)$$

$$I_{avg} = \left(\frac{33.94}{2\pi}\right)(1 + \cos 51.6°) = 8.76 \text{ A}.$$

(f) The switch must block at least the peak source voltage of 339.4 V. The minimum acceptable voltage rating for this component is 400 V. This may not be enough in some situations.

(g)
$$\text{Power factor} = \left(1 - \frac{104}{180} + \frac{\sin 208°}{2\pi}\right)^{0.5} = 0.590. \qquad ∎$$

6.4

HARMONICS: SINGLE-PHASE RESISTIVE LOADS

The current waveform in Figure 6.3 contains appreciable higher-order harmonics, especially as the value of α increases. The harmonic content can be determined from a Fourier series analysis of the waveform: Inspection shows a half-period symmetry; the waveform thus contains only odd-order harmonics. The origin cannot be shifted so that the function becomes either odd or even. The A_n and B_n terms therefore may both exist.

Symmetry allows determination of the coefficients using integration over an interval of $T/2$. A substitution of an angle variable to replace time is used:

$$A_n = \left(\frac{2}{\pi}\right)\int_\alpha^\pi I_m \sin \theta \cos n\theta \, d\theta \qquad (6.8)$$

$$B_n = \left(\frac{2}{\pi}\right)\int_\alpha^\pi I_m \sin \theta \sin n\theta \, d\theta. \qquad (6.9)$$

Evaluation of Equations 6.8 and 6.9 yields the following results:

$$A_1 = \left(\frac{I_m}{2\pi}\right)[(\cos 2\alpha) - 1] \qquad (6.10)$$

$$B_1 = \left(\frac{I_m}{2\pi}\right)[2(\pi - \alpha) + \sin 2\alpha] \qquad (6.11)$$

$$A_n = \left[\frac{I_m}{\pi(n^2 - 1)}\right]\{2 + (n - 1)[\cos (n + 1)\alpha] - (n + 1)[\cos (n - 1)\alpha]\} \qquad (6.12)$$

$$B_n = \left[\frac{I_m}{\pi(n^2 - 1)}\right]\{(n - 1)[\sin (n + 1)\alpha] - (n + 1)[\sin (n - 1)\alpha]\}. \qquad (6.13)$$

The graph in Figure 6.4 shows the manner in which several of the harmonics vary with α. Each value is the relative magnitude of each harmonic and is obtained by combining the A and B coefficients in the usual manner.

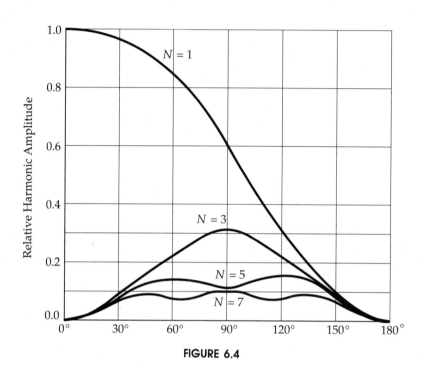

FIGURE 6.4

E X A M P L E   6 . 4

A single-phase resistive load is supplied from a 460-V, 60-Hz source through a phase-control switch. With no phase control, the load power is 15 kW. Find:

(a) the value of α to reduce the average power to 9.0 kW
(b) the magnitude of the peak fundamental current for this value of α
(c) the magnitude of the peak third- and fifth-order harmonic currents.

Solution

(a) With α = 0, the value of the load resistance can be found:

$$R_L = \frac{(460)^2}{15{,}000} = 14.1\ \Omega.$$

Using Equation 6.4 with $P = 9000$ W,

$$I_{LRMS} = \left(\frac{9000}{14.1}\right)^{0.5} = 25.26 \text{ A.}$$

Using Equation 6.3 and an iterative solution, α can be found:

$$\alpha = 1.4124 \text{ rad} = 80.9°.$$

(b) Using Equations 6.10 and 6.11:

$$A_1 = \left(\frac{46.14}{2\pi}\right)[\cos 2(1.4124) - 1] = -14.32 \text{ A.}$$

$$B_1 = \left(\frac{46.14}{2\pi}\right)[2(\pi - 1.4124) + \sin 2(1.4124)] = 27.68 \text{ A.}$$

$$C_1 = (A_1^2 + B_1^2)^{0.5} = 31.16 \text{ A.}$$

(c) Using Equations 6.12 and 6.13:

$$A_3 = \left(\frac{46.14}{8\pi}\right)[2 + 2\cos 4(1.4124) - 4\cos 2(1.4124)]$$

$$= 11.77 \text{ A.}$$

$$B_3 = \left(\frac{46.14}{8\pi}\right)[2\sin 4(1.4124) - 4\sin 2(1.4124)]$$

$$= -4.46 \text{ A.}$$

$$C_3 = (A_3^2 + B_3^2)^{0.5} = 12.59 \text{ A.}$$

$$A_5 = \left(\frac{46.14}{24\pi}\right)[2 + 4\cos 6(1.4124) - 6\cos 4(1.4124)]$$

$$= -3.16 \text{ A.}$$

$$B_5 = \left(\frac{46.14}{24\pi}\right)[4\sin 6(1.4124) - 6\sin 4(1.4124)]$$

$$= 4.17 \text{ A.}$$

$$C_5 = (A_5^2 + B_5^2)^{0.5} = 5.23 \text{ A.} \qquad \blacksquare$$

6.5
PHASE CONTROL: INDUCTIVE LOADS

For an inductive load, the graphs in Figure 6.3 require modification. The circuit is shown in Figure 6.5(a) and the corresponding graphs in Figure 6.5(b). Note in the graph for load current that the load current does not become zero until

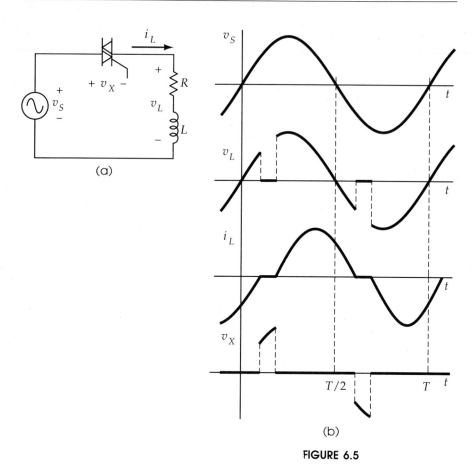

(a)

(b)

FIGURE 6.5

some time after zero voltage. This results, of course, from load inductance. At the time the load current reaches and remains at zero, the voltage across the switch has an ideal discontinuity. This was discussed in Chapter 3 with regard to the possibility of turn on resulting from a rapid change in voltage across the terminals of either an SCR or a TRIAC. A nonpolarized snubber network generally is required in such a case to prevent unwanted turn on when the current becomes zero.

In Figure 6.5, the load current can be found by using standard circuit-analysis methods. Starting at $t = \alpha/\omega$, the current can be found from Equation 6.14:

$$i_L = \left(\frac{V_m}{|Z|}\right)[\sin{(\omega t - \theta)} + A\,e^{-(\omega t/\omega\tau)}]. \qquad (6.14)$$

The relation in Equation 6.14 is valid only in the range $t_1 < t < t_2$ as shown in Figure 6.5(b), where

$$t_1 = \frac{\alpha}{\omega} \tag{6.15}$$

$$t_2 = \frac{\beta}{\omega} \tag{6.16}$$

$$|Z| = |R + j\omega L| \tag{6.17}$$

$$\omega\tau = \frac{\omega L}{R} = \tan\theta \tag{6.18}$$

$$A = -\frac{\sin(\alpha - \theta)}{e^{-(\alpha/\omega\tau)}} \tag{6.19}$$

The angle β is found by finding the time t_2 when the current in Equation 6.14 becomes zero. This is not expressible in closed form but can be found easily by an iterative process. Once β is found, the load current's RMS value and the average power to the load can be determined. All the terms in Equation 6.14 for load current are known, and the equation for a current's RMS value can be evaluated by Equation 6.20:

$$I_{L\mathrm{RMS}} = \frac{V_m}{|Z|} \left[\frac{2}{T} \int_{\alpha/\omega}^{\beta/\omega} [\sin(\omega t - \theta) + A e^{-t/\tau}]^2 \, dt \right]^{0.5}. \tag{6.20}$$

Performing the indicated integration, the result becomes that of Equation 6.21:

$$I_{L\mathrm{RMS}} = \frac{V_m}{(2)^{0.5}|Z|} \left[\begin{array}{l} \dfrac{\beta - \alpha}{\pi} - \dfrac{\sin 2(\beta - \theta)}{2\pi} + \dfrac{\sin 2(\alpha - \theta)}{2\pi} \\[2ex] - \left[\left(\dfrac{A^2 \omega\tau}{\pi} \right) (e^{-2\beta/\omega\tau} - e^{-2\alpha/\omega\tau}) \right] \\[2ex] - \left\{ \left(\dfrac{4A\omega\tau \, e^{-\beta/\omega\tau}}{\pi[1 + (\omega\tau)^2]} \right) [\sin(\beta - \theta) + \omega\tau \cos(\beta - \theta)] \right\} \\[2ex] + \left\{ \left(\dfrac{4A\omega\tau \, e^{-\alpha/\omega\tau}}{\pi[1 + (\omega\tau)^2]} \right) [\sin(\alpha - \theta) + \omega\tau \cos(\alpha - \theta)] \right\} \end{array} \right]^{0.5}. \tag{6.21}$$

Once the load current's RMS value is known, the average load power is found easily. The result is given in Equation 6.22:

$$P_{\mathrm{avg}} = (I_{L\mathrm{RMS}})^2 R_L. \tag{6.22}$$

The power factor of the phase-controlled load can be evaluated by using the relation for RMS current in Equation 6.21. In Equation 6.23, V_{RMS} is the

RMS value of the source voltage:

$$\text{Power factor} = \frac{\text{average power}}{V_{RMS}I_{LRMS}}. \tag{6.23}$$

$$\text{Power factor} = \frac{(I_{LRMS})^2 R}{\left(\dfrac{V_m}{1.414}\right)(I_{LRMS})}. \tag{6.24}$$

$$\text{Power factor} = \frac{R}{|Z|}\left[\begin{array}{l} \dfrac{\beta - \alpha}{\pi} - \dfrac{\sin 2(\beta - \theta)}{2\pi} + \dfrac{\sin 2(\alpha - \theta)}{2\pi} \\[2mm] - \left[\left(\dfrac{A^2\omega\tau}{\pi}\right)(e^{-2\beta/\omega\tau} - e^{-2\alpha/\omega\tau})\right] \\[2mm] - \left\{\left(\dfrac{4A\omega\tau\,e^{-\beta/\omega\tau}}{\pi[1 + (\omega\tau)^2]}\right)[\sin(\beta - \theta) + \omega\tau\cos(\beta - \theta)]\right\} \\[2mm] + \left\{\left(\dfrac{4A\omega\tau\,e^{-\alpha/\omega\tau}}{\pi[1 + (\omega\tau)^2]}\right)[\sin(\alpha - \theta) + \omega\tau\cos(\alpha - \theta)]\right\} \end{array}\right]^{0.5} \tag{6.25}$$

$$\text{Power factor} = \cos\theta\left[\begin{array}{l} \dfrac{\beta - \alpha}{\pi} - \dfrac{\sin 2(\beta - \theta)}{2\pi} + \dfrac{\sin 2(\alpha - \theta)}{2\pi} \\[2mm] - \left[\left(\dfrac{A^2\omega\tau}{\pi}\right)(e^{-2\beta/\omega\tau} - e^{-2\alpha/\omega\tau})\right] \\[2mm] - \left\{\left(\dfrac{4A\omega\tau\,e^{-\beta/\omega\tau}}{\pi[1 + (\omega\tau)^2]}\right)[\sin(\beta - \theta) + \omega\tau\cos(\beta - \theta)]\right\} \\[2mm] + \left\{\left(\dfrac{4A\omega\tau\,e^{-\alpha/\omega\tau}}{\pi[1 + (\omega\tau)^2]}\right)[\sin(\alpha - \theta) + \omega\tau\cos(\alpha - \theta)]\right\} \end{array}\right]^{0.5} \tag{6.26}$$

In Equation 6.26, the power factor is given as the product of two terms. The first would be the circuit power factor if there were no phase control. The second term includes the effect of phase control. Note that the power factor is always less than it would be without phase control.

EXAMPLE 6.5

In the circuit in Figure 6.5(a), the source is 460-V RMS with a frequency of 60 Hz. The load consists of 10 Ω in series with 0.05 H. The combination is operated at $\alpha = 75°$. Find:

(a) an equation for load current valid in the range $\alpha < \omega t < \beta$

(b) the value of β

(c) the RMS value of the load current

(d) average power to the load

(e) the minimum value of α for which phase control is in effect

(f) the circuit power factor.

Solution

(a) Using Equation 6.14, the load current is found to be

$$i_L = \left(\frac{650}{21.34}\right)[\sin(\omega t - 1.083) - 0.449\,e^{-\omega t/1.885}].$$

(b) The value of load current from part (a) becomes zero at $\omega t = \beta = 4.1757$ rad. This is found by an iterative process. When expressed in degrees, β is 239°. In full conduction without intentional phase delay, the load current would become zero at an angle of 242°.

(c) Using Equation 6.21, the RMS current in the load can be found:

$$I_{L\text{RMS}} = 18.68 \text{ A.}$$

(d) Load power now may be found using Equation 6.22 and the result from part (c):

$$P_{\text{avg}} = (I_{L\text{RMS}})^2 R_L = (18.68)^2(10) = 3491 \text{ W.}$$

(e) The angle θ is found from Equation 6.18:

$$\theta = \tan^{-1}\left(\frac{\omega L}{R}\right) = \tan^{-1}\left[\frac{(377)(0.05)}{10}\right] = 62.0°.$$

Any attempt to make α less than this value fails.

(f) The power factor may be found using Equation 6.23:

$$\text{Power factor} = \frac{3491}{(460)(18.68)} = 0.406.$$

Note that the power factor is less than $\cos 62° = 0.470$. ∎

The results expressed by Equations 6.14 through 6.26 can be quite un-wieldy. The graphs in Figures 6.6 and 6.7 can be useful for circuit analysis and design. Figure 6.6 gives the conduction angle $(\beta - \alpha)$ as a function of α using the value of $\cos \theta$ for the circuit as a parameter. Figure 6.7 gives relative load current RMS value as a function of α, again using $\cos \theta$ as a parameter. The graphs provide numerical solutions of the equations cited. Example 6.6 illustrates the use of the graphs.

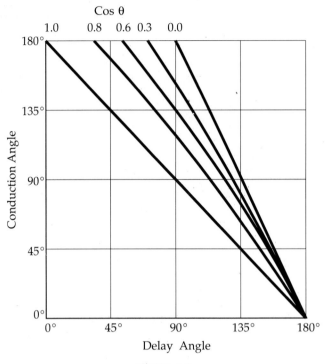

FIGURE 6.6

EXAMPLE 6.6

A load consisting of $R = 12 \; \Omega$ in series with $L = 0.04244$ H is connected to a 240-V RMS, 60-Hz voltage source by a phase-control switch. The average load power must be controlled from 1500 W to 500 W. Find:

(a) the range of load RMS current required

(b) the range of α required

(c) the conduction angle $(\beta - \alpha)$

(d) the peak switch current for the smaller value of α

(e) the power factor for the larger power value.

Solution

(a) Using Equation 6.22 for $P = 1500$ W,

$$1500 = (I_{L_{RMS}})^2 (12)$$

$$I_{L_{RMS}} = 11.18 \text{ A.}$$

Using Equation 6.22 for $P = 500$ W,

$$500 = (I_{L_{RMS}})^2 (12)$$

$$I_{L_{RMS}} = 6.45 \text{ A.}$$

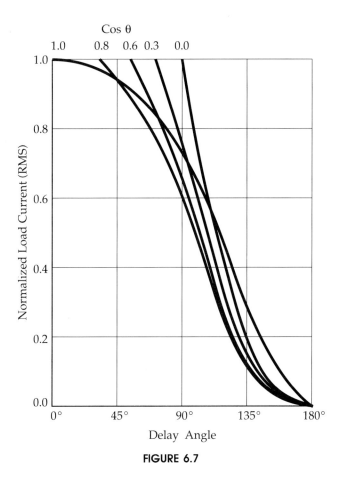

FIGURE 6.7

(b) With no phase control, the maximum value of RMS current is

$$I_{L_{RMS}} = \frac{240}{\left|12 + j(377)(0.04244)\right|} = 12 \text{ A}.$$

For $P = 1500$, the relative load current is

$$\frac{I_{L_{RMS}}}{12} = \frac{11.18}{12} = 0.932.$$

From Figure 6.7, this condition requires $\alpha = 63°$.
For $P = 500$ W, the relative load current is

$$\frac{I_{L_{RMS}}}{12} = \frac{6.45}{12} = 0.538.$$

From Figure 6.7, this condition requires $\alpha = 106°$.

(c) From Figure 6.6, the conduction angle $(\beta - \alpha)$ is found to be $169°$ and $117°$, respectively, for the two cases.

(d) Using Equation 6.14 with an iterative process, the maximum value of i_L is found to be 15.97 A at $\omega t = 145°$.

(e) Using Equation 6.23,

$$\text{Power factor} = \frac{1500}{(240)(11.18)} = 0.559.$$

Without phase control, the power factor is $\cos \theta = \cos 53.1° = 0.60.$ ■

6.6
HARMONICS: SINGLE-PHASE INDUCTIVE LOADS

The harmonic content of the current waveform in Figure 6.5(b) cannot be determined analytically. The coefficients of the Fourier series can be determined by a numerical integration for a given case. The graphs in Figures 6.8 and 6.9 present such results for the cases of $\theta = 30°$ and $\theta = 60°$. The harmonic currents are normalized to a unit value of $|V_m/Z|$, where $|Z| = |R + j\omega L|$.

EXAMPLE 6.7

A single-phase load consisting of 5 Ω in series with an inductance of 0.02297 H is operated in a phase-control mode with α of $90°$. The source is 240-V RMS, 60-Hz. Find:

(a) the conduction angle $(\beta - \alpha)$

(b) the RMS value of load current

(c) the power factor

(d) the size of the first three terms in the Fourier series for the current.

Solution

(a) From the graph in Figure 6.6, the value of $(\beta - \alpha)$ can be read as $144°$, or 2.513 radians.

(b) From Equation 6.17 through 6.21, the current can be determined:

$$Z = 5 + j(2\pi)(60)(0.02297) = 5 + j8.66.$$

$$\theta = \tan^{-1}\left(\frac{8.66}{5}\right) = 60°.$$

$$\omega\tau = \tan \theta = 1.732.$$

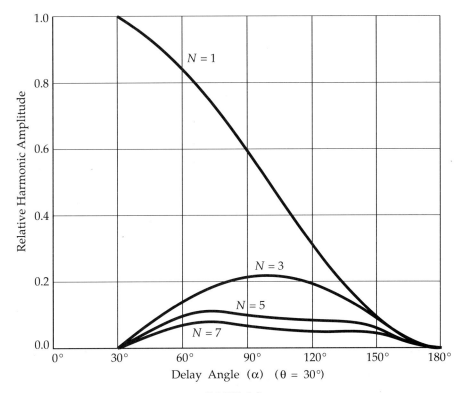

FIGURE 6.8

$$A = -\frac{\sin(90° - 60°)}{e^{-(1.571/1.732)}} = 1.238.$$

$$I_{L_{\mathrm{RMS}}} = (24)(0.810) = 19.45 \text{ A}.$$

(c) From Equation 6.26, we can evaluate the power factor, which consists of two parts. One already has been evaluated in part (b) for $I_{L_{\mathrm{RMS}}}$ and is equal to the bracketed term of 0.810. The other part is the value of $\cos \theta$;

Power factor $= (\cos \theta)(0.810) = (\cos 60°)(0.810) = 0.405.$

(d) From the graph in Figure 6.9, the Fourier coefficients may be determined:

$$C_1 = \frac{(0.65)(240)(1.414)}{10} = 22.1 \text{ A}.$$

$$C_3 = \frac{(0.12)(240)(1.414)}{10} = 4.1 \text{ A}.$$

$$C_5 = \frac{(0.05)(240)(1.414)}{10} = 1.7 \text{ A}.$$ ∎

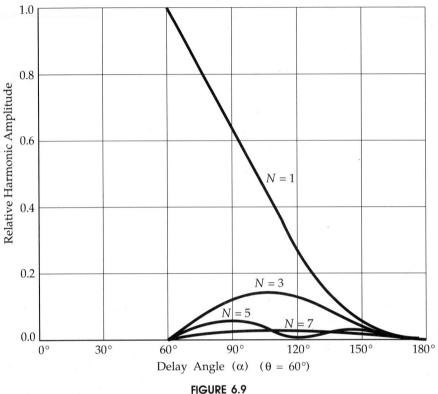

FIGURE 6.9

6.7

PHASE CONTROL: POLYPHASE RESISTIVE LOADS

The phase-control methods applied to single-phase loads in earlier sections also can be applied to polyphase systems. The circuit arrangement in Figure 6.10 can be used to vary the power supplied to a three-phase resistive load. The TRIACs are delayed in turn on by the angle α beyond the normal beginning of conduction. The resulting waveforms are shown in Figure 6.11. The switch in each line also may be implemented by using two SCRs in a back-to-back arrangement.

During those intervals when all three TRIACs are in conduction, the load currents are the same as for a noncontrolled three-phase resistive load. During the intervals when one of the line currents is zero, the remaining two phases are effectively in series and constitute a single-phase load connected to two of the three lines of the voltage source. The conduction pattern during any $60°$ interval is repeated during each following $60°$ interval with a permutation in phases and sign of the current. For example, the current variation for Phase A, during a

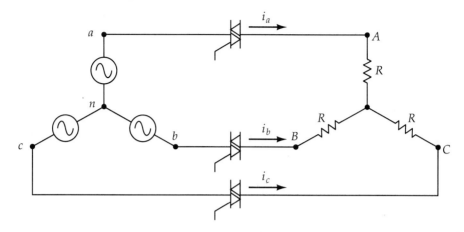

FIGURE 6.10

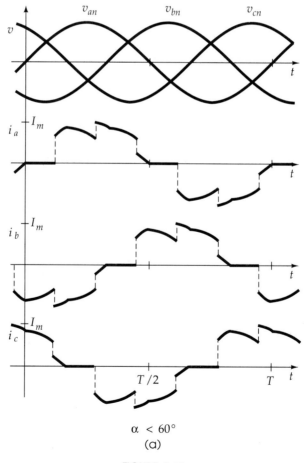

$\alpha < 60°$

(a)

FIGURE 6.11

275

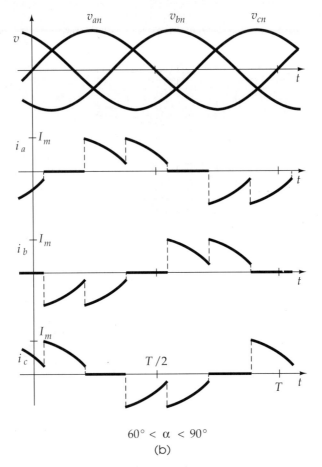

$$60° < \alpha < 90°$$

(b)

FIGURE 6.11 (continued)

given 60°, is repeated during the next 60° for Phase C, except for a change in the algebraic sign of the current.

From the graph in Figure 6.11, we can observe that peak switch current may be less than the case without phase control. For $\alpha < 30°$, peak current is not affected; whereas for $\alpha > 30°$, peak current is reduced. For purposes of design, if the control must operate with a zero value of α, then full-conduction conditions govern the current rating of the switching semiconductors.

To determine the voltage rating of the semiconductors, the circuit diagram in Figure 6.12 may be used. During an interval when Phase A is not conducting, the voltage across the switch may be determined from Equation 6.27:

$$v_S = v_{an} + v_{nb} + v_{BO}. \tag{6.27}$$

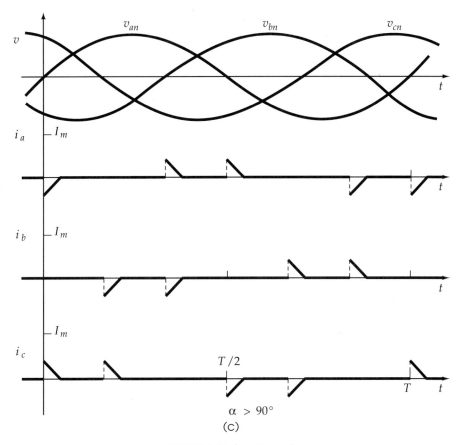

$\alpha > 90°$

(c)

FIGURE 6.11 (continued)

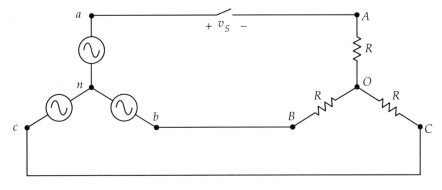

FIGURE 6.12

During the time that Phase A is open, v_{BO} is just one-half of v_{BC}. The result of using this condition in Equation 6.27 is given in Equations 6.28 and 6.29:

$$v_S = v_{an} + v_{nb} + 0.5v_{BC} = v_{ab} + 0.5v_{bc} \tag{6.28}$$

$$v_S = 1.5v_{an}. \tag{6.29}$$

If the phase-control angle is large enough, then two phases may be non-conducting at some point. This means that all currents are zero during some interval. The peak line-to-line voltage must be blocked at some instant by two devices in series. Because of different leakage currents, the two devices may not share this voltage equally. Therefore, a safe design procedure is one that selects devices with voltage ratings of at least the peak value of the system's line-to-line voltage.

Load Power

With a resistive load, the line currents at each instant are determined easily, and the RMS value can be found. The waveform is different in several ranges of α, and the form of the resulting equations depends on the range of α. For $\alpha < 60°$, the current waveforms in Figure 6.11(a) apply. Each half-cycle of current consists of three different 60° intervals. The following equations apply where the usual relations for a three-phase set of voltages apply. The voltage v_{an} is a sine function and the ABC phase sequence is used. The angle θ replaces ωt in the equations:

$$i_a = 0 \qquad \text{for } 0 < \theta < \alpha \tag{6.30}$$

$$i_a = \frac{v_{an}}{R} \qquad \text{for } \alpha < \theta < \frac{\pi}{3} \tag{6.31}$$

$$i_a = \frac{v_{ab}}{2R} \qquad \text{for } \frac{\pi}{3} < \theta < \left(\frac{\pi}{3} + \alpha\right) \tag{6.32}$$

$$i_a = \frac{v_{an}}{R} \qquad \text{for } \left(\frac{\pi}{3} + \alpha\right) < \theta < \frac{2\pi}{3} \tag{6.33}$$

$$i_a = \frac{v_{ac}}{2R} \qquad \text{for } \frac{2\pi}{3} < \theta < \left(\frac{2\pi}{3} + \alpha\right) \tag{6.34}$$

$$i_a = \frac{v_{an}}{R} \qquad \text{for } \left(\frac{2\pi}{3} + \alpha\right) < \theta < \pi. \tag{6.35}$$

The RMS value is found by substituting the preceding six relations into Equation 6.36; the result is given by Equation 6.37:

$$I_{L_{RMS}} = \left\{\left(\frac{1}{\pi}\right)\int_0^\pi [i_a(\theta)]^2 \, d\theta\right\}^{0.5} \tag{6.36}$$

$$I_{L_{RMS}} = I_m\left[\frac{1}{2\pi}(\pi - 1.5\alpha + 0.75\sin 2\alpha)\right]^{0.5}. \tag{6.37}$$

For $60° < \alpha < 90°$, the graph in Figure 6.11(b) applies. The current relations are expressed by Equations 6.38, 6.39, and 6.40:

$$i_a = 0 \qquad \text{for } \alpha - \frac{\pi}{3} < \theta < \alpha \qquad (6.38)$$

$$i_a = \frac{v_{ab}}{2R} \qquad \text{for } \alpha < \theta < \alpha + \frac{\pi}{3} \qquad (6.39)$$

$$i_a = \frac{v_{ac}}{2R} \qquad \text{for } \alpha + \frac{\pi}{3} < \theta < \alpha + \frac{2\pi}{3}. \qquad (6.40)$$

Substituting the preceding relations into Equation 6.36 with new limits of integration gives the result from Equation 6.41:

$$I_{L_{\text{RMS}}} = I_m \left\{ \left(\frac{3}{4\pi} \right) \left[\frac{\pi}{3} + 0.866 \sin\left(2\alpha + \frac{\pi}{6} \right) \right] \right\}^{0.5}. \qquad (6.41)$$

For $90° < \alpha < 150°$, the conduction pattern for a given phase current is not continuous over the entire $120°$ interval; this is shown in Figure 6.11(c). There is a gap in the conduction in Phase A as conduction switches from Phase B to C. The gate terminal of the switch requires continuous excitation for this operation to exist; a short pulse at the start of conduction is not sufficient. For this mode of operation, the current's RMS value can be calculated by an integration over a half-period. The currents are expressed by the following equations:

$$i_a = 0 \qquad \text{for } \frac{\pi}{6} < \theta < \alpha \qquad (6.42)$$

$$i_a = \frac{v_{ab}}{2R} \qquad \text{for } \alpha < \theta < \frac{5\pi}{6} \qquad (6.43)$$

$$i_a = 0 \qquad \text{for } \frac{5\pi}{6} < \theta < \alpha + \frac{\pi}{3} \qquad (6.44)$$

$$i_a = \frac{v_{ac}}{2R} \qquad \text{for } \alpha + \frac{\pi}{3} < \theta < \frac{7\pi}{6}. \qquad (6.45)$$

Substituting the preceding four relations into Equation 6.36 with appropriate limits gives the result in Equation 6.46:

$$I_{L_{\text{RMS}}} = I_m \left\{ \left(\frac{3}{4\pi} \right) \left[\frac{5\pi}{6} - \alpha + 0.5 \sin\left(2\alpha + \frac{\pi}{3} \right) \right] \right\}^{0.5}. \qquad (6.46)$$

EXAMPLE 6.8

A Y-connected resistive load of 20 Ω per phase is connected to a 460-V, 60-Hz, three-phase source. The load power must be made variable from 9 kW to 3 kW by using a phase-controlled switch in each line between source and load. Find:

(a) the peak switch current

(b) the range of α required

(c) the RMS switch current rating

(d) the switch voltage rating.

Solution

(a)
$$I_m = \frac{(460)(\frac{2}{3})^{0.5}}{20} = 18.78 \text{ A.}$$

As long as $\alpha < 30°$, the peak switch current is the same as I_m. If α is $> 30°$, however, as found in later parts of this example, then the peak current is somewhat less than 18.78 A.

(b) For a load power of 9 kW, the RMS load current is found:

$$I_{L_{RMS}} = \left[\frac{9000}{(3)(20)} \right]^{0.5} = 12.24 \text{ A.}$$

Using Equation 6.37, the value of α is calculated by iteration to be 46.67°, or 0.8145 radian.

For a power of 3 kW,

$$I_{L_{RMS}} = \left[\frac{3000}{(3)(20)} \right]^{0.5} = 7.07 \text{ A.}$$

Using Equation 6.46 and solving for α yields a value of $\alpha = 90.8°$, or 1.585 radians.

(c) The switch RMS current rating is the same as the RMS value of the largest load current.

(d) Conservatively, the switch voltage rating should not be less than the peak L–L voltage of the source, or $(460)(1.414) = 650$ V. In practice, a rating of no less than 800 V should be used.   ∎

Power Factor: Resistive Load

Again, the power factor presented to the AC source is less than unity because of the phase control used. The definition of power factor for the single-phase case as expressed in Equation 6.6 is modified to allow for the three-phase case. Note that in this equation $|V_{LN_{RMS}}|$ is the magnitude of the source voltage:

$$\text{Power factor} = \frac{3(\text{average power per phase})}{3|V_{LN_{RMS}}||I_{L_{RMS}}|}. \tag{6.47}$$

Substituting Equation 6.37, 6.41, or 6.46 in Equation 6.47 yields Equation 6.48. The blank within the parentheses of that equation contains the appropriate term of the relation used to obtain the equation:

$$\text{Power factor} = (2)^{0.5}(\qquad)^{0.5}. \tag{6.48}$$

EXAMPLE 6.9

In Example 6.8, find the power factor for each of the two load values.

Solution   For $P = 9$ kW and using Equations 6.37 and 6.48 for $\alpha = 0.8145$ rad:

$$\text{Power factor} = 1.414 \left\{ \left(\frac{1}{2\pi}\right) [\pi - 1.5(0.8145) + 0.75 \sin 1.629] \right\}^{0.5}$$

$$= 0.922.$$

For $P = 3$ kW and using Equations 6.46 and 6.48 for $\alpha = 1.585$ rad:

$$\text{Power factor} = 1.414 \left[\left(\frac{3}{4\pi}\right) \left\{ \frac{5\pi}{6} - 1.585 + 0.5 \sin \left[(2)(1.585) + \frac{\pi}{3} \right] \right\} \right]^{0.5}$$

$$= 0.532. \qquad \blacksquare$$

6.8
PHASE CONTROL: POLYPHASE INDUCTIVE LOADS

With load inductance, the graphs in Figure 6.11 are modified somewhat to elimi-nate current discontinuities at the switching points. The currents are no longer calculated easily because each depends not only on the present voltage but also on previous conditions. Closed forms of the solution are not possible.

The graphs in Figure 6.13 show circuit behavior for an inductive load with $\alpha = 105°$ and $\theta = 60°$. In this figure, note that current variation in one phase during a 60° interval is repeated in another phase in the next 60° interval but with reversed sign. This means that a complete solution for a 60° interval is all that is necessary to describe the circuit operation. The boundary conditions at the beginning and end of such an interval are so related as to meet the conditions described above. The current values in this figure were obtained from the SPICE simulation of Example 6.10.

Selecting the switching devices in such a circuit generally will be governed by the current at $\alpha = 0$. Such a selection can be made without knowing the manner in which the RMS current varies with α.

The value of the peak line-to-line voltage of the three-phase system again will control the voltage rating of the semiconductor switches—if a conservative approach to system design is used. Because the load is inductive, each semi-conductor switch experiences a rapid change in voltage as its current becomes zero. A snubber probably will be required to prevent an unwanted turn on at this time.

The circuit power factor will be less than that dictated by the circuit power factor without phase control. For large loads, the power factor may be econom-

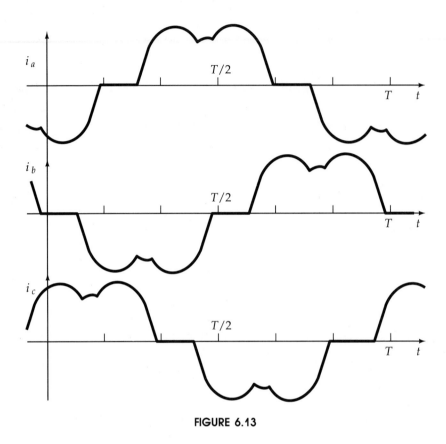

FIGURE 6.13

ically important. The exact value can be determined by numerical calculation if
there is reason to do so.

EXAMPLE 6.10

The current waveforms in Figure 6.13 were generated using a SPICE simulation
program, which was performed for a 60° interval starting at the time that i_a
was switched into conduction at $\alpha = 105°$. Properly oriented diodes were used
to simulate the switching elements of the circuit. The circuit is shown in Figure 6.14. The initial current in the two conducting phases was determined
iteratively.

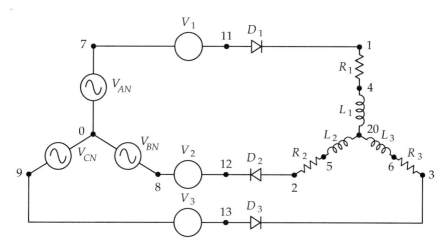

FIGURE 6.14

A portion of the SPICE output is shown below to illustrate the solution that can be obtained.

```
******* 01/12/90 ********************** 12:13:42 ******

        POLYPHASE — PHASE CONTROL — ALPHA=105 THETA=60

            ****        CIRCUIT DESCRIPTION        ****

VAN 7 0 SIN( 0  100 60 -4.8611M 0 )
VBN 8 0 SIN( 0 -100 60 -7.6389M 0 )
VCN 9 0 SIN( 0 -100 60 -2.0833M 0 )
V1  7 11 DC 0
V2  8 12 DC 0
V3  9 13 DC 0
L1 4 20 0.04594407 IC=0
L2 5 20 0.04594407 IC=-1.018
L3 6 20 0.04594407 IC=1.018
R1 1 4 10
R2 2 5 10
R3 3 6 10
D1 11 1 DMOD
D2 2 12 DMOD
D3 13 3 DMOD
.MODEL DMOD D
*
*SOLUTION CONTROL
*
.TRAN 69.4444U 2.77778M 0 2U UIC
*
```

```
.PRINT TRAN I(V1) I(V2) I(V3)
*
.END
**** TRANSIENT ANALYSIS TEMPERATURE = 27.000 DEG C
```

TIME	I(V1)	I(V2)	I(V3)
0.000E+00	5.464E-09	-1.018E+00	1.018E+00
6.944E-05	1.436E-01	-1.038E+00	8.944E-01
1.389E-04	2.839E-01	-1.054E+00	7.700E-01
2.083E-04	4.209E-01	-1.066E+00	6.448E-01
2.778E-04	5.545E-01	-1.073E+00	5.190E-01
3.472E-04	6.847E-01	-1.077E+00	3.926E-01
4.167E-04	8.114E-01	-1.077E+00	2.657E-01
4.861E-04	9.346E-01	-1.073E+00	1.384E-01
5.556E-04	1.054E+00	-1.065E+00	1.080E-02
6.250E-04	1.112E+00	-1.112E+00	-1.279E-10
6.944E-04	1.160E+00	-1.160E+00	-1.299E-10
7.639E-04	1.205E+00	-1.205E+00	-1.318E-10
8.333E-04	1.246E+00	-1.246E+00	-1.337E-10
9.028E-04	1.284E+00	-1.284E+00	-1.354E-10
9.722E-04	1.318E+00	-1.318E+00	-1.370E-10
1.042E-03	1.348E+00	-1.348E+00	-1.386E-10
1.111E-03	1.375E+00	-1.375E+00	-1.400E-10
1.181E-03	1.398E+00	-1.398E+00	-1.414E-10
1.250E-03	1.417E+00	-1.417E+00	-1.427E-10
1.319E-03	1.433E+00	-1.433E+00	-1.438E-10
1.389E-03	1.446E+00	-1.446E+00	-1.449E-10
1.458E-03	1.455E+00	-1.455E+00	-1.459E-10
1.528E-03	1.460E+00	-1.460E+00	-1.467E-10
1.597E-03	1.462E+00	-1.462E+00	-1.475E-10
1.667E-03	1.461E+00	-1.461E+00	-1.482E-10
1.736E-03	1.457E+00	-1.457E+00	-1.487E-10
1.806E-03	1.449E+00	-1.449E+00	-1.492E-10
1.875E-03	1.438E+00	-1.438E+00	-1.495E-10
1.944E-03	1.423E+00	-1.423E+00	-1.498E-10
2.014E-03	1.406E+00	-1.406E+00	-1.500E-10
2.083E-03	1.385E+00	-1.385E+00	-1.500E-10
2.153E-03	1.361E+00	-1.361E+00	-1.500E-10
2.222E-03	1.335E+00	-1.335E+00	-1.498E-10
2.292E-03	1.305E+00	-1.305E+00	-1.495E-10
2.361E-03	1.272E+00	-1.272E+00	-1.492E-10
2.431E-03	1.236E+00	-1.236E+00	-1.487E-10
2.500E-03	1.198E+00	-1.198E+00	-1.482E-10
2.569E-03	1.157E+00	-1.157E+00	-1.475E-10
2.639E-03	1.113E+00	-1.113E+00	-1.467E-10
2.708E-03	1.066E+00	-1.066E+00	-1.459E-10
2.778E-03	1.017E+00	-1.017E+00	-1.449E-10

The RMS value of each line current and thus the load power can be determined numerically from the tabulated current values. An approximate numerical integration can be performed as illustrated in the following relation:

$$I_{RMS} = \left\{ \left(\frac{2\,\Delta t}{T} \right) \sum_{k=0}^{(n-1)} \left[i\left(t_k + \frac{\Delta t}{2} \right) \right]^2 \right\}^{0.5}.$$

In the above, n is the number of intervals in the half-period of the current waveform, t_k is the time at the beginning of each interval, and Δt is the duration of each time interval. The data available for the three line currents for one-sixth of the period provide data for one current for an interval of one-half period. In this example, $n = 60$ and $\Delta t = 138.9\ \mu s$. The result of the indicated numerical integration is

$$I_{RMS} = 1.031\ A.$$

The average load power now may be calculated using this current value;

$$P = (3)(I_{RMS})^2(R) = (3)(1.031)^2(10) = 31.9\ W.$$

The circuit power factor also may be determined:

$$\begin{aligned}
\text{Power factor} &= \frac{P}{(3)(V_{LN_{RMS}})(I_{RMS})} \\
&= \frac{31.9}{(3)(57.7)(1.031)} = 0.179. \quad \blacksquare
\end{aligned}$$

6.9
PHASE CONTROL: MOTOR LOADS

An induction motor with a suitable load can be varied in speed by reducing motor voltage below rated value. This method contrasts with the variable-frequency methods that we will study in Chapter 8. At any given speed, an induction motor with reduced voltage produces less torque than the normal full-voltage torque value. The graph in Figure 6.15 shows the behavior for a single-phase motor whose auxiliary winding with series capacitor is connected permanently. A motor with a centrifugally actuated switch for the auxiliary winding is not suitable for speed control.

The graph has an additional speed torque curve for a fan-type load. For any given voltage, the intersection of the motor and load curves corresponds to the operating speed of the combination. It is possible to vary the motor

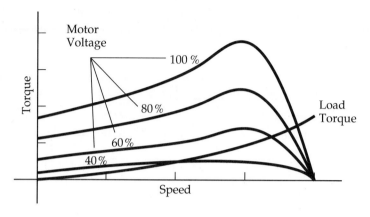

FIGURE 6.15

speed over the full speed range by suitably changing the motor voltage, although the method is suitable only for loads with torque requirements that vary appreciably with speed as shown in Figure 6.15.

The voltage to the motor can be varied, in effect, by using the phase-control technique of Section 6.5. The voltage no longer is sinusoidal and the current has intervals of zero value such as are shown in Figure 6.5(b). Nevertheless, the motor speed can be varied over the full speed range with this method. Motor design, however, is affected if this speed-control means is used. Motor slip increases as voltage decreases, resulting in increased motor current and losses. This increase occurs even though motor voltage has been decreased. Maximum current and losses occur at approximately 65% of synchronous speed. The motor design must provide a means to remove the heat of these losses to safely limit motor temperature. For motor speed less than the speed corresponding to maximum loss, the motor current and losses decrease.

This method of motor-speed control can be applied to either single-phase or polyphase induction motors. For single-phase motors, the circuit diagram in Figure 6.5(a) is representative of the circuit connection. The TRIAC (or other switch) is gated on by a suitable control. The phase-delay angle is determined by some physical quantity that is affected by motor speed. With a three-phase motor, at least three switching devices are required. The circuit in Figure 6.16 represents the type of polyphase circuit used for this purpose. In this case, TRIACs are shown as the switching device, but for larger current requirements, two SCRs can be used to replace each TRIAC. The three gate terminals are each referenced to different MT_1 points in the circuit in Figure 6.16; pulse transformers for the gate circuit thus are required to provide isolation between phases. The control system must generate suitable pulses to turn on the TRIACs at the required $120°$ phase relation for a three-phase system.

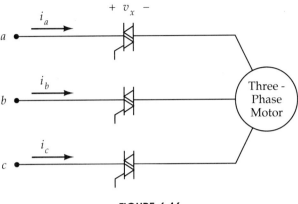

FIGURE 6.16

The graphs in Figure 6.17 show waveforms of the motor current for one phase of a typical three-phase motor controlled in the manner described. The phase-delay angle in this figure has a value that produces an interval of approximately $35°$, during which the current is zero in each half-cycle.

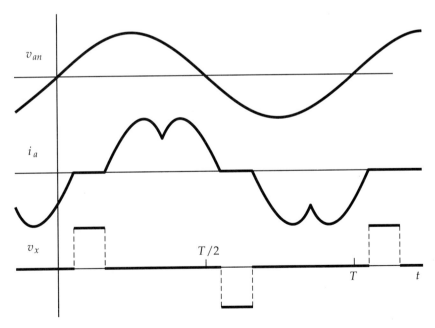

FIGURE 6.17

6.10

PROBLEMS

6.1   An electrical-resistance heater is controlled in an integral cycle manner to provide variable power. The control repeats over a 40-cycle interval; $V_S = 230$-V RMS, 60-Hz; and $R_L = 5\ \Omega$. Find:

(a) the maximum power to the load

(b) the minimum average load power

(c) the value of k for 4-kW load power.

6.2   An electrical-resistance heater of $6\ \Omega$ is provided power from a 230-V, 60-Hz source. The power is controlled in an on–off manner by the use of integral cycles like those in Figure 6.2, with the switch implemented by a TRIAC. The control is to provide power from 8.5 kW to 1.2 kW with a maximum step size of 160 W. Find:

(a) a suitable value of n

(b) the range of k required

(c) the RMS current rating of the TRIAC.

6.3   Repeat Problem 6.2 using two SCRs as in Figure 6.1(b). For part (c), find the average current rating of each SCR.

6.4   The circuit in Figure 6.1 is used for phase control; $V_S = 460$-V RMS, 60-Hz; $R_L = 12\ \Omega$; and $\alpha = 45°$. Find:

(a) peak load current   (b) average load power

(c) switch current rating   (d) power factor.

6.5   The power to a resistive load is to be controlled by a phase-control technique. The power is to range from 2 kW to 8 kW; $V_S = 230$-V RMS, 60-Hz; and $R_L = 6\ \Omega$. Find:

(a) the range of α required

(b) the switch current and voltage rating, if a TRIAC is used

(c) the power factor at the largest power level.

6.6   The circuit in Figure 6.1(b) is used to control the power to a resistive load. The power is required to be variable from 5 kW to 40 kW; $V_S = 460$-V RMS, 60-Hz; and $R_L = 5\ \Omega$. Find:

(a) the range of α required

(b) the SCR current and voltage ratings

(c) the range of power factor presented to the source.

6.7   An inductive load is phase-controlled from a 230-V RMS, 60-Hz source; $\alpha = 80°$, $R_L = 15\ \Omega$, and $L = 0.04$ H. Find:

(a) the value of β

(b) the RMS value of load current

(c) the load power

(d) the peak switch current

(e) the power factor.

6.8 The inductive load given in Problem 6.7 has the average controlled from 1600 W to 100 W. Find:

(a) the range of RMS current required

(b) the range of α required

(c) the range of β required

(d) the average SCR current if the switch is like that in Figure 6.1(b).

6.9 The inductive load in Figure 6.1(a) is phase-controlled in a manner that varies the power from 12 kW to 2 kW; $V_S = 460$-V RMS, 60-Hz; $R_L = 10 \ \Omega$; and $L = 0.015$ H. Find:

(a) the range of RMS current required

(b) the range of α required

(c) the range of β required

(d) the peak TRIAC current

(e) the power factor when delivering 12 kW.

6.10 A balanced three-phase, Y-connected, resistive load of 20 Ω per phase is connected to a 460-V, three-phase, 60-Hz source in a manner similar to that in Figure 6.10. The α value is 75°. Find:

(a) the peak line current

(b) the average load power

(c) the power factor

(d) a voltage rating for each switch

(e) the switch current's RMS value.

6.11 A balanced three-phase, Y-connected, resistive load of 10 Ω per phase is connected to a 230-V, 60-Hz, three-phase source through phase-control switching devices. The load power must be varied from 4 kW to 1 kW. Find:

(a) the required range for α

(b) the switch current and voltage ratings

(c) the power factor at the largest load power.

CHAPTER · 7

DC–DC
Converters

In this chapter, we will consider DC–DC converters or choppers. These converters have many circuit configurations, and thus it is not possible to consider all of the possible circuit variations in an introductory treatment. Both the most basic direct-connected versions and a limited number of magnetically coupled circuit arrangements are considered in this chapter.

7.1
TYPES OF CHOPPER CIRCUITS

Chopper circuits can be classified by circuit function. A very elementary type of buck chopper was considered in Chapter 1. The basic direct-connected types are *buck*, *boost*, and *buck-boost* arrangements. Certain magnetically coupled versions also provide buck and boost functions.

7.2
BUCK CHOPPER

The basic buck chopper provides an average output voltage that is less than the input voltage. The version in Chapter 1 is not very practical because no energy storage was provided. A much more practical arrangement is shown in Figure 7.1.

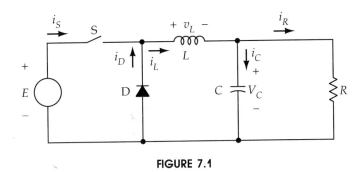

FIGURE 7.1

The inductor and capacitor provide a smoothing action so that the output voltage has only a limited ripple. Just how much filtering is provided depends on the nature of the load requirement. The amount of filtering provided also affects the form of the circuit analysis because two modes of operation depend on the value of circuit inductance. If the inductance is large enough that the inductor current never becomes zero, the mode is described as *continuous inductor current*. If the inductor is smaller, then the inductor current is zero for part of each cycle, and the mode is described as one with *discontinuous inductor current*. A separate analysis is required for each mode, and a relation can be found that sets the boundary between the two modes.

Voltage Relation

In Figure 7.1, switch S is opened and closed periodically. The total period is T, and the fraction of time that the switch is closed is D. The fraction of time the switch is opened, therefore, is $(1 - D)$. For the purpose of this analysis, we assume that C is large enough that negligible ripple occurs in v_C. Let this nonvarying capacitor voltage be denoted by V_C.

During the time that the switch is closed, the circuit arrangement is as shown in Figure 7.2(a). For the time that the switch is open, the inductor current freewheels through the diode and results in the circuit shown in Figure 7.2(b). The circuit voltage equation during the time the switch is closed is given in Equation 7.1:

$$E = v_L + V_C \tag{7.1}$$

$$E = L\left(\frac{di_L}{dt}\right) + V_C \tag{7.2}$$

$$\left(\frac{di_L}{dt}\right) = \frac{E - V_C}{L}. \tag{7.3}$$

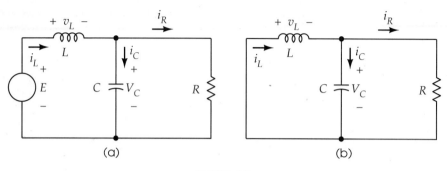

FIGURE 7.2

During this time period of length DT, the inductor current increases with a constant slope (shown in Figure 7.3), as do several other circuit currents and voltages. The inductor current starts at some initial value I_{min} and changes to a value I_{max} at the end of the switch-closure period.

For the interval that the switch is open, the circuit changes to the arrangement shown in Figure 7.2(b); this interval's circuit voltage equation is given in Equation 7.4:

$$0 = v_L + V_C. \tag{7.4}$$

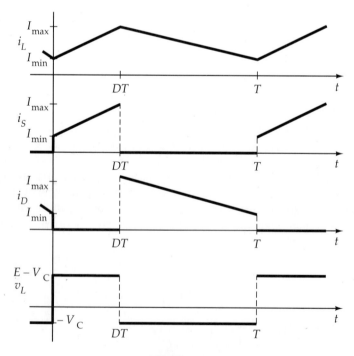

FIGURE 7.3

Equation 7.4 is expanded and rearranged in Equations 7.5 and 7.6:

$$0 = L\frac{di_L}{dt} + V_C \tag{7.5}$$

$$\frac{di_L}{dt} = -\frac{V_C}{L}. \tag{7.6}$$

Thus, during the time interval $(1 - D)T$, the inductor current decreases at a constant rate from I_{max} to I_{min}. The ending value must be the same as that at the beginning of the period, because the operation is periodic. The change during switch closure therefore must be the same as that during the switch's open period. It also is true that I_{min} is greater than or equal to zero, because continuous inductor current is assumed. These statements are expressed in Equations 7.7 and 7.8:

$$I_{max} - I_{min} = \left(\frac{E - V_C}{L}\right)DT \tag{7.7}$$

$$I_{min} - I_{max} = \left(-\frac{V_C}{L}\right)(1 - D)T. \tag{7.8}$$

Solving gives

$$\left(\frac{E - V_C}{L}\right)DT = \left(+\frac{V_C}{L}\right)(1 - D)T \tag{7.9}$$

$$(E - V_C)D = (+V_C)(1 - D) \tag{7.10}$$

$$V_C = DE. \tag{7.11}$$

Thus, the capacitor voltage and hence the chopper's output to the load depend solely on the fraction of time that the switch is closed, provided that the inductor current is continuous.

Circuit Currents

From Figure 7.3, we can find the average value of inductor current easily by inspecting the waveform. This value is given in Equation 7.12:

$$I_L = \frac{I_{max} + I_{min}}{2}. \tag{7.12}$$

A current equation at a load resistor node is given in Equation 7.13. Because the average capacitor current is zero in periodic operation, the result of Equation 7.14 may be written by averaging the terms of Equation 7.13 over one period of operation:

$$i_L = i_C + i_R \tag{7.13}$$

$$I_L = I_R. \tag{7.14}$$

The value of I_R is given by Equation 7.15. A combination of these equations allows a solution for $I_{max} + I_{min}$ in Equation 7.16:

$$I_R = \frac{V_C}{R} \tag{7.15}$$

$$I_{max} + I_{min} = 2\frac{V_C}{R}. \tag{7.16}$$

Combining Equations 7.7 and 7.16 allows us to solve for I_{max} and I_{min}:

$$I_{max} = (DE)\left[\frac{1}{R} + \frac{(1 - D)(T)}{2L}\right] \tag{7.17}$$

$$I_{min} = (DE)\left[\frac{1}{R} - \frac{(1 - D)(T)}{2L}\right]. \tag{7.18}$$

Continuous Current Condition

Solving Equation 7.18 for a zero value of I_{min} yields a relation for the minimum value of circuit inductance that results in continuous inductor current; Equation 7.19 is the result:

$$L = \left(\frac{TR}{2}\right)(1 - D). \tag{7.19}$$

EXAMPLE 7.1

A buck chopper supplies 12 V to a resistive load of 6 Ω from a 30-V source using the circuit in Figure 7.1. The inductor current is continuous. Chopping frequency is 5 kHz. Find:

(a) the value of D

(b) the minimum value of L required

(c) the minimum and maximum values of i_L if L is 1.5 millihenries

(d) power from the source

(e) power to the load.

Solution

(a)
$$D = \frac{V_C}{E} = \frac{12}{30} = 0.4.$$

(b)
$$L = \left[\frac{(T)(R)}{2}\right](1 - D) = \left[\frac{(0.0002)(6)}{2}\right](1 - 0.4)$$
$$= 0.000360 \text{ H}.$$

(c)
$$I_{min} = DE\left[\left(\frac{1}{R}\right) - \frac{(1-D)(T)}{2L}\right]$$
$$= (0.4)(30)\left[\left(\frac{1}{6}\right) - \frac{(1-0.4)(0.0002)}{(2)(0.0015)}\right]$$
$$= 1.52 \text{ A.}$$

$$I_{max} = DE\left[\left(\frac{1}{R}\right) + \frac{(1-D)(T)}{2L}\right]$$
$$= (0.4)(30)\left[\left(\frac{1}{6}\right) + \frac{(1-0.4)(0.0002)}{(2)(0.0015)}\right]$$
$$= 2.48 \text{ A.}$$

(d) Power from the source can be found by using source voltage and average source current:

$$I_{S_{avg}} = \left(\frac{I_{max} + I_{min}}{2}\right)D$$
$$= \left(\frac{2.48 + 1.52}{2}\right)(0.4) = 0.8 \text{ A.}$$
$$P = E(I_{S_{avg}}) = (30)(0.8) = 24 \text{ W.}$$

(e) Because V_C has no ripple, the load power can be found from a simple DC expression:

$$\text{Power to load} = \frac{V_C^2}{R} = \frac{(12)^2}{6} = 24 \text{ W.} \qquad \blacksquare$$

EXAMPLE 7.2

A buck chopper supplies an adjustable voltage to a load of variable resistance. The required range of voltage is from 15 V to 25 V, with a load resistance value ranging from 4 Ω to 10 Ω. Any combination may occur; $E = 40$ V and $f = 8$ kHz. Find:

(a) range of D required

(b) value of L required for continuous inductor current under any condition.

Solution

(a) For $V_C = 15$ V,

$$D = \frac{15}{40} = 0.375.$$

For $V_C = 25$ V,

$$D = \frac{25}{40} = 0.625.$$

(b) The most demanding design condition for L is that which corresponds to the largest value of R and the smallest value of D. By using Equation 7.19, the value of L is determined:

$$L = \left[\frac{(10)(125 \times 10^{-6})}{2} \right] (1 - 0.375)$$

$$= 391 \ \mu\text{H}. \qquad\blacksquare$$

Capacitor Voltage Ripple

The condition of zero ripple in the capacitor voltage now is relaxed to allow a small ripple. This has only a second-order effect on the currents calculated in the previous section, so the previous results can be used without change.

As previously noted, the capacitor current must be entirely alternating to have periodic operation. The graph of capacitor current must be as shown in Figure 7.4 for continuous inductor current. The peak value of this triangular waveform is $(I_{max} - I_{min})/2$. The resulting ripple in capacitor voltage depends on the area under the curve of capacitor current versus time. In Figure 7.4, the charge added to the capacitor in a half-cycle is given by the triangular area

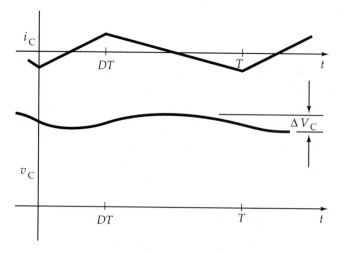

FIGURE 7.4

above the axis:

$$\Delta Q = \frac{1}{2}\left[\frac{I_{max} - I_{min}}{2}\right]\left(\frac{T}{2}\right) \quad (7.20)$$

$$\Delta Q = \left[\frac{(I_{max} - I_{min})(T)}{8}\right]. \quad (7.21)$$

The graph of capacitor voltage also is shown as part of Figure 7.4. The ripple in the voltage is exaggerated to show its effect. Minimum and maximum capacitor voltage values occur at the time of capacitor current zero values. The peak-to-peak value of capacitor voltage ripple is given by

$$\Delta V_C = \frac{\Delta Q}{C} = \left[\frac{(I_{max} - I_{min})(T)}{8C}\right]. \quad (7.22)$$

EXAMPLE 7.3

A buck chopper, operating at 10 kHz, supplies 100 W at 12 V to a load from a 20-V source. Find:

(a) the inductance for continuous inductor current

(b) $I_{max} - I_{min}$

(c) the value of capacitance needed for $\Delta V_C = 0.1$ V.

Solution

(a)
$$I_R = \frac{100}{12} = 8.33 \text{ A}$$

$$R = \frac{12}{8.33} = 1.44 \ \Omega$$

$$D = \frac{12}{20} = 0.6$$

$$T = \frac{1}{10,000} = 0.0001 \text{ s}$$

$$L = \left[\frac{(T)(R)}{2}\right](1 - D) = \left[\frac{(0.0001)(1.44)}{2}\right](1 - 0.6)$$
$$= 0.0000288 \text{ H}.$$

(b) From Equation 7.7:

$$I_{max} - I_{min} = \left[\frac{(20 - 12)(0.6)(0.0001)}{0.0000288}\right]$$
$$= 16.667 \text{ A}.$$

(c) From Equation 7.22:

$$\Delta Q = \frac{(0.000100)(16.667)}{8} = 0.000208 \text{ C}$$

$$C = \frac{\Delta Q}{\Delta V_C} = \frac{0.000208}{0.1} = 0.002080 \text{ F}$$

$$C = 2080 \ \mu F.$$

■

7.3
BOOST CHOPPER

If three buck chopper elements are rearranged as shown in Figure 7.5, a boost-type chopper is created. An analysis similar to that for the buck chopper gives the steady-state operating conditions of this circuit.

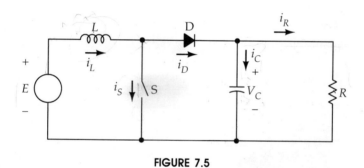

FIGURE 7.5

Voltage Relation

During the time the switch is closed, the inductor current increases with the derivative given by Equation 7.23:

$$\frac{di_L}{dt} = \frac{E}{L}.$$ (7.23)

During this same interval, the diode element is reverse-biased, the capacitor supplies current to the load, and the value of i_C is negative.

Upon opening the switch, the inductor current must decrease so that the current at the end of the cycle can be the same as at the start of the cycle.

For the inductor current to decrease, the V_C value must be greater than E. For this interval with the switch open, the inductor current derivative is given by Equation 7.24:

$$\frac{di_L}{dt} = \frac{E - V_C}{L}.$$ (7.24)

A graph of inductor current versus time is shown in Figure 7.6.

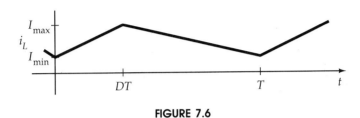

FIGURE 7.6

The increase in i_L during switch closure time must equal the decrease during open-switch time; this fact allows us to determine the voltage relation for the chopper:

$$I_{max} - I_{min} = \left(\frac{E}{L}\right)DT$$ (7.25)

and

$$I_{min} - I_{max} = \left(\frac{E - V_C}{L}\right)(1 - D)T.$$ (7.26)

Equating these two changes results in the voltage relation

$$V_C = \frac{E}{1 - D}.$$ (7.27)

We tacitly assumed in the preceding equations that the inductor current is continuous. We will consider the discontinuous case in a later section.

From Equation 7.27, we can see that the circuit is a boost chopper. As D becomes larger, the value of V_C increases. The equation indicates that the output voltage can be as large a factor times the input voltage as we desire. One factor, however, has been neglected in the analysis leading to Equation 7.27: The inductor resistance becomes important for large values of D. In fact, as D approaches unity, the output voltage decreases rather than increases. The value of D and hence the voltage boost factor must be limited to less than some upper limit to prevent such a problem.

Practical limits to this also become important for an increase on the order of 5:1. The switch may be open only a very short time, with resultant switching-loss problems, and the diode and capacitor currents have large peak values compared to their average values. The resulting RMS value of capacitor current may well be excessive for the capacitance value required. For moderate voltage increases, however, reasonable design conditions result.

Circuit Currents

The complete set of currents in one complete cycle of operation is shown in Figure 7.7. The I_{max} and I_{min} values must be determined so that all other currents can be found. This is done most easily by using the fact that input average power and load average power must be equal, because no losses are included in the circuit models:

$$\text{Input power} = (0.5)(I_{max} + I_{min})(E) \tag{7.28}$$

and

$$\text{Output power} = \frac{V_C^2}{R}. \tag{7.29}$$

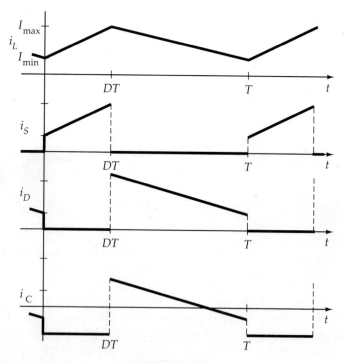

FIGURE 7.7

Equating these power values as well as using the input-to-output voltage relation of Equation 7.27 gives Equation 7.30:

$$I_{max} + I_{min} = \frac{2E}{(R)(1 - D)^2}.$$

(7.30)

Combining Equations 7.26, 7.27, and 7.30 gives:

$$I_{min} = \frac{E}{(R)(1 - D)^2} - \left(\frac{E}{2L}\right)(DT)$$

(7.31)

$$I_{max} = \frac{E}{(R)(1 - D)^2} + \left(\frac{E}{2L}\right)(DT).$$

(7.32)

With the load current value, i_R, known to be V_C/R, the current equation at the capacitor's upper node allows the graph of i_C versus time to be determined, as it is in Figure 7.7.

EXAMPLE 7.4

A boost chopper with the configuration in Figure 7.5 supplies 150 V to a 25-Ω load from a 40-V source. The capacitor is large enough that negligible load voltage ripple occurs; $L = 200\ \mu H$ and $T = 200\ \mu s$. Find:

(a) the value of D

(b) the value of I_{min}

(c) the value of I_{max}

(d) the average diode current

(e) the RMS value of capacitor current.

Solution

(a)
$$V_C = \frac{E}{1 - D}$$

$$150 = \frac{40}{1 - D}$$

$$D = 0.733.$$

The switch is closed for 146.7 μs and open for 53.3 μs each cycle of operation.

(b) From Equation 7.31:

$$I_{min} = \left[\frac{40}{(25)(0.267)^2}\right] - \left[\frac{40}{(2)(0.0002)}\right](0.0001467)$$

$$= 22.50 - 14.67 = 7.83\ \text{A}.$$

(c) From Equation 7.32:

$$I_{max} = 22.50 + 14.67 = 37.17 \text{ A}.$$

(d) The diode current varies linearly from 37.17 A to 7.83 A during the 53.3 μs that the switch is open. Thus,

$$I_D = \left(\frac{53.3}{200}\right)\left(\frac{37.17 + 7.83}{2}\right)$$
$$= (0.267)(22.50)$$
$$= 6.0 \text{ A}.$$

A little reflection shows us an easier way to obtain this value. The capacitor average current must be zero, and thus the diode average current must be the same as the load resistor average current of 150/25, or 6 A.

(e) The capacitor current varies, as in the graph in Figure 7.8, to fit the previously calculated numbers. The RMS value of this current is found using the definition of an RMS value:

$$I_C = \left(\left(\frac{1}{200}\right)\left\{\int_0^{146.7} (-6)^2 \, dt + \int_{146.7}^{200} [31.17 - 0.55(t - 146.7)]^2 \, dt\right\}\right)^{0.5}$$
$$= 10.87 \text{ A},$$

where the integrand for the second integral is the square of the current during the open-switch part of the cycle. ∎

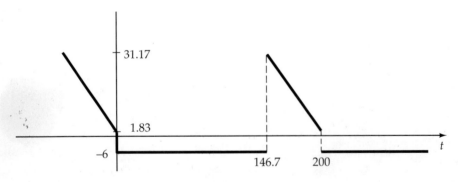

FIGURE 7.8

A comment on Example 7.4 is in order. In designing such a chopper, the components must be selected to withstand the imposed electrical stress. One of the more demanding cases will be the capacitor with its associated ripple current. If a reasonable capacitance value is selected to hold the voltage ripple to perhaps a few tenths of a volt, then the ripple current of 10.87 A in the example may be in excess of the capacitor's ripple-current rating. This is especially true if the capacitor operates much above room temperature. The solution is to use a much larger capacitor than would otherwise be required, although this may not prove economical.

Continuous Current Condition

The preceding relations were all developed with the condition of continuous inductor current. If this is not true, then new relations are required; in particular, the output voltage relation is no longer valid. The boundary for continuous current is found by setting I_{min} to zero; this defines a minimum inductance to ensure continuous inductor current. Using Equation 7.31, Equation 7.33 is obtained:

$$I_{min} = \frac{E}{(R)(1 - D)^2} - \left(\frac{E}{2L}\right)(DT) = 0. \tag{7.33}$$

Solving this equation gives

$$L = \left(\frac{RT}{2}\right)(D)(1 - D)^2. \tag{7.34}$$

EXAMPLE 7.5

Using all the data in Example 7.4, except the inductance value, find the critical inductance value that just permits continuous current in the inductor.

Solution

$$L = \left(\frac{RT}{2}\right)(D)(1 - D)^2$$

$$= \left[\frac{(25)(0.0002)}{2}\right](0.733)(1 - 0.733)^2$$

$$= 0.000130 \text{ H.}$$

Because the inductance in Example 7.4 was greater than this value, the current in the preceding example should have been continuous. This was found to be the case with $I_{min} = 7.83$ A.   ∎

Capacitor Voltage Ripple

The ripple in the capacitor voltage can be found using the graph for capacitor current in Figure 7.7. During the time the switch is closed, the capacitor furnishes the load current with essentially a constant value. In the case in Example 7.4, capacitor current is greater than zero during open-switch time. The example for when this is not true is left as an exercise. The charge removed from the capacitor during this time is given by Equation 7.35:

$$\Delta Q = \left(\frac{V_C}{R}\right)(DT).$$

(7.35)

The resulting voltage ripple is given by Equation 7.36:

$$\Delta V_C = \frac{\Delta Q}{C}.$$

(7.36)

EXAMPLE 7.6

Using the data in Example 7.4, find the value of the capacitor required to limit the peak-to-peak voltage ripple to 0.5 V.

Solution

$$\Delta Q = \left(\frac{150}{25}\right)(0.733)(200)$$

$$= 880 \ \mu C.$$

$$C = \frac{\Delta Q}{\Delta V_C} = \frac{880}{0.5}$$

$$= 1760 \ \mu F.$$ ■

7.4

BUCK-BOOST CHOPPER

A further rearrangement of the circuit elements allows us to realize the buck-boost function as shown in Figure 7.9. In addition to a change in the output-voltage magnitude, a reversal of output-voltage polarity also results in this case.

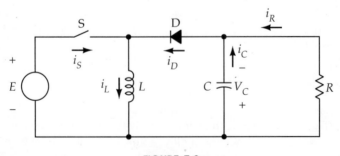

FIGURE 7.9

All previously defined quantities remain the same except for the changes in reference directions as shown in Figure 7.9.

Voltage Relation

With switch S closed, the diode is reverse-biased and i_D is zero. At the same time, the source voltage is impressed on the inductor and i_L increases with time. With S open, the source is disconnected, and the diode current becomes equal to the inductor current. Writing the equations for the changes of inductor current once again yields the relation between input and output voltage.

With the switch closed, inductor current changes as it does in Equations 7.37 and 7.38:

$$\frac{di_L}{dt} = \frac{E}{L} \tag{7.37}$$

and

$$I_{\max} - I_{\min} = \left(\frac{E}{L}\right)(DT). \tag{7.38}$$

With the switch open, similar changes are as in Equations 7.39 and 7.40:

$$\frac{di_L}{dt} = -\frac{V_C}{L} \tag{7.39}$$

and

$$I_{\min} - I_{\max} = \left(-\frac{V_C}{L}\right)(1 - D)(T). \tag{7.40}$$

Equating these two changes in i_L gives the result in Equation 7.41:

$$V_C = \left(\frac{D}{1 - D}\right)E. \tag{7.41}$$

For values of $D < 0.5$, the output voltage is less than the input voltage, whereas the output voltage is greater than the input voltage for values of $D > 0.5$.

Circuit Currents

The currents that exist in this configuration are shown in Figure 7.10. Again, the values of $I_{\min}$ and $I_{\max}$ are required for us to find values for all of the various currents.

The average value of switch current is given by Equation 7.42:

$$I_{S_{\text{avg}}} = \left(\frac{I_{\min} + I_{\max}}{2}\right)(D). \tag{7.42}$$

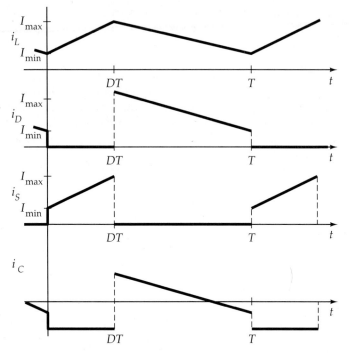

FIGURE 7.10

Input average power then is found from

$$P_{avg} = (E)(I_{S_{avg}}) = \left(\frac{I_{min} + I_{max}}{2}\right)(DE). \qquad (7.43)$$

If the input power in Equation 7.43 is equated to output power and Equation 7.41 is used, then the value of $(I_{min} + I_{max})$ is found in Equation 7.44:

$$I_{min} + I_{max} = \frac{2DE}{(R)(1 - D)^2}. \qquad (7.44)$$

Using the previous relation of Equation 7.38 for $(I_{max} - I_{min})$ yields the result of Equations 7.45 and 7.46:

$$I_{min} = \frac{DE}{(R)(1 - D)^2} - \frac{EDT}{2L} \qquad (7.45)$$

$$I_{max} = \frac{DE}{(R)(1 - D)^2} + \frac{EDT}{2L}. \qquad (7.46)$$

EXAMPLE 7.7

A buck-boost chopper supplies 100 W at 50 V to a resistive load like that in Figure 7.9 from a 35-V source; $T = 200 \ \mu s$ and $L = 700 \ \mu H$. Find:

(a) the value of D

(b) I_{min} and I_{max}

(c) average switch current

(d) average diode current

(e) RMS value of capacitor current.

Solution

(a)
$$V_C = \left[\frac{D}{(1-D)} \right] E$$

$$50 = \left[\frac{D}{(1-D)} \right] (35)$$

$$D = 0.588.$$

(b) Using Equations 7.45 and 7.46,

$$I_{min} = \frac{(0.588)(35)}{(25)(1-0.588)^2} - \frac{(35)(0.588)(200)}{(2)(700)}$$

$$= 7.86 - 2.94 = 1.92 \text{ A.}$$

$$I_{max} = 7.86 + 2.94 = 7.80 \text{ A.}$$

(c) Using Equation 7.42

$$I_{S_{avg}} = \left(\frac{I_{max} + I_{min}}{2} \right)(D)$$

$$= \left(\frac{7.80 + 1.92}{2} \right)(0.588)$$

$$= 2.86 \text{ A.}$$

(d) Average diode current is the same as the average load current, which is 100 W/50 V = 2 A.

(e) Figure 7.11 graphs capacitor current versus time. A somewhat simpler method than the one in Example 7.4 can be used to find the RMS value of the capacitor current. During the interval with the switch closed, the capacitor current can be considered to be a constant value of 2.86 with an added triangular part of $+2.94$ at the beginning and a -2.94 added value at the end. The RMS value of a triangular waveform is its peak value divided by 1.732. During another part of each cycle, the capacitor current is a constant

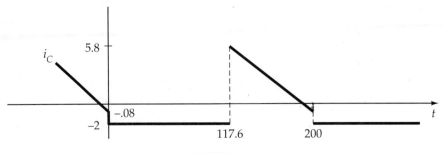

FIGURE 7.11

value of -2 A. Therefore, the overall RMS value can be found by the following relation:

$$I_{C_{RMS}} = \left\{ (-2)^2 \left(\frac{117.6}{200} \right) + \left[(2.86)^2 + \frac{(2.94)^2}{3} \right] \left(\frac{82.4}{200} \right) \right\}^{0.5}$$

$$= 2.63 \text{ A.}$$ ∎

Continuous Current Condition

The condition for continuous inductor current again is determined by the necessary minimum inductance value for $I_{min} = 0$, using Equation 7.45:

$$I_{min} = 0 = \frac{DE}{R(1 - D)^2} - \frac{DET}{2L} \tag{7.47}$$

$$L = \left(\frac{RT}{2} \right) (1 - D)^2. \tag{7.48}$$

This condition, which is similar to previous cases, differs only in the manner in which the switch conduction period, D, enters the equation.

EXAMPLE 7.8

Using all data from Example 7.7 except the inductance value, find the necessary minimum inductance to ensure continuous inductor current.

Solution

$$L = \left[\frac{(25)(200)}{2} \right] (1 - 0.588)^2$$

$$= 424 \text{ }\mu\text{H.}$$

In Example 7.7, L was greater than this value, so the minimum current, I_{min}, would be expected to be greater than zero in Example 7.7. ∎

Capacitor Voltage Ripple

The peak-to-peak value of capacitor voltage ripple is found from the area under one part of the capacitor current curve. If the inductance is large enough, the capacitor current is negative only during the time the switch is closed. During this interval, the current is constant and the charge removed from the capacitor is that of a rectangular area as given by Equation 7.49:

$$\Delta Q = (I_R)DT = \left(\frac{V_C}{R}\right)DT \tag{7.49}$$

$$\Delta V_C = \frac{\Delta Q}{C} = \left(\frac{V_C}{R}\right)\left(\frac{DT}{C}\right). \tag{7.50}$$

Some circuit conditions, such as those in Example 7.7, have a relatively larger value of $(I_{max} - I_{min})$, and the capacitor current also is negative during part of the time the switch is open. This case probably is best treated by a numerical example rather than by an equation expressing the result.

EXAMPLE 7.9

Continuing with Example 7.7, find the value of the capacitor necessary to limit the ripple to 0.2 V peak to peak.

Solution   In Figure 7.11, the time near 200 μs when the capacitor current becomes zero is found easily by using similar triangles. Let t_x be this time;

$$\frac{5.80}{t_x - 117.6} = \frac{0.08}{200 - t_x}$$

$$t_x = 195.7 \ \mu s.$$

The negative part of the area representing ΔQ under the curve of i_C versus time thus has a rectangular part and a triangular part:

$$\Delta Q = (2)(117.6) + \frac{(0.08)(200 - 195.7)}{2}$$

$$= 235.37 \ \mu C.$$

$$\Delta V_C = 0.2 \text{ V}.$$

$$C = \frac{\Delta Q}{\Delta V_C} = \frac{235.37}{0.2}$$

$$= 1177 \ \mu F.$$

In this example, the contribution of the triangular part was quite small and could be neglected. In other cases, with different numerical values, the triangular part can be relatively more important.   ∎

7.5

MAGNETICALLY COUPLED CHOPPERS

The three preceding circuit arrangements are basic chopper versions that are suitable for cases requiring no electrical isolation and cases in which the output voltage did not differ by a very large factor from the input voltage. But for situations in which one or both of the above conditions do not apply, a magnetically coupled version is a better design choice. Many circuit arrangements are possible, so only a few circuits will be considered here.

A list of possible circuits follows:

(a) flyback

(b) forward converter

(c) push-pull

(d) half-bridge

(e) full-bridge.

The choice of which circuit to be used depends on several factors. Output power and input voltage magnitude are two of the major factors. In general, the more involved the circuit, the more suitable it is for higher power output. In this chapter, we will consider the flyback and forward converters.

Flyback Converter

The flyback converter has been used for many years. One long-standing use has been that of providing the high voltage and low power needed for television screens and other CRT applications. Sometimes it is thought suitable only for low-power situations, but its range of power is limited more by economic considerations than by any fundamental power limit. The basic circuit is shown in Figure 7.12.

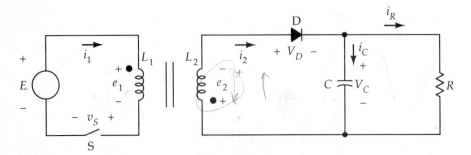

FIGURE 7.12

The initial analysis assumes that the capacitor is large enough that no ripple occurs in its voltage. Switch S is closed periodically for time DT and opened for time $(1 - D)T$ in a manner similar to previous choppers. In the initial analysis, $N_1 = N_2$ for simplicity. This condition is removed later. Furthermore, ideal coupling between the two windings is assumed.

During the time the switch is closed, i_1 increases at a rate given by (E/L_1) A/s. During this time, i_2 is zero and the diode is reverse-biased by the combined effect of V_C and the voltage e_2, which is positive. The value of e_1 is positive and the relative winding directions, indicated by the dots, require a positive e_2 value. At the end of the switch-closure period, the i_1 value drops to zero as a step function. To maintain the same stored magnetic energy, the current i_2 takes on a value to maintain this stored energy. Because $N_1 = N_2$, the value of i_2 becomes the same as the ending value of i_1. Then, because i_2 is greater than zero, the diode conducts in its forward direction, with zero value of v_D, and e_2 thus must equal $(-V_C)$. Figure 7.13 graphs the various quantities.

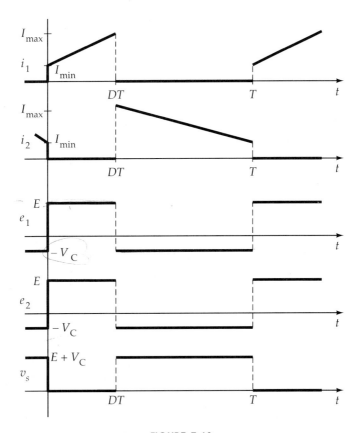

FIGURE 7.13

Circuit Analysis The conditions shown in Figure 7.13 represent a continuous current case in which one of the two coupled inductors always has a current greater than zero. The value of i_1 at the start of the switch closure is the ending value of i_2 from the preceding period. Likewise, the value of i_2 at the start of the open-switch period is the same as i_1 at time DT. Again, these two extreme current values are represented by I_{min} and I_{max}.

During switch closure,

$$\frac{di_1}{dt} = \frac{E}{L_1} \tag{7.51}$$

and

$$I_{max} - I_{min} = \left(\frac{E}{L_1}\right)(DT). \tag{7.52}$$

With the switch open,

$$\frac{di_2}{dt} = -\frac{V_C}{L_2} \tag{7.53}$$

and

$$I_{min} - I_{max} = \left(-\frac{V_C}{L_2}\right)(1 - D)(T). \tag{7.54}$$

In the preceding four equations, $L_1 = L_2$ because $N_1 = N_2$. Using Equations 7.51 through 7.54 gives the voltage relation of Equation 7.55:

$$V_C = \left(\frac{D}{1 - D}\right)E. \tag{7.55}$$

This voltage equation is exactly the same as that for the previous buck-boost chopper in Equation 7.41. The only difference is that electrical isolation has been achieved by the magnetic coupling. Another available option is to change the output voltage by using a different value of N_2; the voltage can be changed appreciably more this way than by using just the duty cycle, D.

One very common situation has a regulated 5-V supply required of a standard 240-V RMS, 60-Hz source. Isolation is required for safety reasons. One possible solution uses a standard 60-Hz transformer to provide isolation and voltage reduction, and then a diode rectifier followed by a buck chopper for regulation. A better solution might be one in which the rectification is done first and then followed by a magnetically coupled chopper with $N_2 < N_1$ to achieve the required voltage reduction. This second solution eliminates the 60-Hz transformer and replaces it with a pair of coupled inductors operating at the chopper frequency. The magnetic portion of the chopper is much smaller than the 60-Hz transformer.

Continuous Current Condition The condition for continuous current is found by solving for the value of I_{min}. The average value of i_1 must be such that the input average power is the same as the output average power:

$$I_{1avg} = \tfrac{1}{2}(I_{min} + I_{max})D \tag{7.56}$$

$$\text{Input power} = EI_{1avg} = \tfrac{1}{2}E(I_{min} + I_{max})D \tag{7.57}$$

$$\text{Output power} = \frac{(V_C)^2}{R}. \tag{7.58}$$

Combining the expression for V_C from Equation 7.55 with Equations 7.57 and 7.58 results in Equation 7.59:

$$I_{min} + I_{max} = \left(\frac{2E}{R}\right)\left[\frac{D}{(1-D)^2}\right]. \tag{7.59}$$

Previously, the equation for $I_{max} - I_{min}$ was obtained as Equation 7.54. Now these two equations can be solved to get I_{min} and I_{max}:

$$I_{min} = \left(\frac{E}{R}\right)\left[\frac{D}{(1-D)^2}\right] - \left(\frac{E}{2L_1}\right)(DT) \tag{7.60}$$

$$I_{max} = \left(\frac{E}{R}\right)\left[\frac{D}{(1-D)^2}\right] + \left(\frac{E}{2L_1}\right)(DT). \tag{7.61}$$

Again, setting $I_{min} = 0$ gives the condition for continuous current operation:

$$L_1 = \left(\frac{RT}{2}\right)(1-D)^2. \tag{7.62}$$

These results are identical to the conductively coupled buck-boost chopper discussed in Section 7.7. It thus becomes evident that there is a very close relation between the flyback chopper and the buck-boost chopper. The flyback version, however, has the added isolation feature as well as flexibility in changing the number of turns on the second winding.

EXAMPLE 7.10

An idealized flyback converter with a 1:1 turn ratio is to supply a variable voltage, ranging from 10 to 40 V, to a 5-Ω load resistor. The source voltage is 30 V. Assume continuous current mode of operation. $T = 100 \ \mu s$. Find:

(a) the range of D required

(b) the inductance of L_1 required for continuous current operation for all values of D

(c) the peak switch current

(d) the peak voltage between switch terminals when switch is open.

Solution

(a) For $V_C = 10$ V, using Equation 7.55:

$$10 = \left(\frac{D}{1-D}\right)(30)$$

$$D = 0.25.$$

For $V_C = 40$ V,

$$40 = \left(\frac{D}{1-D}\right)(30)$$

$$D = 0.571.$$

(b) Using Equation 7.62, the value of L_1 can be found. The smallest value of D requires the largest value of L_1, so the value of $D = 0.25$ is used:

$$L_1 = \left[\frac{(5)(100)}{2}\right](1 - 0.25)^2 \qquad \frac{RT}{2}(1-\delta)^2$$

$$= 140.6 \; \mu\text{H}.$$

This is the smallest value of L_1 that will ensure continuous current over the full range of D.

(c) At $D = 0.25$,

$$I_{max} = \left(\frac{30}{5}\right)\left[\frac{0.25}{(1-0.25)^2}\right] + \left[\frac{30}{(2)(140.6)}\right][(0.25)(100)]$$

$$= 5.33 \; \text{A}.$$

At $D = 0.571$,

$$I_{max} = \left(\frac{30}{5}\right)\left[\frac{0.571}{(1-0.571)^2}\right] + \left[\frac{30}{(2)(140.6)}\right][(0.571)(100)]$$

$$= 24.71 \; \text{A}.$$

The switch device must be capable of a peak current of at least 25 A.

(d) With $D = 0.571$ and the switch open, the voltage e_2 in Figure 7.13 is -40 V. With the 1:1 turn ratio, e_1 is the same value. Thus, during this time, v_S is 70 V and any semiconductor device performing the switch function must be rated for a value in excess of 70 V. ∎

Capacitor Voltage Ripple   If the filter capacitor is no longer given a very large value, but instead has a realistic one, there is a ripple in the output voltage. Figure 7.14 graphs capacitor current versus time for the circuit in Figure 7.12. A closer look at Figure 7.14 shows that it is identical to the capacitor current graph in Figure 7.10. Likewise, the analysis for ripple voltage is identical to that for the buck-boost chopper in the section on capacitor voltage ripple as given in Equation 7.50.

FIGURE 7.14

Turn Ratio Not 1:1 In most cases, the turn ratio, N_1/N_2, is not unity. A new analysis is not required, however, because the actual situation can be referred to an equivalent 1:1 turn ratio. This is very similar to the process used in referring quantities from one side to the other in standard transformer analysis.

Winding 2's actual quantities are referred to an equivalent 1:1 ratio in a manner that depends on the particular quantity. The load power is unchanged in the process. Let the primed quantities be the new or referred quantities. All quantities of Winding 1 are unchanged:

$$P' = P \tag{7.63}$$

$$N'_2 = N_1 \tag{7.64}$$

$$V'_C = \left(\frac{N_1}{N_2}\right) V_C \tag{7.65}$$

$$R' = \left(\frac{N_1}{N_2}\right)^2 R \tag{7.66}$$

$$i'_2 = \left(\frac{N_2}{N_1}\right) i_2 \tag{7.67}$$

$$L'_2 = \left(\frac{N_1}{N_2}\right)^2 L_2 = L_1 \tag{7.68}$$

$$C' = \left(\frac{N_2}{N_1}\right)^2 C. \tag{7.69}$$

EXAMPLE 7.11

A flyback converter is to supply 100 A at 5 V from a 300-V DC source. The chopping frequency is 40 kHz. A step-down turn ratio of $\left(\frac{N_1}{N_2}\right) = 60$ is to be used in the actual converter. Find:

(a) the problem restatement for a 1:1 turn ratio

(b) the value of D required

(c) the value of L_1 for continuous current operation

(d) the actual value of L_2

(e) the switch-blocking voltage

(f) the value of C for $\Delta V_C = 0.05$ V if L_1 is large enough that the capacitor current is negative only during the time the switch is closed.

Solution

(a)
$$V'_C = (60)(5) = 300 \text{ V}$$

$$R' = (60)^2 \left(\frac{5}{100} \right) = 180 \text{ } \Omega$$

$$P' = P = 500 \text{ W.}$$

(b) From Equation 7.55:

$$V'_C = \left(\frac{D}{1-D} \right) E$$

$$300 = \left(\frac{D}{1-D} \right) 300$$

$$D = 0.5.$$

(c) From Equation 7.62:

$$L_1 = \left(\frac{R'T}{2} \right)(1-D)^2$$

$$= \left[\frac{(180)(25)}{2} \right](1-0.5)^2$$

$$= 563 \text{ } \mu\text{H.}$$

(d) From Equation 7.68:

$$L_2 = \left(\frac{N_2}{N_1} \right)^2 L_1$$

$$= \left(\frac{1}{60} \right)^2 (563)$$

$$= 0.156 \text{ } \mu\text{H.}$$

(e) When the switch is open, $e_1 = e'_2 = -300$ V, so the switch must block a minimum of

$$v_S = 300 - (-300) = 600 \text{ V.}$$

(f) From Equations 7.49 and 7.50 modified for a flyback converter:

$$\Delta Q' = \left(\frac{300}{180}\right)(0.5)(25 \times 10^{-6}) = 20.8 \times 10^{-6} \text{ C}$$

$$\Delta V'_C = (60) \Delta V_C = 3 \text{ V}$$

$$C' = \frac{\Delta Q'}{\Delta V'_C} = \frac{20.8 \times 10^{-6}}{3} = 6.94 \times 10^{-6} \text{ F}$$

$$C = (60)^2 C' = (3600)(6.94 \times 10^{-6}) = 0.025 \text{ F}. \qquad \blacksquare$$

Example 7.11 illustrates a converter supplied directly from the power line by a noncontrolled rectifier. The switching semiconductor must be capable of blocking a very appreciable voltage. Typically, this value is twice the peak source voltage, a minimum requirement because the turn ratio is usually set so that D is approximately 0.5.

Forward Converter

A second magnetically coupled converter is the forward converter shown in Figure 7.15. In this circuit, energy is delivered to the load, the external inductor, and the storage capacitor during the period the switch is closed, just the opposite of the flyback converter case. To accomplish this, the winding connections with respect to the dot notation are the reverse of the flyback case. Furthermore, as will be seen in the analysis, the value of D must be less than 50% to allow time for the magnetic core flux to reset during the open-switch time.

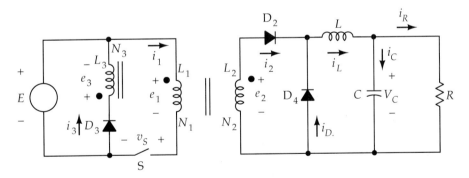

FIGURE 7.15

Circuit Analysis   We assume that $N_1 = N_2 = N_3 = N$, that the three windings are ideally coupled magnetically, and that the self-inductances of the three windings are each large when compared to the external inductor of value

L. This large self-inductance is obtained by using a core without intentional air gaps, much as would be done with a conventional AC transformer.

With the switch closed, the three winding voltages satisfy Equation 7.70:

$$e_1 = e_2 = e_3 = E. \tag{7.70}$$

A voltage equation through the source and D_3 shows that D_3 is reverse-biased and thus i_3 is zero:

$$v_{D_3} = -(E + e_3) = -2E. \tag{7.71}$$

Voltage equations for the secondary circuit are as follow:

$$e_2 = L\left(\frac{di_L}{dt}\right) + V_C \tag{7.72}$$

$$\frac{di_L}{dt} = \frac{E - V_C}{L}. \tag{7.73}$$

The excursion of i_L during switch closure time is given in Equation 7.74:

$$I_{max} - I_{min} = \left(\frac{E - V_C}{L}\right)(DT). \tag{7.74}$$

Thus, i_L and consequently i_2 increase linearly with time as long as S is closed. Note that $i_2 = i_L$ because the FWD, D_4, is reverse-biased. The value of i_1 is closely related to i_2 because the two windings ideally are coupled magnetically. The self-inductances, although large, are not infinite, so there must be a magnetizing current component of i_1. We also assume that the inductances are linear. In Equation 7.75, ϕ is the magnetic flux in the core and t is measured from the time the switch is closed:

$$e_1 = E = N_1\left(\frac{d\phi}{dt}\right) \tag{7.75}$$

$$\phi = \left(\frac{E}{N_1}\right)(t). \tag{7.76}$$

Now let i_m be the magnetizing part of i_1 with the results shown in Equations 7.77 and 7.78:

$$i_m = \left(\frac{N_1}{L_1}\right)\phi = \left(\frac{N_1}{L_1}\right)\left(\frac{E}{N_1}\right)(t) = \left(\frac{E}{L_1}\right)(t) \tag{7.77}$$

$$i_1 = i_2 + i_m. \tag{7.78}$$

When S is opened, the magnetizing component of i_1 can no longer exist in Winding 1 and transfers to Winding 3. The energy stored magnetically in the core is returned to the source. As it does, the value of e_3 becomes equal to $-E$, as do the values of e_1 and e_2.

The magnetic flux and the corresponding value of i_m (and also i_3) begin to decrease linearly to zero. Because $N_1 = N_3$, the time required to reset the core or to reduce the magnetic flux to zero is the same as the time the switch was closed. This condition sets an upper limit of 0.5 on the value of D.

During this same interval, with $e_2 = -E$, the current in the inductor L freewheels through diode D_4. This current decreases, according to Equation 7.79. Again, the current in this inductor may be in either the continuous or the discontinuous mode. The continuous mode is assumed here:

$$\frac{di_L}{dt} = -\frac{V_C}{L}. \tag{7.79}$$

The change occurring during the open-switch time is given by Equation 7.80:

$$I_{min} - I_{max} = \left(-\frac{V_C}{L}\right)(1 - D)(T). \tag{7.80}$$

Combining Equations 7.74 and 7.80 for the changes in i_L during the two switch intervals allows a solution for V_C in Equation 7.81:

$$V_C = DE. \tag{7.81}$$

Thus, we can see that the forward converter basically is a buck converter. The performance is quite similar to the conductively coupled buck converter in Section 7.2. Figure 7.16 graphs several of the currents and voltages applying to this converter.

EXAMPLE 7.12

A forward converter operating at 40 kHz supplies 500 W at 30 V to a load from an 80-V source. For this problem, all windings have the same number of turns and an inductance of 0.01 H. The external inductor is 25 μH. Find:

(a) the value of D

(b) the values of I_{min} and I_{max} in the external inductor

(c) the peak magnetizing current

(d) the energy, stored in the magnetic core, that is returned to the source each cycle

(e) the voltage, v_S, across the switch when it is open.

Solution

(a)
$$D = \frac{V_C}{E} = \frac{30}{80} = 0.375.$$

This is satisfactory because it is less than 0.5.

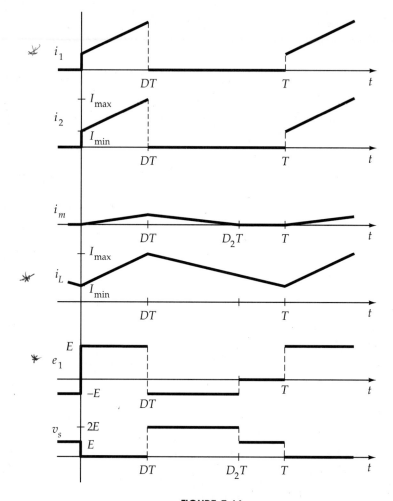

FIGURE 7.16

(b) The average current to the load is $(I_{max} + I_{min})/2$:

$$\frac{I_{max} + I_{min}}{2} = \frac{P}{V_C} = \frac{500}{30} = 16.67 \text{ A}$$

$$I_{max} + I_{min} = 33.33 \text{ A}.$$

From Equation 7.74:

$$I_{max} - I_{min} = \left(\frac{E - V_C}{L}\right)(DT)$$

$$= \left(\frac{80 - 30}{25}\right)[(0.375)(25)]$$

$$= 18.75 \text{ A}.$$

Solving these two conditions on the currents gives values for I_{min} and I_{max}:

$$I_{min} = 7.29 \text{ A}$$

$$I_{max} = 26.04 \text{ A.}$$

(c)
$$\text{Peak } i_m = \left(\frac{E}{L_1}\right)(DT)$$

$$= \left(\frac{80}{0.01}\right)[(0.375)(25 \times 10^{-6})] = 0.075 \text{ A.}$$

The peak value of i_1 thus is 75 mA greater than the peak value of i_2. The peak of i_1 is 26.12 A. The difference resulting from the magnetizing current is small, but this does not mean the time to reset the core or allow i_m to go to zero is unimportant. The upper limit of 0.5 on D must be observed.

(d)
$$\text{Energy} = \tfrac{1}{2}(L_1)(\text{Peak } i_m)^2 = \tfrac{1}{2}(0.01)(0.075)^2$$
$$= 28.1 \times 10^{-6} \text{ J.}$$

(e) When the switch is open, e_3 and e_1 each equal -80 V as long as i_m is greater than zero. A voltage equation around the path of the source, e_1, and v_S gives

$$E = e_1 + v_S$$

$$v_S = 80 - (-80) = 160 \text{ V.} \qquad \blacksquare$$

Continuous Current Condition   The condition for continuous inductor current is identical to that for the conductively coupled buck converter discussed in an earlier section (see page 294), if the turn ratio in this converter is the same $1:1:1$. If another turn ratio is used because of a change in N_2, then the analysis should be done in terms of an equivalent $1:1:1$ problem.

Capacitor Voltage Ripple   This quantity is likewise identical in the form of the equation with that of the buck converter just discussed.

7.6

DISCONTINUOUS CURRENT ANALYSIS

The value of output voltage in the case of discontinuous inductor current requires a different analysis for each of the three basic converter types. The analysis differs in detail for each case, although the basic procedure is the same in each.

Three variables are unknown in the analysis. The minimum inductor current is now zero, so it is not a consideration. The time that the inductor current becomes zero, however, is an unknown. The inductor current time variation is shown in Figure 7.17 with the new variable D_2. The three variables are now V_C, I_{max}, and D_2. The equations required to solve the values of these three variables are obtained by:

(a) finding I_{max} from the circuit equation while the switch is closed,

(b) finding I_{max} from the circuit equation while the switch is open, and

(c) equating average source power over one period to the average load power over the same period.

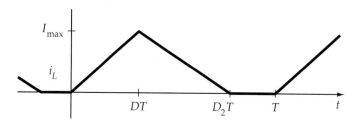

FIGURE 7.17

Buck Chopper

These equations are written and solved for each of the three circuit variations. Using the circuit diagram in Figure 7.1 for a buck chopper and the notation of Figure 7.17, the following equations can be written; the first two are modifications of Equations 7.7 and 7.8:

$$I_{max} = \left(\frac{E - V_C}{L}\right)DT \tag{7.82}$$

$$I_{max} = \left(\frac{V_C}{L}\right)(D_2 - D)T. \tag{7.83}$$

The third equation finds the average input power by using the waveform of i_L during the interval the switch is closed, namely the interval $0 < t < DT$. This average power is equated to the output power in Equation 7.84:

$$\left(\frac{I_{max}}{2}\right)(DE) = \frac{V_C^2}{R}. \tag{7.84}$$

The preceding three equations can be solved for V_C, D_2, and I_{max}. It is convenient to solve for the dimensionless quantities (V_C/E) and $(I_{max}R/E)$ rather than the actual voltage and current. It also is helpful to define a frequently recurring combination of terms as shown in Equation 7.85:

$$K = \frac{RTD^2}{4L}.$$ (7.85)

The results are given by Equations 7.86, 7.87, and 7.88:

$$\frac{V_C}{E} = K\left[-1 + \left(1 + \frac{2}{K}\right)^{0.5}\right]$$ (7.86)

$$D_2 = \left(\frac{D}{2}\right)\left[1 + \left(1 + \frac{2}{K}\right)^{0.5}\right]$$ (7.87)

$$\frac{I_{max}R}{E} = \left(\frac{4K}{D}\right)\left[1 + K - K\left(1 + \frac{2}{K}\right)^{0.5}\right].$$ (7.88)

The output voltage for a buck chopper is shown in the graph in Figure 7.18 for the full range of D. In this particular example, the circuit operates in the discontinuous mode for $0 < D < 0.7$; note that for this range V_C is greater than would be the case for continuous inductor current. For larger values of D, the circuit changes to the continuous mode. The slope of this characteristic is variable, and consequently so is the incremental gain expressed as the rate of change of output voltage with respect to D. In addition, the dynamic behavior changes between the discontinuous and continuous modes. Both conditions require consideration in a closed-loop system design.

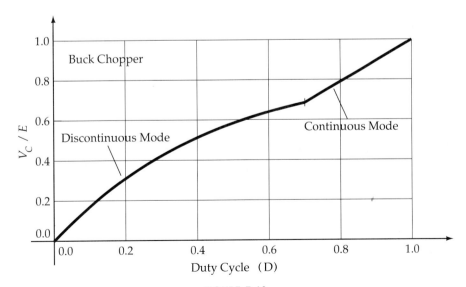

FIGURE 7.18

EXAMPLE 7.13

A buck chopper furnishes 200 W at 30 V to a load from a 40-V source at a chopping frequency of 20 kHz. The inductance is 10 μH. Find:

(a) load resistance, R

(b) D

(c) D_2

(d) peak inductor current

(e) the value of filter capacitor to limit load voltage ripple to 0.1 V peak-to-peak

(f) the value of output voltage at which the inductor current becomes continuous.

Solution

(a)
$$R = \frac{V_C^2}{P} = \frac{(30)^2}{200} = 4.5 \ \Omega.$$

(b) For continuous inductor current and using Equation 7.19, the required value of L is found to be 28.13 μH. Because L is less than this value, the mode is discontinuous. Equations 7.85 and 7.86 are used to find K and D:

$$\frac{V_C}{E} = \frac{30}{40} = 0.75$$

$$0.75 = -K + K\left(1 + \frac{2}{K}\right)^{0.5}$$

$$K = 1.125$$

$$1.125 = \frac{(4.5)(0.000050)D^2}{(4)(0.000010)}$$

$$D = 0.447.$$

(c) Use Equation 7.87 to find D_2:

$$D_2 = \left(\frac{0.447}{2}\right)\left[1 + \left(1 + \frac{2}{1.125}\right)^{0.5}\right] = 0.596.$$

(d) From Equation 7.88:

$$I_{max} = \left(\frac{40}{4.5}\right)\left[\frac{(4)(1.125)}{0.447}\right]\left[1 + 1.125 - 1.125\left(1 + \frac{2}{1.125}\right)^{0.5}\right]$$
$$= 22.36 \text{ A}.$$

(e) $$\text{Average load current} = \frac{V_C}{R} = \frac{30}{4.5} = 6.67 \text{ A}.$$

The graph in Figure 7.19 shows the capacitor current versus time. This is found from Figure 7.17, the value of I_{max}, and the load current value of 6.67 A.

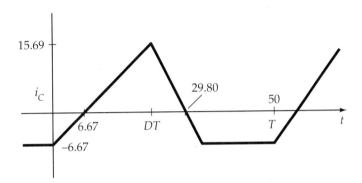

FIGURE 7.19

A calculation of the zero crossing points gives values of 6.67 μs and 29.80 μs. The area under the triangular part of the curve is found easily in order to find ΔQ:

$$\Delta Q = (0.5)(15.69)(29.80 - 6.67) = 181 \ \mu C$$

$$C = \frac{\Delta Q}{\Delta V_C} = \frac{181}{0.1} = 1810 \ \mu F.$$

(f) Using Equations 7.19 and 7.11:

$$10 = \left[\frac{(50)(4.5)}{2} \right] (1 - D)$$

$$D = 0.911$$

$$V_C = DE = (0.911)(40) = 36.4 \text{ V.} \qquad \blacksquare$$

Boost Chopper

In a similar manner, three equations can be written for the boost chopper using the circuit in Figure 7.5 and the graph in Figure 7.17. In the third equation, average power from the source is determined by the period when current exists in the source. This interval is now $D_2 T$ as compared to DT for the buck chopper:

$$I_{max} = \frac{EDT}{L} \tag{7.89}$$

$$I_{max} = \left(\frac{V_C - E}{L}\right)(D_2 - D)T \tag{7.90}$$

$$\left(\frac{I_{max}}{2}\right)D_2 E = \frac{V_C^2}{R}. \tag{7.91}$$

The solutions from these three circuit equations is expressed in Equations 7.92, 7.93, and 7.94:

$$\frac{V_C}{E} = 0.5[1 + (1 + 8K)^{0.5}] \tag{7.92}$$

$$D_2 = \left(\frac{D}{4K}\right)[1 + 4K + (1 + 8K)^{0.5}] \tag{7.93}$$

$$\frac{I_{max}R}{E} = \frac{4K}{D}. \tag{7.94}$$

The output voltage for a boost chopper is graphed in Figure 7.20 as a function of D. In the example shown, two ranges of D have continuous inductor

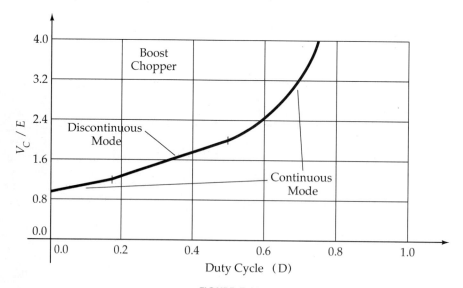

FIGURE 7.20

current, while a middle range has discontinuous current. In the discontinuous range, the output voltage is larger than it would be for the case of continuous inductor current. A sufficiently large value of L can eliminate the region of discontinuous current operation.

EXAMPLE 7.14

Design a boost converter to supply 25 V to a resistive load of 10 Ω. The design objective is to use the smallest possible value of inductance without exceeding a peak source current of 12 A; $E = 15$ V and $f = 50$ kHz.

Solution From Equation 7.92:

$$\frac{V_C}{E} = \frac{25}{15} = 0.5[1 + (1 + 8K)^{0.5}]$$

$$K = 0.556.$$

From Equation 7.94:

$$\frac{12}{15/10} = \frac{4K}{D} = \frac{(4)(0.556)}{D}$$

$$D = 0.278.$$

From Equation 7.85:

$$0.556 = \frac{(10)(20)(0.278)^2}{4L}$$

$$L = 6.94 \ \mu\text{H}. \qquad\qquad\blacksquare$$

Buck-Boost Chopper

For the buck-boost chopper, the circuit equations are written for Figure 7.9 and the graph in Figure 7.17:

$$I_{\text{max}} = \frac{EDT}{L} \tag{7.95}$$

$$I_{\text{max}} = \left(\frac{V_C}{L}\right)(D_2 - D)T \tag{7.96}$$

$$\left(\frac{I_{\text{max}}}{2}\right)DE = \frac{V_C^2}{R}. \tag{7.97}$$

Solving the above equations yields the results of Equations 7.98, 7.99, and 7.100:

$$\frac{V_C}{E} = (2K)^{0.5} \tag{7.98}$$

$$D_2 = D\left[1 + \left(\frac{1}{2K}\right)^{0.5}\right] \tag{7.99}$$

$$\frac{I_{max}R}{E} = \frac{4K}{D}. \tag{7.100}$$

The graph in Figure 7.21 shows operation of a buck-boost chopper with discontinuous inductor current occurring for $D < 0.5$. In the discontinuous mode, the output voltage is a linear function of D and is larger than it would be for the continuous mode. For the range $D > 0.5$, the chopper operates in the continuous current mode.

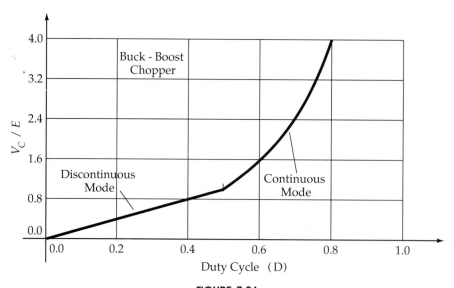

FIGURE 7.21

EXAMPLE 7.15

A buck-boost converter supplies a variable voltage to a 15-Ω resistive load from a 20-V source. With the output voltage at 30 V, the inductor current is just continuous. Find the operating conditions at an output of 15 V and $f = 50$ kHz.

Solution   The value of L corresponding to the continuous conduction state must be found first. From Equation 7.41:

$$30 = 20\left(\frac{D}{1 - D}\right)$$

$$D = 0.6.$$

From Equation 7.48, the value of L can be found:

$$L = \left[\frac{(15)(20)}{2}\right](1 - 0.6)^2 = 24 \ \mu\text{H}.$$

For an output of 15 V, the value of K can be found by using Equation 7.98:

$$\frac{15}{20} = (2K)^{0.5}$$

$$K = 0.281.$$

From Equation 7.85, we can find the value of D:

$$0.281 = \frac{(15)(20)D^2}{(4)(24)}$$

$$D = 0.30.$$

The value of D_2 is found by using Equation 7.99:

$$D_2 = 0.30\left\{1 + \left[\frac{1}{(2)(0.281)}\right]^{0.5}\right\} = 0.7.$$

The value of maximum inductor current is found by using Equation 7.100:

$$I_{\text{max}} = \left(\frac{20}{15}\right)\left[\frac{(4)(0.281)}{0.3}\right] = 5.00 \ \text{A.} \quad \blacksquare$$

7.7
NONIDEAL EFFECTS

Several nonideal or undesirable effects have not yet been considered. Generally, these have second-order effects on converter performance. For design purposes, they certainly must be included, although their effects usually can be considered separately and allowances made as needed in the design process.

Nonideal Magnetic Coupling

In the two magnetically coupled converters that have been considered, we assumed the completely ideal case of magnetic coupling. This will not be true in the real world, and additional steps must be taken to compensate for the non-ideal case. The major problem is that the switch current cannot go to zero instantaneously as we have assumed. For example, if a BJT is used as the switch and if no additional elements are used, the leakage inductance between the switch and the other winding(s) causes the collector current to be maintained at turnoff. The result is a large collector-to-emitter voltage and a probable transistor failure. Several general approaches can be used to prevent the problem. In one, a snubber network can be connected across the switch to limit the switch voltage. Another solution is to provide another winding that is closely coupled to the switched winding and to use this additional winding to return the energy stored in the leakage inductance to the source. Sometimes both approaches are used. The forward converter previously discussed already includes this additional winding as part of its basic circuit.

Snubber Control   The example to be used is that of a flyback converter with a BJT used as the switch. The two windings, together with the nonideal coupling, are modeled by the circuit shown in Figure 7.22. For simplicity, the turn ratio is $1:1$. In this model, the two inductors of value L_x represent leakage inductances, and the inductor of value L_m is the system's magnetizing inductance.

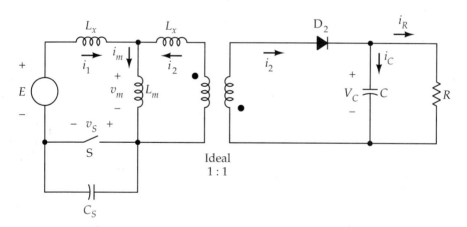

FIGURE 7.22

Upon switch closure, i_1 builds to some value at the time the switch is to be opened, although i_1 may not suddenly become zero because of the leakage inductance, L_x. In the ideal case, L_x is zero and no such restriction exists. So that i_1 is reduced to zero and the current i_m is transferred to i_2, the value of v_S

must be greater than $(E + V_C)$ for a period of time. During the interval that i_1 decreases, the value of i_2 increases in both primary and secondary windings of the ideal transformer portion of the model. The capacitor C_S, the major component of the snubber, acts to limit the switch voltage to a value within the switch capability. For the continuous current case, these various currents are shown in Figure 7.23.

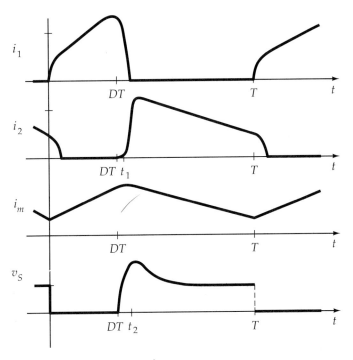

FIGURE 7.23

At the end of the open-switch period, the switch voltage will be equal to $(E + V_C)$, according to Equation 7.109, and a certain energy will be stored in the snubber capacitor. When the switch is closed, the capacitor is discharged and the energy is dissipated. As we showed in Chapter 4 for a BJT, the snubber requires a resistor and a diode to limit the peak discharge current. The energy stored in the snubber capacitor in each cycle then is largely dissipated in the snubber resistor. The snubber circuit also aids in solving the RBSOA problem that was discussed in Chapter 4.

Converter efficiency is the one significant problem that occurs with this solution. A certain amount of energy is lost each cycle, and in conjunction with the chopping frequency, the losses resulting from the nonideal magnetic coupling are fixed. If these losses are excessive, the basic solution is to reduce the effect that is responsible for them. The coupling between the two windings needs to be improved. Well-known techniques of using bifilar windings or sub-dividing each winding into parts and interleaving of the parts are used. These techniques should be used as necessary until an acceptable design is obtained.

Such methods for improving the magnetic coupling are not without their problems, however. The capacitance between the two windings is increased by any process that improves the coupling. In addition, bifilar winding techniques cannot be used in those cases where the two windings have an unequal number of turns.

In the circuit in Figure 7.22, the switch is assumed to be ideal and opens in zero time. Initially i_1 continues to increase because v_S is zero, and because v_m is positive, diode D_2 continues to be reverse-biased. The circuit in Figure 7.24 applies initially.

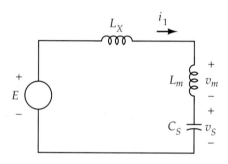

FIGURE 7.24

Initial conditions for this interval are $v_S = 0$ and $i_1 = i_m = I$. The solution for this interval can be written by inspection using the methods in Appendix A:

$$v_S = E(1 - \cos \omega t) + I\left(\frac{L_x + L_m}{C_S}\right)^{0.5} \sin \omega t \qquad (7.101)$$

$$i_1 = I \cos \omega t + E\left(\frac{C_S}{L_x + L_m}\right)^{0.5} \sin \omega t, \qquad (7.102)$$

where

$$\omega = \frac{1}{[(L_x + L_m)C_S]^{0.5}}. \qquad (7.103)$$

These relations are valid until D_2 becomes forward-biased at t_1, which occurs when v_m becomes equal to $-V_C$. The value of t_1 can be calculated as shown in the following equations.

From Figure 7.24, v_m is given by Equation 7.104:

$$v_m = \left[\frac{L_m}{L_m + L_x}\right](E - v_S).$$ (7.104)

Replacing v_m with $-V_C$ provides an equation for switch voltage at which i_2 begins. This result is given in Equation 7.105:

$$v_S = E + \left(\frac{L_m + L_x}{L_m}\right)V_C.$$ (7.105)

Using this value for v_S, Equation 7.101 now can be solved for the value of t_1 when D_2 becomes forward-biased.

The circuit for $t > t_1$ is shown in Figure 7.25(a). This circuit may be reduced to that in Figure 7.25(b) by obtaining a Thévenin equivalent for a portion of the circuit. In Figure 7.25(b), the new element values are given by Equations 7.106 and 7.107:

$$L'_x = \frac{L_m L_x}{L_m + L_x}$$ (7.106)

$$V'_C = \frac{L_m V_C}{L_m + L_x}.$$ (7.107)

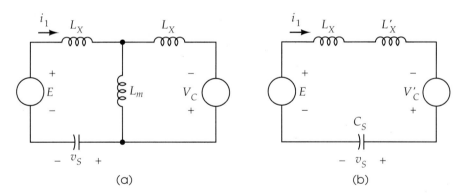

(a)   (b)

FIGURE 7.25

The maximum capacitor voltage in Figure 7.25(b) occurs when i_1 becomes zero. Equations for i_1 and v_S can be written for this new interval beginning at $t = t_1$. The value of ω has changed from the value applying for $t < t_1$:

$$i_1 = [i_1(t_1)]\cos\omega(t - t_1) + [E + V'_C - v_S(t_1)]\left(\frac{C_S}{L}\right)^{0.5}\sin\omega(t - t_1)$$

(7.108)

$$v_S = (E + V'_C)[1 - \cos \omega(t - t_1)] + [v_S(t_1)] \cos \omega(t - t_1)$$
$$+ [i_1(t_1)]\left(\frac{L}{C_S}\right)^{0.5} \sin \omega(t - t_1), \tag{7.109}$$

where

$$L = L_x + L'_x \tag{7.110}$$

and

$$\omega = \frac{1}{(LC_S)^{0.5}}. \tag{7.111}$$

Equation 7.108 can be solved to find t_2, when maximum capacitor voltage occurs, by setting i_1 to zero. The result is given in Equation 7.112:

$$\tan \omega(t_2 - t_1) = \frac{-i_1(t_1)}{[E + V'_C - v_S(t_1)]\left(\dfrac{C_S}{L}\right)^{0.5}}. \tag{7.112}$$

Equation 7.109 can be rewritten as Equation 7.113:

$$v_S = (E + V'_C) + (V_1^2 + V_2^2)^{0.5} \cos [\omega(t - t_1) + \theta]. \tag{7.113}$$

Equation 7.113's V_1 and V_2 are given by the following two equations:

$$V_1 = v_S(t_1) - E - V'_C \tag{7.114}$$

$$V_2 = \left(\frac{L}{C_S}\right)^{0.5} i_1(t_1). \tag{7.115}$$

The maximum value of v_S occurs when the cosine function in Equation 7.113 is unity. Maximum switch voltage is given by Equation 7.116:

$$v_{S_{max}} = (E + V'_C) + (V_1^2 + V_2^2)^{0.5}. \tag{7.116}$$

The energy stored in the snubber capacitor is returned to the source, delivered to the load, or dissipated in the snubber resistor. During the remaining time from t_2 that the switch is open, the snubber capacitor discharges from its peak voltage toward the value $(E + V'_C)$. This discharge occurs through the snubber resistor, C_S, and the transformer leakage inductance. For usual values of snubber resistance, this process is highly damped and essentially is an RC-type discharge. The power dissipated in the snubber resistor is small but nonzero. At the time the switch turns on, the snubber capacitor is discharged rapidly from the value of $(E + V'_C)$ to zero. The remaining snubber capacitor energy then is dissipated in the snubber resistor. As a close approximation, the energy in each discharge is given by Equation 7.117:

$$\text{Energy} = 0.5C_S(E + V'_C)^2. \tag{7.117}$$

EXAMPLE 7.16

A flyback converter supplies 80 V from a 100-V source. Initial design assumes an ideal transformer. The windings have just sufficient inductance for the continuous current mode; $T = 80$ μs, $R = 75$ Ω, and $N_1/N_2 = 1$. Find:

(a) the value of D

(b) the winding self-inductance, L_1

(c) I_{max}

(d) the value of t_1 with $C_S = 0.05$ μF and each value of $L_x = 10$ μH

(e) $i_1(t_1)$

(f) the value of t_2

(g) the maximum switch voltage

(h) the approximate snubber resistor power rating.

Solution

(a) From Equation 7.55:

$$80 = \left(\frac{D}{1-D}\right)100$$

$$D = 0.444.$$

(b) From Equation 7.62, for continuous current:

$$L_1 = \left[\frac{(75)(80)}{2}\right](1 - 0.444)^2 = 926 \ \mu H.$$

(c) From Equation 7.61:

$$I_{max} = \left(\frac{100}{75}\right)\left[\frac{0.444}{(1-0.444)^2}\right] + \left[\frac{100}{(2)(926 \times 10^{-6})}\right][(0.444)(80 \times 10^{-6})]$$

$$= 1.92 + 1.92 = 3.84 \text{ A}.$$

(d) Using Equation 7.105:

$$v_S = 100 + \left(\frac{926}{916}\right)(80) = 180.9 \text{ V}.$$

Using Equation 7.103:

$$\omega = \frac{1}{[(926 \times 10^{-6})(0.05 \times 10^{-6})]^{0.5}} = 147,000 \text{ rad/s}.$$

Using Equation 7.101:

$$180.9 = 100(1 - \cos \omega t_1) + (3.84)\left(\frac{926}{0.05}\right)^{0.5} \sin \omega t_1$$

$$t_1 = 3.65 \times 10^{-6} \text{ s}.$$

(e) From Equation 7.102:

$$i_1(t_1) = 3.84 \cos \omega t_1 + (100)\left(\frac{0.05}{926}\right)^{0.5} \sin \omega t_1$$

$$= 3.68 \text{ A.}$$

(f)
$$L'_x = \frac{(916)(10)}{926} = 9.89 \ \mu H$$

$$L = L_x + L'_x = 19.89 \ \mu H.$$

From Equation 7.111:

$$\omega = \frac{1}{[(19.89 \times 10^{-6})(0.05 \times 10^{-6})]^{0.5}} = 1.003 \times 10^6 \text{ rad/s}$$

$$V'_C = \frac{(916)(80)}{926} = 79.14 \text{ V.}$$

From Equation 7.112:

$$\tan \omega(t_2 - t_1) = \frac{-3.68}{(100 + 79.14 + 180.9)\left(\dfrac{0.05}{19.89}\right)^{0.5}}$$

$$\tan \omega(t_2 - t_1) = -0.2039$$

$$\omega(t_2 - t_1) = 2.941$$

$$t_2 - t_1 = 2.93 \ \mu s$$

$$t_2 = 6.58 \ \mu s.$$

(g) From Equations 7.114 and 7.115:

$$V_1 = 180.9 - 100 - 79.14 = 1.76 \text{ V}$$

$$V_2 = \left(\frac{19.89}{0.05}\right)^{0.5}(3.68) = 73.40 \text{ V.}$$

From Equation 7.116:

$$v_{S_{max}} = (100 + 79.14) + (1.76^2 + 73.40^2)^{0.5} = 252.6 \text{ V.}$$

(h) Assuming a snubber time constant that is short enough, most of the power comes from discharging the snubber capacitor from 179.14 V, $(E + V'_C)$, to 0 V. The energy from each snubber discharge can be found using Equation 7.117.

$$\text{Energy} = (0.5)(0.05 \times 10^{-6})(179.14)^2 = 0.000802 \text{ J.}$$

At a switching frequency of 12.5 kHz,

$$\text{Power} = (0.000802)(12,500) = 10.0 \text{ W.} \qquad \blacksquare$$

Voltage Clamp   The snubber circuit in the preceding example functions to limit the switch voltage at turnoff, but there is no direct control on the limiting value. The larger the snubber capacitor, the smaller the peak switch voltage. Furthermore, an increase in capacitance means increased losses in the snubber resistor, which affects the overall efficiency.

A voltage clamp added to the snubber serves two purposes. First, it limits the switch voltage to the clamping voltage, which can be set at any desired level. The leakage inductance may not be known precisely, in which case the switch voltage becomes variable, depending on the leakage inductance. Second, with the voltage clamp, the snubber capacitor probably can be reduced in value along with the losses in the snubber resistor.

This voltage clamp can be provided by a zener diode connected in parallel with the switch and the snubber. The clamping level should be set high enough to effect a rapid transfer of current from Winding 1 to Winding 2. It also must be greater than the switch voltage during the remainder of the period that the switch is open. In Figure 7.26, the intermediate voltage level at the end of the cycle must not cause the lamp to function when the switch is supposed to be open.

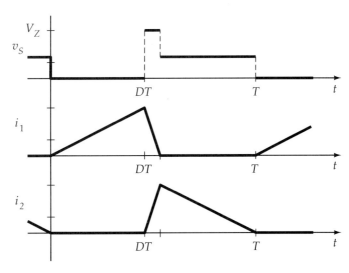

FIGURE 7.26

To illustrate the effect of such a voltage clamp, the following analysis uses *only* the voltage clamp; that is, no snubber capacitor is used. The switch is assumed to open in zero time at $t = 0$. The source current, i_1, must be continuous; therefore, the voltage clamp is effective immediately and produces the voltage V_Z across the switch. The circuit in Figure 7.22 is redrawn as Figure 7.27 to reflect these changes. To be effective, V_Z must be large enough that D_2 begins to conduct immediately.

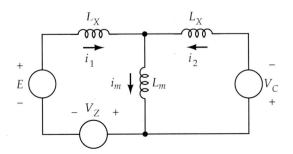

FIGURE 7.27

The circuit in Figure 7.27 can be simplified with a Thévenin equivalent as shown in Figure 7.28. In this figure, L'_x and V'_C have the same definitions as in the previous section. The voltage equation for this circuit is given in Equation 7.118:

$$(L_x + L'_x)\left(\frac{di_1}{dt}\right) = E + V'_C - V_Z.$$ (7.118)

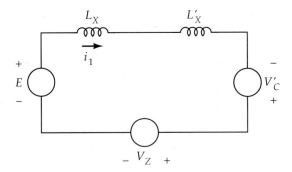

FIGURE 7.28

The time, t_1, required for i_1 to become zero is found by using Equation 7.119 and assuming an initial value of I for i_1:

$$t_1 = \frac{-I}{\dfrac{di_1}{dt}}.$$ (7.119)

A further rearrangement of Figure 7.27 using a Thévenin equivalent yields Figure 7.29, with the value of V_X given by Equation 7.120:

$$V_X = (V_Z - E)\left(\frac{L_m}{L_m + L_x}\right). \tag{7.120}$$

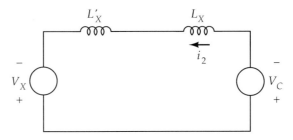

FIGURE 7.29

To ensure that the current i_2 increases upon opening the switch, the value of V_X must be greater than V_C. Using this condition sets a lower limit on the value of V_Z. These requirements result in Equation 7.121:

$$V_Z > E + \left(\frac{L_m + L_x}{L_m}\right)V_C. \tag{7.121}$$

For a closely coupled transformer, $(L_m + L_x)/L_m$ is not much greater than 1. The value of V_Z is not required then to be much greater than $(E + V_C)$.

The peak value of i_2 occurs at the same time that i_1 becomes zero. The circuit in Figure 7.29 is used to get equations for i_2's rate of change and peak value:

$$\frac{di_2}{dt} = \frac{V_X - V_C}{L_x + L_x'} \tag{7.122}$$

$$i_2 \text{ peak} = \left(\frac{di_2}{dt}\right)(t_1). \tag{7.123}$$

The energy delivered to the voltage clamp is calculated easily. The value of i_1 decays linearly to zero in the time t_1. The energy and power are given by Equations 7.124 and 7.125:

$$\text{Energy} = 0.5It_1V_Z \tag{7.124}$$

$$\text{Power} = 0.5It_1V_Zf, \tag{7.125}$$

where f is the switching frequency.

EXAMPLE 7.17

A flyback converter with $N_1/N_2 = 1$ has the following data:

$$E = 100 \text{ V} \qquad L_x = 10 \text{ }\mu\text{H} \qquad T = 80 \text{ }\mu\text{s}$$

$$V_Z = 250 \text{ V} \qquad L_m = 990 \text{ }\mu\text{H} \qquad D = 0.45.$$

$$V_C = 81 \text{ V}$$

The current mode is just continuous. The value of V_C is slightly less than predicted by the ideal case of Equation 7.55. Find:

(a) the value of i_1 at the end of the time that the switch is closed

(b) the time required for i_1 to be reduced to zero after the switch is opened

(c) the peak value of i_2

(d) the average power to the switch voltage clamp.

Solution

(a) During the time the switch is closed,

$$\frac{di_1}{dt} = \frac{100}{1000 \times 10^{-6}} = 100,000 \text{ A/s}.$$

The switch is closed for 36 μs;

$$\text{Peak } i_1 = (10^5)(36 \times 10^{-6}) = 3.6 \text{ A}.$$

(b)
$$L'_x = \frac{(10)(990)}{1000} = 9.9 \text{ }\mu\text{H}$$

$$V'_C = \left(\frac{990}{1000}\right)(81) = 80.19 \text{ V}.$$

Using Equation 7.118,

$$\frac{di_1}{dt} = \frac{100 + 80.19 - 250}{10 + 9.9}$$

$$= -3.508 \text{ A/}\mu\text{s}.$$

Using Equation 7.119,

$$t_1 = \frac{-3.6}{-3.508} = 1.0262 \text{ }\mu\text{s}.$$

(c) Using Equation 7.120, the value of V_X can be found:

$$V_X = (250 - 100)\left(\frac{990}{1000}\right) = 148.5 \text{ V}.$$

Then, using Equation 7.122 the value of di_2/dt is found:

$$\frac{di_2}{dt} = \frac{148.5 - 81}{10 + 9.9} = 3.392 \ A/\mu s.$$

The peak value of i_2 is found using Equation 7.123:

$$i_2 \ peak = (3.392)(1.0262) = 3.481 \ A.$$

(d) Using Equation 7.125, the average power is obtained:

$$Power = (0.5)(3.6)(1.0262 \times 10^{-6})(250)(12,500)$$
$$= 5.77 \ W. \qquad\blacksquare$$

Energy Recovery As the preceding example shows, the power to a clamping voltage that assists the turnoff process can be quite large and can have a significant effect on the conversion efficiency. Unless some other technique is used, a reduction in the lost power can be obtained only by better coupling between the two windings. This better coupling, however, may not be feasible for various reasons. One might be the need for a high level of insulation between the windings, which results in a certain amount of separation.

Another reason might be that the two windings have different numbers of turns, thus preventing use of a bifilar winding technique. In this situation, an energy-recovery process that uses a third winding may be appropriate. Winding 3 can have the same number of turns as Winding 1, thus allowing these two windings to be wound as bifilar windings. If done, Windings 1 and 3 can be coupled very closely with small leakage reactance. The need for a switch snubber or voltage clamp is reduced greatly. Most of the energy stored in the leakage reactance between Windings 1 and 2 is returned to the voltage source. This energy does not have to be dissipated, and it does not reduce the converter's efficiency. Figure 7.30 shows such an arrangement.

For this analysis, we will assume ideal coupling between Windings 1 and 3 but not with 2, and that all windings have the same number of turns; the

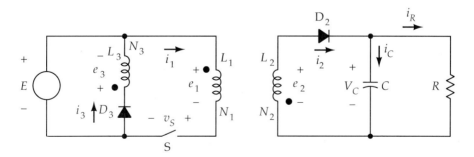

FIGURE 7.30

equivalent circuit of Figure 7.31 results. With the switch closed, the current in Winding 1 has reached a value, I_1, which is the same as the current i_x in the model. During this time, the combined effect of E and e_3 reverse biases D_3 by the value $2E$. The switch is opened and i_1 may go to zero immediately because its magnetic effect may be replaced by i_3. This current in Winding 3 causes an energy return to the source.

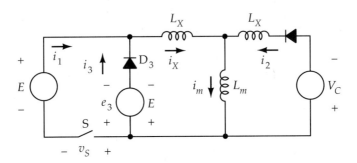

FIGURE 7.31

The solution is found easily by using Thévenin-equivalent circuits for the circuit in Figure 7.31. The circuit in Figure 7.32(a) is used to obtain i_3, and that in Figure 7.32(b) is used to obtain i_2. Equations for the rates of change of i_2 and i_3 may be written for these circuits. The results are given in Equations 7.126 and 7.127:

$$\frac{di_3}{dt} = \frac{V'_C - E}{L_x + L'_x} \qquad (7.126)$$

$$\frac{di_2}{dt} = \frac{E' - V_C}{L_x + L'_x} \qquad (7.127)$$

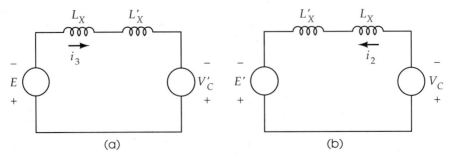

(a)   (b)

FIGURE 7.32

The graph in Figure 7.33 shows the manner in which i_2 and i_3 change in the interval just after the switch opens. The initial value of i_1 and the rate at which i_3 changes determine how long i_2 requires to reach its peak value. This interval is shown in exaggerated scale in the graph in Figure 7.33.

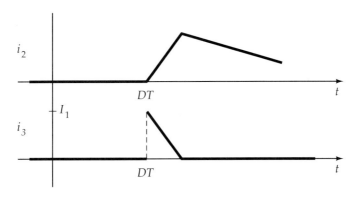

FIGURE 7.33

If the equation for (di_2/dt) is examined, we obtain an upper limit on V_C. This derivative must be positive for the given conditions to represent an equilibrium condition:

$$V_C < \left(\frac{L_m}{L_m + L_x}\right)E. \tag{7.128}$$

For a flyback converter with $N_1 = N_3$, this energy recovery method limits D to less than 0.5 and to a value for which the above inequality holds. For a value of V_C that requires $D > 0.5$, an alternate procedure is to design the converter with $N_2/N_1 > 1$ such that $D < 0.5$.

EXAMPLE 7.18

A flyback converter with $N_1 = N_2 = N_3$ has the following data:

$$E = 100 \text{ V} \qquad L_x = 0.00002 \text{ H} \qquad T = 200 \text{ } \mu s$$

$$V_C = 64.8 \text{ V} \qquad L_m = 0.00098 \text{ H} \qquad D = 0.4$$

$$R = 29.67 \text{ } \Omega.$$

The current mode is just continuous. Find:

(a) the peak value of i_1

(b) the time for i_3 to decay to zero

(c) the peak value of i_2

(d) the energy returned to source for each switch operation.

Solution

(a) The switch is closed for $(0.4)(200) = 80 \ \mu s$;

$$I_1 = \left(\frac{100}{0.001}\right)(80 \times 10^{-6}) = 8.0 \ \text{A}.$$

(b) After the switch is opened, (di_3/dt) is found by using Equation 7.126;

$$V'_C = \left(\frac{980}{1000}\right)(64.8) = 63.504 \ \text{V}$$

$$\frac{di_3}{dt} = \frac{63.504 - 100}{20 + 19.6} = -0.9216 \ \text{A}/\mu s$$

$$\Delta t = \frac{8.0}{0.9216} = 8.68 \ \mu s.$$

(c) Using Equation 7.127, the value of di_2/dt is found;

$$E' = \left(\frac{980}{1000}\right)(100) = 98 \ \text{V}$$

$$\frac{di_2}{dt} = \frac{98 - 64.8}{20 + 19.6} = 0.838 \ \text{A}/\mu s$$

$$i_2 \ \text{peak} = \left(\frac{di_2}{dt}\right)(\Delta t) = (0.838)(8.68) = 7.28 \ \text{A}.$$

(d) Energy to source $= \frac{1}{2}(i_3 \ \text{peak})(E)(\Delta t)$
$= \frac{1}{2}(8.0)(100)(8.68 \times 10^{-6})$
$= 0.00347 \ \text{J}.$ ∎

Inductor Resistance

In earlier sections, the inductor resistance was neglected. This was reasonable because an efficient converter is possible only if such resistance is relatively small. Its actual effect now will be considered.

Buck Chopper   The circuit diagram in Figure 7.1 is altered to include R_L in series with the inductor as shown in Figure 7.34. This resistance is small enough that the time constant, L/R_L, is large when compared to the switching period.

The equations that describe circuit operation are altered to account for this change, with the voltage across R_L variable in response to the time variation in i_L. The value of this voltage is small compared to E, and as an approximation

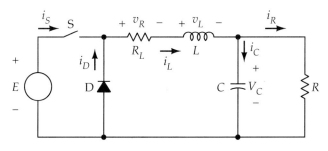

FIGURE 7.34

v_R is calculated using the average value of inductor current. Inasmuch as the inductor time constant is large compared to the time interval involved, the effect of this approximation on the inductor current as a function of time is negligible. The average value of the inductor current is represented by I_L. Equations 7.7 and 7.8 are altered to account for the inductor resistance and are as shown in Equations 7.129 and 7.130:

$$I_{max} - I_{min} = \left(\frac{E - I_L R_L - V_C}{L}\right) DT \tag{7.129}$$

$$I_{min} - I_{max} = \left(\frac{-I_L R_L - V_C}{L}\right)(1 - D)T. \tag{7.130}$$

As Equations 7.12, 7.14, and 7.15 show, the value of I_L is the same as the current in the load resistance. Making use of all these relations, the solution for V_C is given in Equation 7.131:

$$V_C = E\left[\frac{D}{(1 + R_L/R)}\right]. \tag{7.131}$$

For the usual case where R_L/R is small, perhaps 0.01, the value of V_C is reduced slightly as compared to the ideal situation. In a closed-loop system, the value of D would be changed as necessary to achieve the desired value of V_C.

EXAMPLE 7.19

A buck chopper supplies power to a load at 20 V from a source of 50 V; $R = 10\ \Omega$, $R_L = 0.15\ \Omega$, $L = 250\ \mu H$, and $f = 25$ kHz. Find:

(a) the value of D required for the ideal case

(b) the value of D including the effect of R_L.

Solution

(a)
$$D = \frac{20}{50} = 0.4.$$

(b) From Equation 7.131:

$$20 = 50 \frac{D}{1 + \left(\dfrac{0.15}{10}\right)}$$

$$D = 0.406.$$

A small adjustment of D from the ideal value compensates for the inductor resistance. ∎

Boost Chopper   For the boost chopper case, the circuit in Figure 7.5 is altered to include a resistor, R_L, in series with L. The new circuit is shown in Figure 7.35. As we did for the buck chopper, the voltage across R_L is evaluated as $I_L R_L$. Equations 7.25 and 7.26 are modified as shown in Equations 7.132 and 7.133:

$$I_{max} - I_{min} = \left(\frac{E - I_L R_L}{L}\right) DT \tag{7.132}$$

$$I_{min} - I_{max} = \left(\frac{E - I_L R_L - V_C}{L}\right)[(1 - D)T]. \tag{7.133}$$

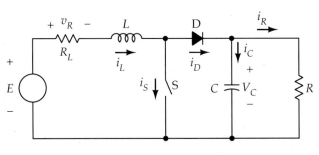

FIGURE 7.35

We need another relation for I_L to solve these two equations. Equation 7.134, in fact, relates this current, I_L, to the average value of load current. This is done by noting that the average value of i_D is the same as the average value of the load current:

$$(I_L)(1 - D) = I_R = \frac{V_C}{R}. \tag{7.134}$$

Combining these three equations gives the result of Equation 7.135 for V_C:

$$V_C = \frac{E}{1 - D + \dfrac{R_L}{R(1 - D)}}. \tag{7.135}$$

In this relation, the effect of R_L can be substantial as D increases. In fact, the value of V_C has a maximum that does not exist in the ideal case. The graph in Figure 7.36 shows the effect for the case of $R_L/R = 0.015$; the ordinate is (V_C/E), or as sometimes denoted, the value M.

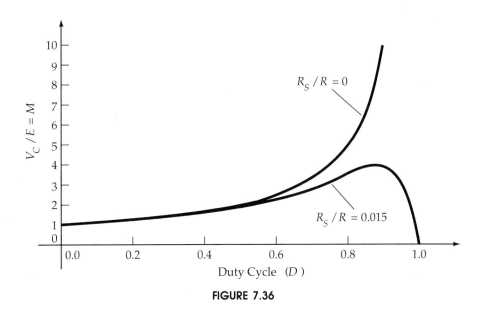

FIGURE 7.36

The maximum value of M at some value of D presents a problem in closed-loop operation. Normally, an increase in D increases the output voltage. If a system operating at a large value of D experiences a decrease in its E value, the normal action is to increase D to change the output voltage as required. But increasing D decreases the output voltage. This in turn further increases D until it approaches unity. The system has become unstable as a result of operating beyond the value of D for which maximum V_C occurs. The remedy is to restrict the D value to something less than that for which maximum V_C occurs.

E X A M P L E   7 . 2 0

A boost chopper is required to deliver 50 W at 40 V from a 15-V source. $R_L = 0.3\ \Omega$, and the inductor current is continuous. Find:

(a) the value of D if R_L is neglected

(b) the new value of D if R_L is included.

Solution

(a)
$$40 = \frac{15}{1 - D}$$
$$D = 0.625.$$

(b)
$$R = \frac{(40)^2}{50} = 32 \ \Omega$$

$$\frac{R_L}{R} = 0.00938.$$

From Equation 7.135:

$$40 = \frac{15}{\left[1 - D + \left(\dfrac{0.00938}{1 - D} \right) \right]}$$

$$D = 0.652 \quad or \quad D = 0.973.$$

We reject the larger value because it is beyond the peak conversion voltage. This solution corresponds to large currents and correspondingly large losses. ∎

Nonideal Switches

The effect of nonideal switches can be included by modeling switches with voltage sources, resistance elements, or both in series with ideal switches. This modeling, of course, does not include the dynamic effects at switching times.

Voltage Source Addition   A first-order model for many switching elements is a voltage source in series with an ideal element. A circuit for a buck chopper that includes such modeling for the switch and the freewheeling diode is shown in Figure 7.37, which is a modification of Figure 7.1.

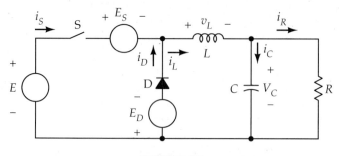

FIGURE 7.37

The analysis is similar to that in Section 7.2, with Equations 7.7 and 7.8 modified here to become Equations 7.136 and 7.137:

$$I_{max} - I_{min} = \left(\frac{E - E_S - V_C}{L}\right)DT \tag{7.136}$$

$$I_{min} - I_{max} = \left(\frac{-E_D - V_C}{L}\right)(1 - D)T. \tag{7.137}$$

Solving these two equations gives V_C as a function of D:

$$V_C = D(E - E_S + E_D) - E_D. \tag{7.138}$$

The effect is small and can be corrected by a change in the value of D. A closed-loop system can adjust the D value automatically as required. A similar analysis for the boost chopper gives the result expressed by Equation 7.139.

$$V_C = \left(\frac{E - DE_S}{1 - D}\right) - E_D. \tag{7.139}$$

Again, a closed-loop system can compensate for the fact that V_C is affected by nonideal switches.

EXAMPLE 7.21

A boost chopper operates to supply 40 V from a 20-V source. The switches are nonideal and may be represented by voltage sources in series with ideal elements. $E_S = 1.2$ V, $E_D = 0.9$ V, and the inductor is large. Find:

(a) the ideal value of D

(b) the value of D necessary to compensate for the nonideal switches.

Solution

(a)
$$40 = \frac{20}{1 - D}$$
$$D = 0.5.$$

(b)
$$40 = \left(\frac{20 - 1.2D}{1 - D}\right) - 0.9$$
$$D = 0.526.$$

A small increase in D from the ideal case compensates for the nonideal switches.

∎

Addition of Switch Resistance   Some switches such as a MOSFET are better represented by a resistance than by a voltage source. Figure 7.38 shows a buck chopper with such a representation.

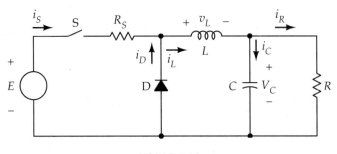

FIGURE 7.38

The switch current varies with time during the interval that the switch is closed. The time constant represented by L/R_S must be large if the chopper is to be efficient. Therefore, a satisfactory representation of switch current during this interval is a constant that is the average current in the inductor, and which is represented as I_L. The equations for the circuit in Figure 7.38 are as follow:

$$I_{max} - I_{min} = \left(\frac{E - I_L R_S - V_C}{L}\right) DT \qquad \textbf{(7.140)}$$

$$I_{min} - I_{max} = \left(-\frac{V_C}{L}\right)(1 - D)T. \qquad \textbf{(7.141)}$$

The value of I_L is the same as the load current and is given by Equation 7.142:

$$I_L = \frac{V_C}{R}. \qquad \textbf{(7.142)}$$

Solving these three equations results in Equation 7.143:

$$V_C = \frac{DE}{[1 + (R_S/R)D]}. \qquad \textbf{(7.143)}$$

The effect of switch resistance is small and can be compensated by a small change in the value of D as compared to the ideal case.

EXAMPLE 7.22

A buck chopper supplies 25 V to a load resistance of 5 Ω from a source of 50 V. The switching element is a MOSFET that can be modeled in the conducting state by $R_{DS(ON)} = 0.15\ \Omega$. The inductor current is continuous. Find the value of D required.

Solution   From Equation 7.143, the value of D can be determined:

$$25 = \frac{(D)(50)}{\left[1 + \left(\dfrac{0.15}{5}\right)(D)\right]}$$

$$D = 0.508.$$ ∎

For the boost chopper case, the circuit in Figure 7.5 is modified to include a switch resistance. This is shown in Figure 7.39. Relations for the analysis of this circuit are given in Equations 7.144 and 7.145 (Equation 7.134 also is needed to express the relation for I_L):

$$I_{max} - I_{min} = \left(\frac{E - I_L R_S}{L}\right)DT \tag{7.144}$$

$$I_{min} - I_{max} = \left(\frac{E - V_C}{L}\right)(1 - D)T. \tag{7.145}$$

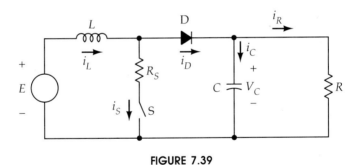

FIGURE 7.39

Solving these relations results in Equation 7.146:

$$V_C = \frac{E}{\left\{1 - D + \left[\dfrac{D}{(1 - D)}\right]\left(\dfrac{R_S}{R}\right)\right\}}. \tag{7.146}$$

This relation for V_C has a maximum value as a function of D. The effect is somewhat the same as for the inductor resistance modeled by Equation 7.135. All of the problems described in the previous section on boost choppers can occur in this situation.

EXAMPLE 7.23

The boost chopper in Figure 7.39 is modeled by the following elements: $E = 25$ V, $R = 10\ \Omega$, and $R_S = 0.18\ \Omega$. The inductor current is continuous. Find:

(a) the value of V_C for $D = 0.6$

(b) the largest possible value of V_C.

Solution

(a) From Equation 7.146:

$$V_C = \frac{25}{\left[1 - 0.6 + \left(\dfrac{0.6}{0.4}\right)\left(\dfrac{0.18}{10}\right)\right]}$$

$$= 58.5 \text{ V}.$$

(b) The maximum value of V_C can be obtained by finding the minimum of the denominator of Equation 7.146. This is done by differentiating with respect to D:

$$f = 1 - D + \left(\frac{D}{1-D}\right)\left(\frac{R_S}{R}\right)$$

$$\frac{df}{dD} = -1 + \left(\frac{R_S}{R}\right)\left[\frac{1}{1-D} + \frac{D}{(1-D)^2}\right].$$

Setting this derivative to zero and using $R_S/R = 0.018$ yields $D = 0.866$. For this D value, the value of V_C is 99.9 V. In the ideal case, this D value corresponds to $V_C = 186.6$ V. ∎

EXAMPLE 7.24

A buck chopper is modeled by including switch resistance, inductor resistance, and diode voltage. The inductance is large; $E = 50$ V, $E_D = 0.9$ V, $V_C = 20$ V, $R = 4\ \Omega$, $R_S = 0.08\ \Omega$, and $R_L = 0.06\ \Omega$. Find:

(a) a relation between V_C, E, and D that includes the nonideal elements

(b) the required value of D

(c) the ratio of output power to input power (this neglects switching loss).

Solution

(a) Combining the several effects into one relation that expresses the change in inductor currents gives the following relations:

$$D[E - I_L(R_L + R_S) - V_C] = -(1 - D)(-E_D - I_L R_L - V_C)$$

$$V_C = \frac{D(E + E_D) - E_D}{1 + \left(\dfrac{R_L}{R}\right) + D\left(\dfrac{R_S}{R}\right)}.$$

The form of the preceding expression could have been anticipated from previous results.

(b)
$$20 = \frac{D(50 + 0.9) - 0.9}{1 + 0.015 + 0.02D}$$

$$D = 0.420.$$

(c)
$$I_L = \frac{V_C}{R} = \frac{20}{4} = 5 \text{ A}.$$

This current does not vary appreciably during the switching cycle. The average value of the source current during the time the switch is closed is the same as I_L:

$$I_S = DI_L = (0.420)(5) = 2.10 \text{ A}$$

$$\text{Input power} = EI_S = (50)(2.10) = 105 \text{ W}$$

$$\text{Output power} = V_C I_L = (20)(5) = 100 \text{ W}$$

$$\text{Efficiency} = \frac{100}{105} = 95.2\%.$$

This calculation neglects certain losses. ∎

Input Harmonics

The input current to each of the various choppers investigated is a time-varying current. Thus far the source voltage has been modeled with an ideal voltage source that is capable of providing such a current without adverse effects on other connected equipment. Actual real-world sources may not have such capabilities. Calculating the harmonic content of the input current is important to determine whether adverse effects exist. Another area of interest is the suppression of such harmonic currents in the source; a buck chopper is used as an illustration.

Calculation of Harmonic Currents The input current waveform for a buck chopper for i_S, as a function of time, is shown in Figure 7.3. Determining the Fourier series for such a waveform is straightforward:

$$A_0 = \left(\frac{1}{T}\right) \int_0^T i_s(t) \, dt \tag{7.147}$$

$$A_0 = \left(\frac{1}{T}\right) \int_0^{DT} \left[I_{min} + \frac{(I_{max} - I_{min})t}{DT} \right] dt \tag{7.148}$$

$$A_0 = (I_{max} + I_{min})\left(\frac{D}{2}\right) \tag{7.149}$$

$$A_n = \left(\frac{2}{T}\right) \int_0^{DT} \left[I_{min} + \frac{(I_{max} - I_{min})t}{DT} \right] \cos n\omega_0 t \, dt \qquad (7.150)$$

$$B_n = \left(\frac{2}{T}\right) \int_0^{DT} \left[I_{min} + \frac{(I_{max} - I_{min})t}{DT} \right] \sin n\omega_0 \, dt \qquad (7.151)$$

$$\omega_0 = \frac{2\pi}{T}. \qquad (7.152)$$

Performing the indicated integration of Equations 7.150 and 7.151 yields the results of Equations 7.153 and 7.154:

$$A_n = \left(\frac{1}{\pi n}\right) \left\{ I_{max} \sin(n\omega_0 DT) - \frac{(I_{max} - I_{min})[1 - \cos(n\omega_0 DT)]}{2\pi nD} \right\} \qquad (7.153)$$

$$B_n = \left(\frac{1}{\pi n}\right) \left[I_{min} - (I_{max})(\cos n\omega_0 DT) + \frac{(I_{max} - I_{min})(\sin n\omega_0 DT)}{2\pi nD} \right] \qquad (7.154)$$

$$C_n = (A_n^2 + B_n^2)^{0.5}. \qquad (7.155)$$

Harmonic Reduction   A low-pass filter can be inserted between the DC source and the chopper to reduce the harmonic currents in the source. An effective filter should have a cutoff frequency that is appreciably less than the chopping frequency. The circuit in Figure 7.40 is used to perform the analysis.

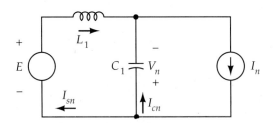

FIGURE 7.40

Added inductor L_1 and capacitor C_1 provide the required filtering action. The sinusoidal current source with current of value I_n represents one harmonic current required by the chopper. Analysis of the circuit enables us to calculate the fraction of I_n that has a path through the DC source. In addition, we can calculate the harmonic voltage across C_1.

Generally, the lowest-order harmonic at the chopping frequency is most important. The circuit analysis of Figure 7.40 yields the following results for

I_{sn} and V_n in response to the harmonic current:

$$I_{sn} = \frac{\dfrac{1}{(j\omega_0 L_1)}(I_n)}{j\omega_0 C_1 + \dfrac{1}{j\omega_0 L_1}} = \frac{I_n}{1 - \omega_0^2 L_1 C_1} \qquad (7.156)$$

$$I_{cn} = \frac{(j\omega_0 C_1)(I_n)}{j\omega_0 C_1 + \dfrac{1}{j\omega_0 L_1}} = -\frac{\omega_0^2 L_1 C_1 I_n}{1 - \omega_0^2 L_1 C_1} \qquad (7.157)$$

$$V_n = \frac{I_{cn}}{j\omega_0 C_1}. \qquad (7.158)$$

The value of ω_0 generally is large compared to the cutoff frequency of the filter as determined by L_1 and C_1. A reasonable approximation is to neglect the "1" term in the denominators of the above equations. The equations then can be replaced by simpler forms involving only the magnitude of the quantities:

$$|I_{sn}| = \left| \frac{I_n}{\omega_0^2 L_1 C_1} \right| \qquad (7.159)$$

$$|V_n| = \left| \frac{I_n}{\omega_0 C_1} \right|. \qquad (7.160)$$

EXAMPLE 7.25

A buck chopper supplies 5 A to a resistive load at 35 V from a 60-V source. The inductor is twice as large as necessary to cause continuous inductor current. $T = 25$ μs.

Design an LC filter to be connected between the chopper and the 60-V source. The filter must limit the 40-kHz peak source current to 0.2 A and the peak 40 kHz voltage at the input to the chopper shall not exceed 0.5 V.

Solution

$$D = \frac{35}{60} = 0.583$$

$$\omega_0 = (2\pi)(40,000) = 251,300 \text{ rad/s.}$$

The values of I_{max} and I_{min} are required initially. With minimum inductance, $I_{min} = 0$ and $I_{max} = (2)(5) = 10$ A. Because the inductance is twice the minimum value, $I_{max} = 7.5$ A and $I_{min} = 2.5$ A.

From Equations 7.153, 7.154, and 7.155, we can determine the lowest-order harmonic components:

$$D\omega_0 T = 3.665 \text{ rad}$$

$$A_1 = \left(\frac{1}{\pi}\right)\left\{7.5 \sin(3.665) - \left(\frac{5}{3.665}\right)[1 - \cos(3.665)]\right\}$$

$$= -2.004 \text{ A}$$

$$B_1 = \left(\frac{1}{\pi}\right)\left\{2.5 - 7.5 \cos(3.665) + \left(\frac{5}{3.665}\right)[\sin(3.665)]\right\}$$

$$= 2.646 \text{ A}$$

$$C_1 = (A_1^2 + B_1^2)^{0.5} = 3.319 \text{ A}.$$

Using Equations 7.159 and 7.160, the values of L_1 and C_1 can be determined:

$$0.2 = \frac{3.319}{(251,300)^2 (L_1 C_1)}$$

$$0.5 = \frac{3.319}{(251,300) C_1}$$

$$C_1 = 26.4 \ \mu\text{F}$$

$$L_1 = 9.95 \ \mu\text{H}. \qquad \blacksquare$$

7.8

DYNAMIC PERFORMANCE

Most DC–DC converters are operated in a closed-loop mode. The output voltage is sensed, compared to a desired output voltage, and the error is used to adjust the duty cycle, D, to obtain the desired output. Changes in output voltage that result from load changes or input voltage are eliminated or reduced by using such feedback.

To model the converter to study system stability or transient performance, we need some means to represent the converter in the frequency domain. With a given switching frequency, experience has shown that it is possible to close the feedback loop and obtain reasonable closed-loop frequency response from zero to some frequency that is a fraction of the switching frequency.

For this purpose, we need a means to represent the converter in a small signal manner. The duty cycle is set at some quiescent value and then varied a small amount sinusoidally above and below the quiescent value. The frequency of variation is kept small compared to the switching frequency. This process is complicated because the circuit takes on two (or more) states during each switching cycle with the result that there is more than one circuit to analyze for frequency response. To solve the problem, we use state-space averaging. The circuit for each state of a converter is weighted according to the fraction of the time the converter remains in a given state. The procedure is best illustrated by a particular configuration.

The analysis that follows is restricted to the buck converter and results in a dynamic model in which L and C appear unchanged from their physical values. For the case of the boost and buck-boost circuits, which are not considered here, the dynamic model includes an inductor that is a function of the duty cycle D. In addition, the transfer function between small signal duty cycle, $\hat{d}$, and the output voltage contains a term with a zero in the right half-plane. These two conditions make the dynamic analysis of these latter circuits more difficult than for the buck converter.*

State-Space Averaged Buck Converter Model

A conductively coupled buck converter provides a basic circuit to illustrate the process. In Figure 7.1, the circuit elements are assumed to have ideal characteristics. Switch S remains closed for a fraction D of each period. The switch is open for the fraction $(1 - D)$ of each period (for static values of D, this circuit already has been analyzed in Section 7.2). Figure 7.41 shows a buck converter in its two states, with the switch closed in (a) and the switch open in (b). The equations for these two states are given below.

With S closed:

$$\frac{dv_C}{dt} = \left(\frac{1}{C}\right)\left(\frac{i_L - v_C}{R}\right) \tag{7.161}$$

$$\frac{di_L}{dt} = \left(\frac{1}{L}\right)(e - v_C). \tag{7.162}$$

With S open:

$$\frac{dv_C}{dt} = \left(\frac{1}{C}\right)\left(\frac{i_L - v_C}{R}\right) \tag{7.163}$$

$$\frac{di_L}{dt} = \left(\frac{1}{L}\right)(0 - v_C). \tag{7.164}$$

---

* Further development of these topics can be found in Severns, R. P., and Bloom, G. E. *Modern DC-to-DC Switchmode Power Converter Circuits.* New York: Van Nostrand Reinhold, 1985.

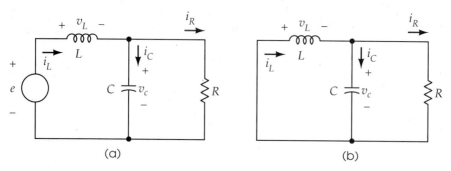

FIGURE 7.41

Now let d be the fractional interval that switch S is closed. This is now a time-varying interval, and a lowercase letter is used in contrast to the static case in which D was used. The fractional interval that the switch is open is d' or $(1 - d)$.

The next step is to weight the equations according to the relative time the circuit is in each state. The relation of Equation 7.161 is multiplied by d to obtain Equation 7.165. In a like manner, Equation 7.163 is multiplied by d' to obtain Equation 7.166:

$$d\left(\frac{dv_C}{dt}\right) = d\left(\frac{1}{C}\right)\left(\frac{i_L - v_C}{R}\right) \tag{7.165}$$

$$d'\left(\frac{dv_C}{dt}\right) = d'\left(\frac{1}{C}\right)\left(\frac{i_L - v_C}{R}\right). \tag{7.166}$$

If the two equations are added and $d + d' = 1$ is noted, the result is that of Equation 7.167:

$$\frac{dv_C}{dt} = \left(\frac{1}{C}\right)\left(\frac{i_L - v_C}{R}\right). \tag{7.167}$$

Equations 7.162 and 7.164 are modified in a like manner to obtain Equations 7.168 and 7.169:

$$d\left(\frac{di_L}{dt}\right) = d\left(\frac{1}{L}\right)(e - v_C) \tag{7.168}$$

$$d'\left(\frac{di_L}{dt}\right) = d'\left(\frac{1}{L}\right)(0 - v_C). \tag{7.169}$$

These two equations are added to obtain Equation 7.170:

$$\frac{di_L}{dt} = \left(\frac{1}{L}\right)(de - v_C). \tag{7.170}$$

The result in Equation 7.170 is a function of the switch duty cycle; this contrasts with Equation 7.167, which does not depend upon d.

The next step in the development process is to introduce a small signal component to each variable, which is represented by a fixed value plus a small signal portion. The following notation, in which the symbol "$\hat{\ }$" represents the small signal portion, is used:

$$
\begin{aligned}
e &= E + \hat{e} & i_S &= I_S + \hat{i}_S \\[6pt]
i_L &= I_L + \hat{i}_L & \frac{di_L}{dt} &= \frac{d\hat{i}_L}{dt} \\[6pt]
v_C &= V_C + \hat{v}_C & \frac{dv_C}{dt} &= \frac{d\hat{v}_C}{dt} \\[6pt]
d &= D + \hat{d} & i_C &= 0 + \hat{i}_C \\[6pt]
d' &= (1 - D) - \hat{d} & i_R &= I_R + \hat{i}_R.
\end{aligned}
\tag{7.171}
$$

The relations of Equation 7.171 are substituted in Equations 7.167 and 7.170. The results are shown in Equations 7.172 and 7.173:

$$
\frac{d\hat{v}_C}{dt} = \left(\frac{1}{C}\right)\left(I_L + \hat{i}_L - \frac{V_C}{R} - \frac{\hat{v}_C}{R}\right)
\tag{7.172}
$$

$$
\frac{d\hat{i}_L}{dt} = \left(\frac{1}{L}\right)[(D + \hat{d})(E + \hat{e}) - V_C - \hat{v}_C].
\tag{7.173}
$$

That there are zero-, first-, and second-order terms allows us to simplify the equations. The second-order terms, which are products of two small signal terms, can be dropped in consideration of their relative size. Equations 7.172 and 7.173 become Equations 7.174 and 7.175:

$$
\frac{d\hat{v}_C}{dt} = \left(\frac{1}{C}\right)\left[I_L - \left(\frac{V_C}{R}\right) + \hat{i}_L - \left(\frac{\hat{v}_C}{R}\right)\right]
\tag{7.174}
$$

$$
\frac{d\hat{i}_L}{dt} = \left(\frac{1}{L}\right)(DE - V_C + E\hat{d} + D\hat{e} - \hat{v}_C).
\tag{7.175}
$$

These equations can be separated into two sets of equations. The first represents the fixed part of the equations, and the second set the small signal portion. The fixed portion is given by Equations 7.176 and 7.177:

$$
0 = \left(\frac{1}{C}\right)\left(I_L - \frac{V_C}{R}\right)
\tag{7.176}
$$

$$
0 = \left(\frac{1}{L}\right)(DE - V_C).
\tag{7.177}
$$

Equations 7.176 and 7.177 are the same as those developed in Section 7.2 for a fixed value of D. The second set of equations for the small signal portion is that of Equations 7.178 and 7.179:

$$\frac{d\hat{v}_C}{dt} = \left(\frac{1}{C}\right)\left(\hat{i}_L - \frac{\hat{v}_C}{R}\right) \tag{7.178}$$

$$\frac{d\hat{i}_L}{dt} = \left(\frac{1}{L}\right)(E\hat{d} + D\hat{e} - \hat{v}_C). \tag{7.179}$$

A circuit model, which is represented by the above equations, is shown in Figure 7.42. This figure simultaneously includes the zero-order and first-order terms from the preceding equations.

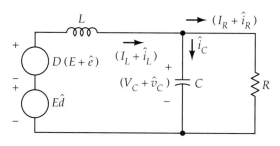

FIGURE 7.42

It is useful to create a generalized transformer that is capable of operating at zero frequency as well as with normal, nonzero, alternating frequencies. This generalized transformer may have a time-varying turn ratio. It obeys all the normal current and voltage relations of the usual ideal transformer. The circuit in Figure 7.42 is changed to include such a transformer and is redrawn as Figure 7.43. The symbol used there for the transformer has gained acceptance in the technical literature.

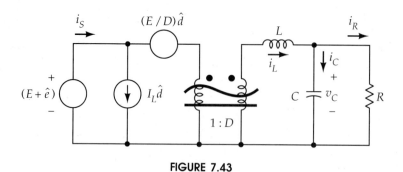

FIGURE 7.43

The equivalent circuit in Figure 7.43 is useful for analyzing several parts of the buck chopper performance. These may be either the DC or the small signal portions of the performance. If $\hat{d}$ and $\hat{e}$ are set to zero, then the resulting circuit yields the performance for fixed values of D. If $\hat{e}$ is allowed to have a nonzero value, then the circuit models the response to ripple voltage occurring in the input source voltage.

If the DC source voltage is not ideal, then the current source in Figure 7.43 becomes important. There is a modulation of the source voltage available to the chopper. A low-pass filter between the source and the chopper could be inserted into the circuit model in Figure 7.43 to reduce the effect of this current component.

Probably the most useful information available from the model is the response to variations in $\hat{d}$. This information allows us to study closed-loop performance, with the output fed back to the input to help control the duty cycle of the ON state.

Frequency Response

The open-loop frequency response of a DC–DC chopper is needed to design a complete closed-loop system successfully. In the analysis that follows, the results apply to the case of an idealized buck chopper that has only the minimum number of ideal circuit elements. There are no parasitic resistance values that might be included in a more complete analysis.

In Figure 7.43, the small signal analysis for the output in response to $\hat{d}$ is desired. Accordingly, all DC quantities and $\hat{e}$ are set to zero. The figure is redrawn with these changes in Figure 7.44. Note that with $(E + \hat{e})$ as a voltage source, the controlled current source has no effect on the voltage equations. The controlled voltage source with value of $(E/D)\hat{d}$, however, is not zero.

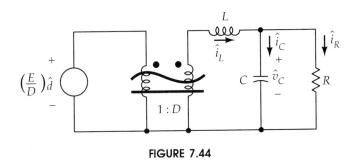

FIGURE 7.44

A further change to the circuit eliminates the transformer and yields the circuit shown in Figure 7.45. The voltage, $\hat{v}_C$, in response to $\hat{d}$ is that of a damped second-order system. The system response in the s domain is given by

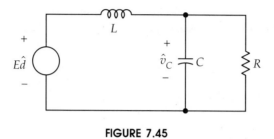

FIGURE 7.45

Equation 7.180.

$$\frac{\hat{v}_C(s)}{\hat{d}(s)} = \frac{E}{1 + \left(\dfrac{L}{R}\right)s + LCs^2} = EF(s). \tag{7.180}$$

A graph of $F(s)$ as a function of angular frequency is shown in Figure 7.46.

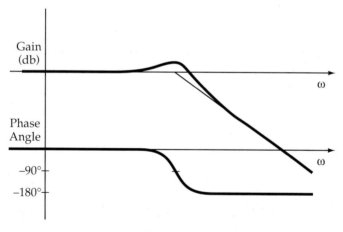

FIGURE 7.46

Closed-Loop Response

If the converter output is used as feedback, then the output can be made to follow some input command. One analysis determines the small signal response to a step in the input command. The circuit shown in Figure 7.47 is typical of such a system. For this arrangement, the system error is given by Equation 7.181:

$$v_e = v_i - v_C. \tag{7.181}$$

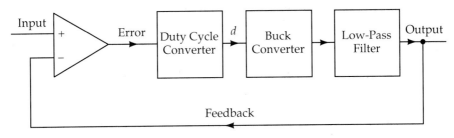

FIGURE 7.47

The duty cycle converter relates system error to duty cycle. In this example, the converter is assumed to be a simple integrator. Equation 7.182 expresses the desired relation:

$$d = \left(\frac{K}{s}\right)(v_e) = \left(\frac{K}{s}\right)(v_i - v_C). \tag{7.182}$$

The above relation is valid for the total quantities, the DC part, or the small signal part. Therefore, Equation 7.183 expresses the small signal part:

$$\hat{d} = \left(\frac{K}{s}\right)(\hat{v}_i - \hat{v}_C). \tag{7.183}$$

Combining Equation 7.180 with 7.183 results in Equations 7.184 and 7.185:

$$\hat{v}_C = EF(s)\hat{d} = [EF(s)]\left(\frac{K}{s}\right)(\hat{v}_i - \hat{v}_C) \tag{7.184}$$

$$G = \frac{\hat{v}_C}{\hat{v}_e} = EF(s)\left(\frac{K}{s}\right). \tag{7.185}$$

These results may be combined into a block diagram representation as in Figure 7.48.

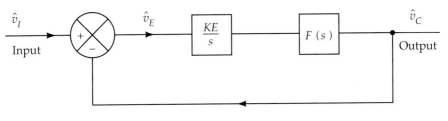

FIGURE 7.48

Equation 7.184 gives an open-loop gain as shown in Equation 7.185. This general relation is illustrated in the graph in Figure 7.49. The overall gain must be set so that the system gain peak at the LC resonant frequency does not cause loop instability. If the resonant peak is removed, the overall system gain can be increased and system performance improved.

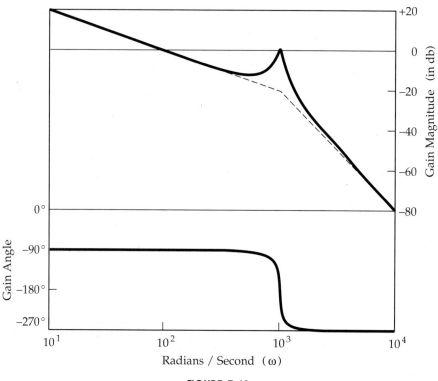

FIGURE 7.49

The next example illustrates closed-loop design using an unmodified LC filter. A later example (7.27) illustrates possible improvement.

EXAMPLE 7.26

The buck chopper in Figure 7.47 has feedback to sense the output voltage and to adjust the switching duty cycle as shown in Figure 7.50 so that the output voltage remains fixed as conditions change; $E = 40$ V, $R = 10\ \Omega$, $V_C = 15$ V, and $f = 100$ kHz. Find:

(a) values of L and C (set L equal to twice the value necessary to maintain continuous inductor current and C to a value that limits the switching ripple to a peak-to-peak value of 0.1 V)

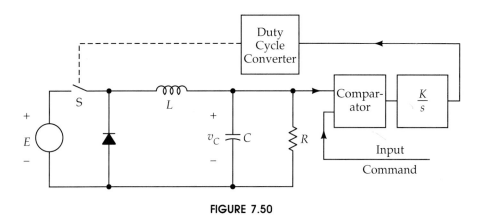

FIGURE 7.50

(b) a K value that results in a stable system

(c) the time domain response for $\hat{v}_C$.

Solution

(a) From Equation 7.177:

$$D = \frac{V_C}{E} = \frac{15}{40} = 0.375.$$

Using Equation 7.19:

$$L_{\min} = \left(\frac{RT}{2}\right)(1 - D) = \frac{(10)(10 \times 10^{-6})(1 - 0.375)}{2}$$

$$= 31.25 \times 10^{-6} \text{ H}.$$

Therefore, use $L = 62.5 \times 10^{-6}$ H.
From Equations 7.17 and 7.18:

$$I_{\max} = (0.375)(40)\left[\left(\frac{1}{10}\right) + \frac{(1 - 0.375)(10 \times 10^{-6})}{(125 \times 10^{-6})}\right]$$

$$= 1.5 + 0.75 = 2.25 \text{ A}.$$

$$I_{\min} = 1.5 - 0.75 = 0.75 \text{ A}.$$

Using Equation 7.22:

$$0.1 = (2.25 - 0.75)\frac{(10 \times 10^{-6})}{8C}$$

$$C = 18.75 \times 10^{-6} \text{ F}.$$

(b) From Equations 7.180 and 7.185 the open-loop response can be found:

$$G = \frac{\hat{v}_C}{\hat{v}_e} = \left(\frac{K}{s}\right)(40)\left(\frac{1}{1 + 6.25 \times 10^{-6}s + 1.1719 \times 10^{-9}s^2}\right)$$

This function is plotted in Figure 7.51 for $K = 1$. From the graph, it is evident that K could be set equal to 31.62 (30 db) and still maintain the resonant peak well below 0 db for stability.

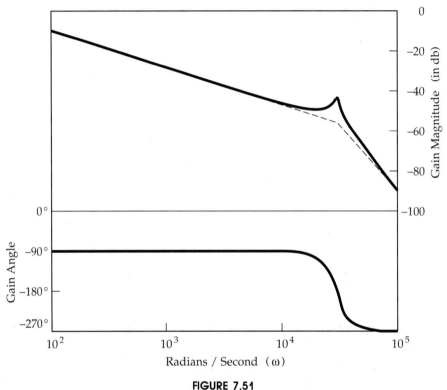

FIGURE 7.51

With the value of K included, the small signal open-loop response using Equation 7.185 becomes:

$$G = \frac{\hat{v}_C(s)}{\hat{v}_e(s)} = \frac{(31.62)(40)}{s(1 + 6.25 \times 10^{-6}s + 1.172 \times 10^{-9}s^2)}.$$

(c) With the loop closed, the step response to a small change in the input command may be determined:

$$\frac{\hat{v}_C(s)}{\hat{v}_i(s)} = \frac{G}{1 + G}$$

$$\frac{\hat{v}_C(s)}{\hat{v}_i(s)} = \frac{1264.8}{1264.8 + s + (6.25 \times 10^{-6}s^2) + (1.172 \times 10^{-9}s^3)}$$

$$\hat{v}_C(s) = \frac{1.079 \times 10^{12}\hat{v}_i(s)}{(s + 1272.5)(s^2 + 4061s + 8.48 \times 10^8)}$$

For a time-domain unit-input step of $\hat{v}_i(t)$, the solution for $\hat{v}_C(t)$ becomes

$$\hat{v}_C(t) = 1.0 - 1.0042\,e^{-1273t} + 0.0439\,e^{-2030t}\sin(29052t - 3.24).$$

The response consists of a constant, an exponential, and a small damped sinusoid. The transient essentially is complete in approximately 3 or 4 milliseconds. It is not the intent of this example to design an optimum feedback compensation, only to illustrate one possibility. Further shaping of the open-loop response may be used to yield an improved transient response. ∎

The resonant peak in the open-loop response can be reduced by increasing the damping in the LC filter circuit. The direct addition of a resistor to increase damping would increase system losses and thus is not a suitable solution. A resistor in series with a capacitor and placed in parallel with the filter capacitor is a suitable answer. The circuit in Figure 7.52 is one possible solution.

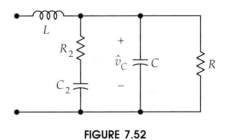

FIGURE 7.52

The design of the circuit requires that R_2 provide appreciable damping at the LC resonant frequency. Capacitor C_2 blocks any DC component of current in R_2. The load resistor R provides some damping, although its effect is small. The values of L and C required to filter the chopping frequency are always such that the load resistance is too large to be effective in damping the resonant peak.

The value of C_2 should be large enough that its effect at the resonant frequency is small. In combination with R, the value of R_2 should effect significant damping. A reasonable relation for design is to set R_2 according to Equation 7.186:

$$R_2 = \left(\frac{L}{C}\right)^{0.5}. \tag{7.186}$$

This R_2 value in combination with R reduces the peak of the resonant response to an acceptable design level. Using the circuit in Figure 7.52, the new expression for $F(s)$ is given in Equation 7.187:

$$F(s) = \frac{1 + R_2 C_2 s}{1 + \left(R_2 C_2 + \frac{L}{R}\right)s + \left(\frac{L}{R}\right)(RC + RC_2 + R_2 C_2)s^2 + R_2 C_2 CLs^3}. \tag{7.187}$$

EXAMPLE 7.27

The response in Example 7.26 can be improved by adding damping to the LC filter, which allows the system gain to be increased. Find:

(a) damping elements to improve response

(b) a new value of system gain

(c) the new response in the time domain.

Solution

(a) Using Equation 7.186, select R_2:

$$R_2 = \left(\frac{L}{C}\right)^{0.5} = \left(\frac{62.5}{18.75}\right)^{0.5} = 1.83 \ \Omega.$$

Select C_2 to have only a moderate effect at the old resonant frequency as compared to R_2. The old resonant frequency is 29,212 rad/s.

$$\left(\frac{1}{\omega C_2}\right) = \frac{R_2}{3}$$
$$C_2 = 56.1 \times 10^{-6} \ \text{F}.$$

The factor of 3 in calculating C_2 is selected arbitrarily.

(b) A new expression for $F(s)$ is computed for the new circuit arrangement in Figure 7.52:

$$F(s) = \frac{1 + (102.66 \times 10^{-6})s}{1 + (108.9 \times 10^{-6})s + (5.32 \times 10^{-9})s^2 + (120.3 \times 10^{-15})s^3}.$$

A graph of system gain is plotted in Figure 7.53 for $K = 1$. The peak close to the old resonant frequency is nearly eliminated. From this graph, it is evident that K can be 41 db (112.2) and still leave the resonant peak about 15 db below the 0-db axis. This is approximately the same criterion as used in Example 7.26. If this is done, the solution for $\hat{v}_C(s)$ gives the following results:

$$\hat{v}_C(s) = \frac{(35.64 \times 10^{15})(1 + 102.7 \times 10^{-6}s)\hat{v}_i(s)}{s^4 + 44217s^3 + (905 \times 10^6)s^2 + (11.97 \times 10^{12})s + 35.64 \times 10^{15}}.$$

If $\hat{v}_i(s)$ is set equal to $1/s$, the solution for $\hat{v}_C(t)$ becomes

$$\hat{v}_C(t) = 1 - 0.807\,e^{-3950t} - 0.178\,e^{-24851t} + 0.444\,e^{-7708t}\sin(17426t - 3.109).$$

The third and fourth terms above are relatively smaller and decay more rapidly than the first two terms. The solution essentially is an exponential of approximately 250 μs time constant. This compares to Example 7.26 in which the solution was essentially an exponential with a 785 μs time constant. The transient is nearly complete in 1 ms. The technique used in this

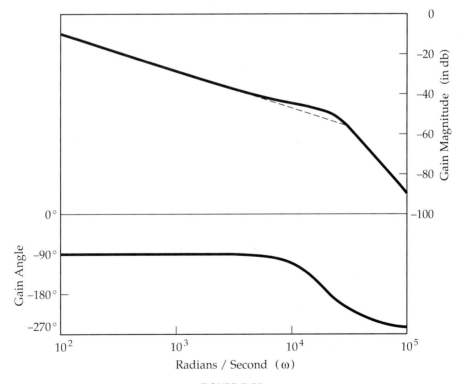

FIGURE 7.53

example has permitted an increase in gain with a resulting improvement in the system response.   ∎

Input Ripple Response

Variations in the input source voltage may cause variations of the output voltage even with a regulating closed-loop control system. The model developed in the previous sections may be used to determine such an effect. The arrangement in Figure 7.54 depicts a situation with the input small signal command at zero. The supply voltage to the converter is not constant but varies with time. This might represent a ripple voltage that results from incomplete filtering following a rectifier stage. Thus, the value of $\hat{e}$ is not zero.

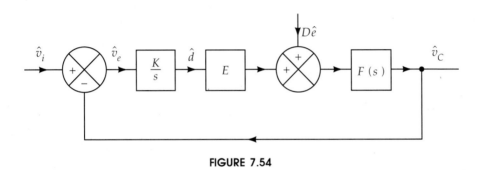

FIGURE 7.54

Equations can be written to describe the circuit operation. The following relation can be written using Figures 7.42 and 7.54 and Equation 7.183:

$$\hat{v}_C = DF(s)\hat{e} + E\left(\frac{K}{s}\right)F(s)(\hat{v}_i - \hat{v}_C). \qquad (7.188)$$

In Equation 7.188, $\hat{v}_i$ then is set equal to zero, with Equation 7.189 resulting:

$$\frac{\hat{v}_C(s)}{\hat{e}(s)} = \frac{sDF(s)}{s + KEF(s)}. \qquad (7.189)$$

The preceding closed-loop response equation can be solved for any desired steady-state response to changes in the converter supply voltage.

EXAMPLE 7.28

The converter in Example 7.27 operates with a fixed input command that corresponds to an output of 15 V. The 40-V value of the input supply voltage has a superimposed ripple of 1-V peak value (2-V peak-to-peak). This ripple has a frequency of 120 Hz and results from incomplete filtering of the rectified supply voltage. Find the peak value of the 120-Hz ripple in the converter output voltage.

Solution   Using the results from Example 7.27, the following values are known:

$$K = 112.2 \qquad D = 0.375 \qquad E = 40 \text{ V}$$

$$F(s) = \frac{1 + (102.7 \times 10^{-6})s}{1 + (108.9 \times 10^{-6})s + (5.32 \times 10^{-9})s^2 + (120.3 \times 10^{-15})s^3}.$$

Using these values in Equation 7.189 for $\hat{v}_C(s)$ yields

$$\frac{\hat{v}_C(s)}{\hat{e}(s)}$$

$$= \frac{0.375s(1 + 102.7 \times 10^{-6}s)}{4488 + 1.461s + (108.9 \times 10^{-6})s^2 + (5.32 \times 10^{-9})s^3 + (120.3 \times 10^{-15})s^4}.$$

For a ripple voltage of 120 Hz, this function can be evaluated at $s = j754$.

$$\left| \frac{\hat{v}_C(j\omega)}{\hat{e}(j\omega)} \right| = 0.062.$$

Approximately 6% of the input ripple appears at the output of the converter, a surprisingly large ripple. There are two reasons for this. First, the output LC filter has a resonant frequency of 4650 Hz, so it has little effect on a frequency of 120 Hz. The LC filter is meant only to be effective at the chopping frequency of 100 kHz. Second, a simple integrator is present in the loop. This certainly causes the response to be slower than it might be if some more nearly optimum shaping of the open-loop response were used. Further development of this topic is beyond the scope of this text.   ∎

7.9
PROBLEMS

7.1   A buck chopper like that in Figure 7.1 has the following data: $E = 40$ V, $T = 50$ μs, $L = 250$ μH, $D = 0.4$, $C = 60$ μF, and $R = 10$ Ω. Find:

(a) the value of L necessary for the continuous current mode

(b) V_C

(c) I_{max} and I_{min}

(d) ΔV_C.

7.2   A buck chopper like that in Figure 7.1 requires an output power of 100 W at an output voltage of 24 V from a 60-V supply. The switching frequency is 60 kHz. The permitted value of ΔV_C is 0.15 V. Find values for D, L, and C assuming L is three times as large as required for continuous current.

7.3   A buck chopper operates with a source that varies from 50 V to 70 V. The output is 200 W at 30 V. Assuming a switching frequency of 60 kHz, design the remaining elements so that L is just large enough to maintain continuous current under all conditions and without ΔV_C exceeding 0.1 V.

7.4   A boost chopper like that in Figure 7.5 has the following values: $E = 18$ V, $T = 15$ μs, $L = 20$ μH, $D = 0.4$, $C = 200$ μF, and $R = 6$ Ω. Find:

(a) the value of L necessary for the continuous current mode

(b) V_C

(c) I_{max} and I_{min}

(d) ΔV_C.

7.5   A boost chopper like that in Figure 7.5 supplies a load of 40 V and 100 W from a 30-V source. The switching frequency is 25 kHz. Design values for L and C such that peak switch current does not exceed 5 A and ΔV_C is 1.0 V.

7.6   A boost chopper like that in Figure 7.5 supplies a load of 50 V and 200 W from a source that varies from 20 V to 30 V. The switching frequency is 60 kHz. Find a value for L such that L is just sufficient so that the inductor current is never in the discontinuous mode. Find C such that ΔV_C is 0.3 V in the worst condition.

7.7   A buck-boost chopper like that in Figure 7.9 supplies a load of 100 Ω from a 50-V source with $D = 0.45$, $T = 25$ μs, $L = 378$ μH, and $C = 20$ μF. Find:

(a) the value of L necessary for continuous inductor current

(b) the value of V_C

(c) I_{max} and I_{min}

(d) the value of ΔV_C.

7.8   A buck-boost chopper like that in Figure 7.9 supplies a load of 25 Ω with 35 V from a 25-V source. The switching frequency is 40 kHz. Find:

(a) the value of L for just continuous inductor current

(b) the value of C for ΔV_C of 0.25 V (for this part use a value of L that is twice that found in part (a)).

7.9   A buck-boost chopper like that in Figure 7.9 has a source voltage of 24 V. The output is to a load of 10 Ω and is required to be variable from 10 V to 40 V. The switching frequency is 60 kHz. Design for values of L and C that provide continuous inductor current and that limit ΔV_C to 0.5 V.

7.10 A flyback converter has the following data:

$$E = 200 \text{ V} \qquad D = 0.4 \qquad L_1 = L_2 = 600 \text{ } \mu\text{H}$$

$$\frac{N_1}{N_2} = 1 \qquad T = 15 \text{ } \mu\text{s} \qquad R = 150 \text{ } \Omega \qquad C = 40 \text{ } \mu\text{F}.$$

(a) Find the value of the minimum inductance that causes continuous inductor current.

(b) Find the value of V_C.

(c) Find I_{max} and I_{min}.

(d) Find the value of ΔV_C.

7.11 Design a flyback converter to provide 160 V from a 150-V source to a load of 200 Ω. The switching frequency is 40 kHz, the inductor current is just continuous, and the output ripple may not exceed 0.5 V. Assume the flyback transformer has a 1:1 turn ratio.

7.12 Design a flyback converter to provide 2 A at 15 V from a 250-V source. The switching frequency is 50 kHz. The inductor current should be continuous and the value of ΔV_C should not exceed 0.05 V. As part of the solution, a suitable turn ratio should be chosen.

7.13 A forward converter like that in Figure 7.15 has the following characteristics:

$$L_1 = L_2 = L_3 = 12 \text{ mH} \qquad T = 25 \text{ } \mu\text{s} \qquad L = 50 \text{ } \mu\text{H} \qquad C = 40 \text{ } \mu\text{F}$$

$$N_1 = N_2 = N_3 \qquad R = 4 \text{ } \Omega \qquad D = 0.35 \qquad E = 60 \text{ V}.$$

(a) Find the values of I_{max} and I_{min}.

(b) Find the value of V_C.

(c) Find the value of ΔV_C.

(d) Find the peak value of i_m.

(e) Find the energy per cycle and the power returned to the source by Winding 3.

7.14 A forward converter is to supply 100 W at 25 V from a 65-V source. The operating frequency is 50 kHz. Design the converter to operate in the continuous mode with $\Delta V_C = 0.5$ V. Limit the value of i_m to 5% of I_{max}.

7.15 A forward converter is to supply 150 W at 12 V from a 230-V source. Select a suitable ratio of turns on Winding 2 as compared to Windings 1 and 3. The switching frequency is 50 kHz. The value of ΔV_C should not exceed 0.12 V, and i_m should not exceed 5% of I_{max}. The output inductor should operate in the continuous mode.

7.16   A conductively coupled buck converter supplies a load of 5 A at 12 V from a 24-V source; $f = 50$ kHz, $L = 8$ μH, and $C = 200$ μF. Find:

(a) the mode of operation, whether continuous or discontinuous

(b) D

(c) D_2

(d) I_{max}

(e) ΔV_C.

7.17   A buck chopper is designed to operate in the discontinuous mode with as small an inductor as possible. The output power is 120 W at 24 V from a 60-V source. Switching frequency is 100 kHz. Switch current may not exceed 14 A. Find:

(a) the values of L and D that fit the requirements

(b) the value of C to limit ΔV_C to 0.5 V.

7.18   A boost chopper operates over an extended range of the output voltage; $E = 20$ V, $R = 20$ Ω, $L = 19.2$ μH, $C = 50$ μF, and $T = 20$ μS. Find:

(a) the range of D for both continuous and discontinuous operation

(b) the output voltage for $D = 0.4$

(c) I_{max} under the condition of (b)

(d) the value of ΔV_C under the condition of (b).

7.19   A buck-boost chopper supplies 20 V to a resistive load of 25 Ω from a 16-V source; $L = 40$ μH and $T = 20$ μS. Find:

(a) the value of D

(b) I_{max}

(c) the value of C that limits ΔV_C to 0.15 V.

7.20   A flyback converter operates to supply 150 V to a load from a 150-V source. Initially, assume ideal transformer coupling; $T = 75$ μS, $R = 50$ Ω, $N_1/N_2 = 1$, and $L_1 = L_2 = 1$ mH. Find:

(a) the value of D

(b) I_{max}

(c) the value of t_1 if the transformer is nonideal ($L_x = 5$ μH and $C_S = 0.05$ μF)

(d) $i_1(t_1)$

(e) the value of t_2

(f) the maximum switch voltage.

7.21   Repeat Problem 7.20 with $L_x = 3$ μH.

7.22 A flyback converter with $N_1/N_2 = 1$ has the following data for Figure 7.27. The current mode is just continuous.

$$E = 150 \text{ V} \qquad L_x = 4 \text{ } \mu\text{H} \qquad T = 40 \text{ } \mu\text{s}$$

$$V_Z = 325 \text{ V} \qquad L_m = 496 \text{ } \mu\text{H} \qquad D = 0.4$$

$$V_C = 99.3 \text{ V} \qquad C \text{ is large enough that } \Delta V_C \text{ is negligible.}$$

(a) Find the peak value of i_1.
(b) Find the value of t_1.
(c) Find the peak value of i_2.
(d) Find the average power to the voltage clamp.
(e) Find the average load power.

7.23 A flyback converter uses a voltage clamp across the switch to produce an equivalent circuit like that in Figure 7.27. The following operating conditions are known:

$$E = 240 \text{ V} \qquad L_x = 5 \text{ } \mu\text{H} \qquad T = 50 \text{ } \mu\text{s}$$

$$V_Z = 600 \text{ V} \qquad L_m = 495 \text{ } \mu\text{H} \qquad D = 0.3$$

$$V_C = 110 \text{ V} \qquad N_1/N_2 = 1 \qquad C = 100 \text{ } \mu\text{F}.$$

(a) Find the peak value of i_1 at the time the switch opens.
(b) Find the time to reduce i_1 to zero.
(c) Find the peak value of i_2.
(d) Find the time to reduce i_2 to zero.
(e) Find the load resistance.
(f) Find the load ripple voltage.

7.24 A flyback converter with the arrangement of that in Figure 7.30 has the following data. The inductor current is just continuous.

$$E = 100 \text{ V} \qquad L_x = 5 \text{ } \mu\text{H} \qquad N_1 = N_3$$

$$V_C = 13.2 \text{ V} \qquad L_m = 495 \text{ } \mu\text{H} \qquad N_1/N_2 = 5$$

$$D = 0.4 \qquad T = 50 \text{ } \mu\text{s} \qquad C \text{ is large.}$$

(a) Find the time required to reduce i_3 to zero after the switch is opened.
(b) Find the load resistance.
(c) Find the energy returned to the source at each turnoff operation.

7.25   A buck chopper supplies 5 A at 30 V to a load from a 50-V source. The inductor current is continuous. $R_L = 0.05\ \Omega$. Other circuit elements are ideal. Find the required value of D.

7.26   A boost chopper supplies 5 A at 60 V to a load from a 20-V source. The inductor current is continuous. Other circuit elements are ideal. Find the maximum inductor resistance such that D does not exceed 0.71.

7.27   The nonideal switches of a buck chopper with continuous current may be represented by $E_S = 1.5$ V and $E_D = 1.0$ V. $R_L = 0.06\ \Omega$, $E = 100$ V, $V_C = 60$ V, and $R = 7.2\ \Omega$. Find the required value of D.

7.28   A boost chopper is controlled by a MOSFET switch. The inductor current is continuous. $E = 35$ V, $V_C = 78$ V, $E_D = 1.4$ V, and $R = 27.0\ \Omega$. Find the maximum value of R_S such that D does not exceed 0.58.

7.29   A boost chopper with a large inductance value has the following data: $E = 15$ V, $V_C = 35$ V, $R = 10\ \Omega$, $R_S = 0.15\ \Omega$, $E_D = 1.1$ V, $R_L = 0.12\ \Omega$, and $f = 40$ kHz. Find:

(a) the value of D required

(b) the input current

(c) the power loss in each circuit element

(d) the ratio of output power to input power (neglect the switching losses).

7.30   A boost chopper using the minimum value of inductance for continuous current supplies 100 W at 50 V from a 25-V source. All switching elements may be considered ideal. $T = 25\ \mu s$. Design a low-pass filter to be inserted between the source and the chopper to reduce the 40-kHz component of source current to 0.4-A peak value. The 40 kHz component of voltage to the chopper shall not exceed 0.5-V peak value.

7.31   A buck chopper has the following element values: $E = 50$ V, $V_C = 35$ V, $T = 25\ \mu s$, $L = 30\ \mu H$, $C = 100\ \mu F$, and $R = 8\ \Omega$. Design a filter to be inserted between the DC source voltage and the chopper. The lowest frequency component of source current shall not exceed 0.2-A peak value, and the lowest frequency component of voltage to the chopper shall not exceed 0.5-V peak value.

7.32   A conductively coupled buck chopper supplies 12 V from a 30-V source to a load of 6 Ω. The switching frequency is 60 kHz.

(a) Find values of L and C such that the inductor is twice as large as required for continuous current and C is as required for ΔV_C of 0.05 V.

(b) Find the open-loop transfer function with $K = 1$.

(c) Select a K value such that the system is stable with reasonable gain margin.

(d) Evaluate the response to a small step in the command for output voltage.

7.33 Repeat Problem 7.32 using elements R_2 and C_2 to dampen the LC filter response.

7.34 A buck chopper with the following data has an input voltage with a peak ripple of 10% at a frequency of 120 Hz superimposed on the DC source of 50 V. Find the peak 120-Hz voltage in the output if a reasonable closed-loop gain is chosen.

$$T = 15 \ \mu s \qquad D = 0.35 \qquad L = 80 \ \mu H \qquad C = 20 \ \mu F$$

$$R_2 = 2.0 \ \Omega \qquad C_2 = 60 \ \mu F \qquad R = 10 \ \Omega.$$

7.35 Using the data and solution from Problem 7.34, find the output voltage time response for a small step in the input command.

C H A P T E R · 8

Inverters

In this chapter we will consider inverters that supply an alternating output from a DC source. The AC output is generated by a multiplicity of switch operations, and the resulting waveform consists of several voltage segments. The values of these segments may be positive, negative, or zero but generally there is only one nonzero magnitude.

8.1

SPLIT SOURCE: HALF-BRIDGE

The circuit in Figure 8.1 can be used to supply a rectangular alternating voltage to a load that consists of resistance and inductance. The DC source consists of two equal parts, which are arranged as in the figure; this arrangement is known as a *split source*. The circuit also is known as a half-bridge because it uses two switches (this contrasts with the full bridge in Figure 8.5, which requires four switches).

The ideal switches in Figure 8.1 are opened and closed alternately, each 50% of the time, with one switch open while the other is closed. The switches may be implemented with BJTs, SCRs, or MOSFETs.

During the interval that S_1 is closed and S_2 is open, the KVL for the upper loop requires $v_L = E$. After a suitable time, S_1 is opened and S_2 is closed. The

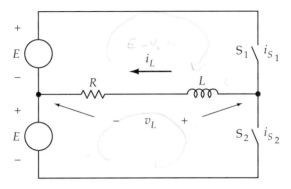

FIGURE 8.1

KVL equation for the lower loop requires that $v_L = -E$. The result is an alternating rectangular waveform for v_L as shown in Figure 8.2. The figure also shows the graph for the resulting load current.

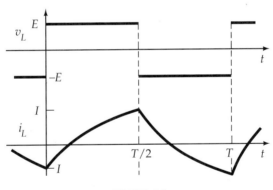

FIGURE 8.2

A few comments about Figure 8.2 are in order here. At $t = T/2$, just before S_1 is opened, i_L is positive. Upon opening S_1 and closing S_2, i_L must be continuous in time and therefore must remain positive for some interval even though v_L reverses sign. After some period of time, i_L does indeed change sign along with the direction of current in S_2. Thus we can see that the switches must conduct in both directions and so cannot be simply a BJT, for example. In addition to the main element, it generally is necessary to include a diode element in parallel to conduct current in the reverse direction. To further appreciate the circuit operation, Figure 8.1 is redrawn as Figure 8.3 with BJTs used as part of S_1 and S_2.

Consider an instant when the end of S_1 closure is attained. Transistor Q_1 is assumed to turnoff in an ideal manner in zero time. Transistor Q_2 is turned

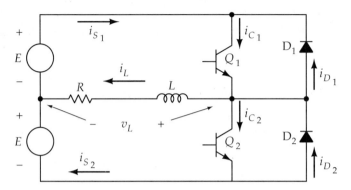

FIGURE 8.3

on by providing it with base current. Because i_L is positive, transistor Q_2 cannot conduct the load current. The only path available for i_L is by way of diode D_2. At the instant that i_L switches from Q_1 to D_2, the connection of the right-hand terminal of the load is moved from the upper terminal to the lower terminal of the two power sources. At this same instant, the load voltage changes polarity. Thus, turning on Q_2 does not accomplish anything directly and immediately.

After an interval during which the load current decreases, the load current goes through zero and becomes negative. At this point in time, Q_2 actually must begin to conduct. The graphs in Figure 8.4 show the time relationships of the currents.

One more point to note is that transistor turnoff usually occurs more slowly than transistor turn on. Usually, then, transistor turn on is intentionally delayed until the other transistor has completed its turnoff process. This practice causes no problem, of course, because the transistor to be turned on does not actually conduct for some period as a result of the inductive load.

The behavior of the load current can be found using the following equations. From the circuit in Figure 8.1 with S_1 closed, Equation 8.1 results:

$$E = v_L = Ri_L + L\frac{di_L}{dt}. \tag{8.1}$$

During the interval that S_2 is closed, Equation 8.2 applies:

$$-E = v_L = Ri_L + L\frac{di_L}{dt}. \tag{8.2}$$

The boundary condition that permits solution of Equation 8.1 is that the current at $t = T/2$ is the same as that at $t = 0$ except for the reversal of sign. Using this condition from Equation 8.1 gives us the result of Equation 8.3:

$$i_L = \left(\frac{E}{R}\right)(1 - e^{-t/\tau}) - Ie^{-t/\tau}, \tag{8.3}$$

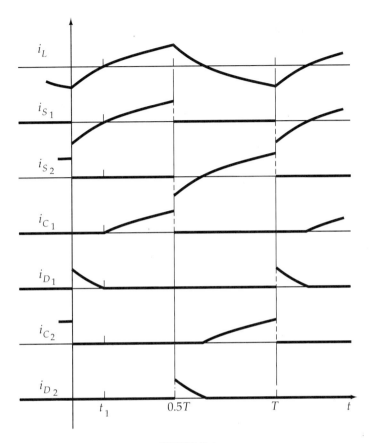

FIGURE 8.4

where

$$I = \left(\frac{E}{R}\right)\left(\frac{1 - e^{-T/2\tau}}{1 + e^{-T/2\tau}}\right) \tag{8.4}$$

and

$$\tau = \frac{L}{R}. \tag{8.5}$$

In Figure 8.4, the start or end of certain currents occurs when i_L is zero. This time can be found by setting i_L to zero in Equation 8.3 and also by using Equation 8.4 as shown in Equation 8.6:

$$t_1 = \tau \ln\left(\frac{2}{1 + e^{-T/2\tau}}\right). \tag{8.6}$$

From the graph in Figure 8.4, average current in the two parts of the switch can be calculated. Transistor current occurs from t_1 to $T/2$ and is zero the remainder of a period. Diode current occurs from $t = 0$ to t_1 and likewise is zero for the remainder of the period. Average currents are given by Equations 8.7 and 8.8:

$$I_C = \left(\frac{1}{T}\right) \int_{t_1}^{T/2} i_L \, dt \tag{8.7}$$

$$I_D = \left(\frac{1}{T}\right) \int_0^{t_1} -i_L \, dt. \tag{8.8}$$

EXAMPLE 8.1

In Figure 8.3 the following data are given: $E = 300$ V, $R = 10\ \Omega$, $f = 60$ Hz, and $L = 0.05$ H. Find:

(a) peak load current

(b) time of current zero crossing after start of a half-cycle

(c) average transistor current

(d) average diode current.

Solution

(a) From Equation 8.5:

$$\tau = \frac{0.05}{10} = 0.005 \text{ s}.$$

From Equation 8.4:

$$I = \left(\frac{300}{10}\right)\left(\frac{1 - e^{-0.01667/0.01}}{1 + e^{-0.01667/0.01}}\right)$$

$$= 20.47 \text{ A}.$$

(b) From Equation 8.6:

$$t_1 = (0.005) \ln\left(\frac{2}{1 + e^{-0.01667/0.01}}\right)$$

$$= 0.00260 \text{ s}.$$

(c) From Equation 8.7:

$$I_C = \left(\frac{1}{0.01667}\right)\int_{0.00260}^{0.00833} (30 - 50.47\, e^{-t/0.005})\, dt = 4.18 \text{ A}.$$

(d) From Equation 8.8:

$$I_D = \left(\frac{1}{0.01667}\right)\int_0^{0.0026} -(30 - 50.47\, e^{-t/0.005})\, dt = 1.46 \text{ A}. \quad \blacksquare$$

The graphs in Figure 8.4 for the case of the BJT-implemented switch show that collector current in Q_1 begins somewhere in the interval for which $0 < t < T/2$. The exact time generally is unknown. For the circuit to function successfully, base current for Q_1 must be provided at the proper time. This problem can be solved by providing base current for Q_1 during the entire half-period interval from 0 to $T/2$ except for an initial short delay to ensure that Q_2 has completed its prior turnoff.

In the situation in which an SCR is used as the switch, continuous gate current can be provided during the half-period interval. Even though an SCR can be gated into conduction by a short pulse of gate current, this method is not suitable here because the proper time to provide this pulse generally is unknown. An alternate turn-on procedure provides several short gate-current pulses that are uniformly spaced in the half-period interval. Each pulse is sufficient to turn on the SCR provided that circuit conditions are proper for SCR conduction. If the SCR anode-to-cathode voltage is not yet positive, then the SCR does not begin conduction. After a short time, another gate-current pulse occurs and, provided that the SCR anode-to-cathode voltage now is positive, the SCR begins conduction. This process continues until such time as the SCR's anode-to-cathode voltage is positive when the gate-current pulse occurs. The spacing between gate-current pulses is made short enough that any interval in which conduction should occur but does not is not long enough to cause significant circuit effect. The obvious benefit of this method is a reduction in the size and cost of the circuit elements that provide gate-current pulses.

If an SCR implements the switches, then commutating means such as those discussed in Chapter 3 must be provided to cause SCR turnoff at the end of each half-cycle. This is in contrast to a BJT or MOSFET situation in which the turn-on drive to the switch simply is removed. These design requirements generally dictate the use of BJT or MOSFET switches for small and moderate size equipment. Very large equipment may justify the use of SCRs as switch elements even though commutating capacitors are required. In some cases, recent developments in GTO devices may have changed the particular semiconductor device that is selected for the design of an inverter switch. The evolution of semiconductor devices continues to influence their economical selection for particular inverter designs.

8.2

BRIDGE INVERTER

The preceding circuit arrangement presents the essential inverter concepts. The need for two sources of equal amplitude, however, makes this solution less than desirable in most cases. Instead, a bridge inverter arrangement can be used. The bridge inverter uses one source, but this improvement is partially offset by the need for four switches.

The circuit in Figure 8.5 is a bridge inverter using one DC source and four bidirectional switches. All of the switch requirements from the preceding section remain in effect. The DC source now supplies current to the inverter on both half-cycles, whereas each of the two DC sources in the half-bridge supplies current in only one of the half-cycles of each inverter cycle.

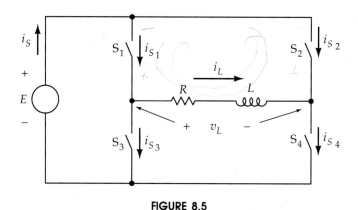

FIGURE 8.5

During inverter operation, switches S_1 and S_4 are closed at the same time and provide a positive value of v_L together with a path for i_L. After the end of one half-cycle, the switches are opened, and switches S_2 and S_3 are closed. Again, as a result of the inductive load, the switches must be capable of bidirectional currents.

The current i_S in the voltage source in Figure 8.5 has intervals during which it is negative. Energy is returned from the load to the source during these intervals. The nature of the source must be such that it can accept this energy. If a rectifier, a capacitor must be at the output terminals so that the rectifier is capable of accepting this energy by storing it in the capacitor.

The bridge configuration requires that the elements that make up S_1 and S_2 may not have a terminal in common with the negative side of E. The circuits that turn on S_1 and S_2 therefore must be isolated from that which turns on S_3 and S_4 because they do not have terminals in common. For example, if these four switches are NPN-type BJTs, then the four emitter terminals are not common and all of the base drive circuits may not have the same reference. The problem usually is solved by coupling the turn-on signals to S_1 and S_2 in one of two ways: by using a pulse transformer to provide coupling isolation or by using the optical isolation of an LED driving a phototransistor to turn on base current.

8.3

OUTPUT CONTROL

For the inverter output to be useful, it must be controlled in a manner required by the load to be supplied. In the very simple circuits presented thus far, the only control indicated is the ability to control output frequency by choosing the times at which the switches are operated. Additional control frequently is necessary to permit the output voltage to be adjusted or to permit the harmonic content of the output to be controlled.

Depending on the method by which these characteristics are controlled, voltage amplitude and harmonic content may be either separate functions or dependent on each other. The following sections discuss several control methods.

Voltage Control

If the objective is only inverter output-voltage control, it is simplest to control the DC source voltage. The inverter output voltage then varies directly with the input voltage. The variable DC source can be obtained from a phase-controlled rectifier as in Chapter 5 or from a DC–DC converter as in Chapter 7.

There are situations when the DC source cannot be variable or when the losses that accompany an added process cannot be tolerated. This latter case would occur if the only purpose of a DC–DC conversion was to provide a variable DC voltage for inverter input. In these situations, the inverter process also will have to provide the variation in output voltage.

One basic way to accomplish this is simply to vary the fraction of time that the output voltage is nonzero during each inverter half-cycle. The graph in Figure 8.6 shows an inverter output that is zero part of each half-cycle and either

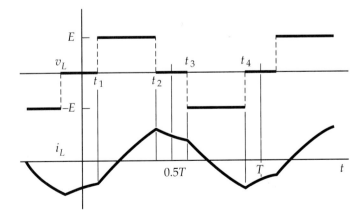

FIGURE 8.6

$+E$ or $-E$ during the remaining part of the half-cycle. This is accomplished in the inverter in Figure 8.5 in the following manner. When S_1 and S_4 have been closed and $i_L > 0$, S_4 is opened. The load current must continue, because the load is inductive. The path that is available is through the diode part of S_2. No circuit action is required to turn on S_2. It is automatic that the path exists because it is through a diode element. Examination of the path of S_1, the load, and S_2 shows that $v_L = 0$ for the time this occurs.

After the time when zero load voltage is desired, switch S_1 is opened and switches S_2 and S_3 are closed. S_2 has been closed by way of its diode, but now it is closed actively by turning on the transistor part of S_2. This circuit action causes the load voltage to change to $-E$ as shown in the graph.

The fundamental component of the Fourier series for v_L is a function of the time interval when the voltage is nonzero. Inspection of the graph for v_L shows an odd function for which the value of B_1 is found from Equations 8.9 through 8.11:

$$B_1 = \left(\frac{2}{T}\right)\int_0^T [v_L(t)](\sin \omega_0 t)\, dt \tag{8.9}$$

$$= \left(\frac{2}{T}\right)\left[\int_{t_1}^{t_2} E \sin \omega_0 t\, dt + \int_{t_3}^{t_4} -E \sin \omega_0 t\, dt\right] \tag{8.10}$$

$$= \left(\frac{4E}{\pi}\right)(\cos \alpha_1), \tag{8.11}$$

where

$$t_3 = t_1 + \frac{T}{2},$$

$$t_4 = t_2 + \frac{T}{2},$$

$$t_2 = \frac{T}{2} - t_1,$$

$$\alpha_1 = \omega_0 t_1, \quad \text{and}$$

$$\omega_0 = \frac{2\pi}{T}.$$

Equation 8.11 shows that the fundamental component of the inverter output can be varied by controlling the conduction time, $(t_2 - t_1)$, during each half-cycle. The remaining terms of the Fourier series have not been determined, but they also vary with the value of t_1. A more general analysis gives the result of Equation 8.12:

$$B_n = \left(\frac{4E}{n\pi}\right)(\cos n\alpha_1).\qquad(8.12)$$

A specific case is one in which $\omega_0 t = 30°$. The fundamental voltage is reduced by a factor of 0.866, whereas the third harmonic is reduced to zero by the factor $\cos[(3)(30°)] = \cos 90° = 0$.

EXAMPLE 8.2

(a) In the arrangement in Figure 8.6, what is the value of α_1 so that the fundamental component of v_L is 50 V for $E = 250$ V?

(b) What is the resulting value of the third harmonic component of v_L?

Solution

(a) From Equation 8.11:

$$50 = \left[\frac{(4)(250)}{\pi}\right]\cos\alpha_1$$

$$\alpha_1 = 80.96°.$$

(b) From Equation 8.12:

$$B_3 = \left[\frac{(4)(250)}{(3)(\pi)}\right][\cos(3)(80.96°)]$$

$$= -48.37 \text{ V}.$$

Note the very substantial value of the lowest-order harmonic. True, the fundamental is reduced by this process, but it is at the expense of harmonic components similar in size to the fundamental. ∎

Another means of voltage amplitude control can be used in those cases when the entire inverter is composed of two or more units operating in series. Sometimes this is done in large equipment where the size dictates that the output of two or more units be combined. The individual inverters are isolated from one another by transformers and are in series on the AC side. Each inverter is operated with full switch conduction for each half-period as shown in the graph in Figure 8.2. The individual inverters are operated so that there is a phase shift between the two (or more) output voltages. The total voltage is one having the same wave shape as that in Figure 8.6. The output voltage is controlled in the same manner as in Equations 8.11 and 8.12 with the exception that α_1 is now one-half the delay angle between the output of the two inverters. It still is possible to control the conduction interval within each inverter so that an additional control objective can be realized.

Harmonic Control

The switching action described in the preceding section can be used to cause control (reduction) of the harmonics in the inverter output. A very basic example was given in Example 8.2. To control more than one harmonic, multiple switch operations per half-cycle are required.

If two additional independent switching times are provided, then two harmonic values may be controlled or eliminated. The waveform symmetry is maintained so that the function remains an odd function and also has half-period symmetry so that only odd-order harmonics occur. In the graph in Figure 8.7, the switching points are at t_1 and t_2 with corresponding angles $\alpha_1 = \omega_0 t_1$ and $\alpha_2 = \omega_0 t_2$.

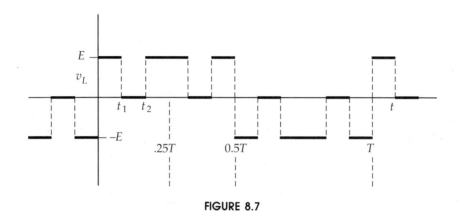

FIGURE 8.7

Using all of the waveform's symmetry suggests that only the odd-order sine terms are present and that these can be found by integrating over one-fourth the period. The following general term of the Fourier series results in Equation 8.14. The variable of integration has been changed by substituting $\theta = \omega_0 t$:

$$B_n = 4\left(\frac{2}{2\pi}\right)\left(\int_0^{\alpha_1} E\sin n\theta \, d\theta + \int_{\alpha_2}^{\pi/2} E\sin n\theta \, d\theta\right) \tag{8.13}$$

$$= \left(\frac{4E}{n\pi}\right)(1 - \cos n\alpha_1 + \cos n\alpha_2). \tag{8.14}$$

If the objective of harmonic control is to eliminate certain harmonics from the inverter output, usually the low-order ones should be eliminated, because they are the largest in amplitude and the most difficult to be removed by any load-filtering action. For that reason, consider the case in which the third and fifth harmonics are to be eliminated. This can be done by setting B_3 and B_5 to zero. Two conditions result from these constraints:

$$1 - \cos 3\alpha_1 + \cos 3\alpha_2 = 0 \qquad \text{(8.15)}$$

$$1 - \cos 5\alpha_1 + \cos 5\alpha_2 = 0. \qquad \text{(8.16)}$$

These equations are transcendental and do not have a closed-form solution. A numerical solution yields the values $\alpha_1 = 17.8°$ and $\alpha_2 = 38.0°$.

In this process, the fundamental component is whatever the values of α_1 and α_2 yield. A calculation using Equation 8.14 gives $B_1 = (0.836)(4E/\pi)$. If only two switching points are controlled to reduce the third and fifth harmonics to zero, the fundamental output voltage cannot be independently adjusted. Additional control obviously requires an additional independent switching point.

EXAMPLE 8.3

Using a method similar to that in Figure 8.7, but with the purpose of controlling the fundamental and simultaneously reducing the third harmonic component to zero, find values for α_1 and α_2. In particular, the fundamental component is to be 0.85E.

Solution   From Equation 8.14:

$$B_1 = \left(\frac{4E}{\pi}\right)(1 - \cos\alpha_1 + \cos\alpha_2)$$

$$B_3 = \left(\frac{4E}{3\pi}\right)(1 - \cos 3\alpha_1 + \cos 3\alpha_2).$$

Now set $B_1 = 0.85E$ and $B_3 = 0$. Then,

$$1 - \cos\alpha_1 + \cos\alpha_2 = 0.668$$

$$1 - \cos 3\alpha_1 + \cos 3\alpha_2 = 0.$$

Solving the above two equations yields values of $\alpha_1 = 29.8°$ and $\alpha_2 = 57.6°$.

In solving the above equations, it soon becomes evident that some combinations of the fundamental and the third harmonic cannot be met. The method therefore has its limitations.   ∎

Pulse-Width Modulation

Extending the switching in the preceding section to many switching points per cycle is called *pulse-width modulation* (PWM) because the end result is several or many pulses per cycle, each of which is controlled in duration. The usual methods to implement PWM are arranged so as to produce an integral number of pulses per half-cycle and also to arrange the pulses so that each half-cycle is symmetrical about the center of the half-cycle. The function is arranged as in Figure 8.8 so that it is an odd function. The result of this arrangement is that there are no even harmonics in the Fourier series for the waveform and that all of the A coefficients are zero.

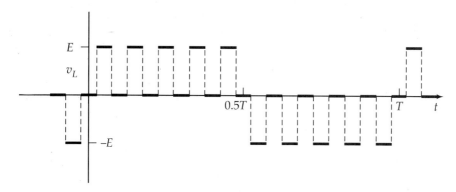

FIGURE 8.8

The purpose of PWM is to control both the output voltage amplitude and, at least in some cases, the size of one or more of the output's harmonic components. One possible implementation is to use a certain number of pulses in each half-cycle such that all pulses have the same width. An example with five pulses per half-cycle is shown in Figure 8.8. The pulse width is variable as required to provide the desired fundamental output voltage.

The pulses are spaced $180°/5$, or $36°$, apart with the pulse width as needed. A pulse width of $36°$ reverts to the waveform of a simple inverter as shown previously in Figure 8.2. An approximate analysis of the waveform in Figure 8.8 follows. As is evident in the figure, the waveform is an odd function and has half-period symmetry. Thus, the Fourier series contains only sine terms of odd order. Each pulse is represented by an impulse function of value equal to the area of the actual pulse. The impulse is located at the center of the actual pulse. This is an approximation, but to the extent that a sinusoid can be represented by a straight line over the pulse width, the approximation is exact.

In the following equations, there are k pulses per half-cycle, each with a width of t_p. Each pulse is located at the discrete time of value t_i:

$$t_i = \left(\frac{T}{2k}\right)(i + 0.5) \qquad i = 0, 1, 2, \ldots, (k - 1) \qquad \textbf{(8.17)}$$

$$t_p = \frac{mT}{2k}. \qquad \textbf{(8.18)}$$

In Equation 8.18, m is the fraction of possible maximum pulse width. Substitution of the preceding conditions in an evaluation of the Fourier coefficients gives Equations 8.19 and 8.20. In this process, each pulse of finite width is replaced by an impulse function, $\delta(t_i)$, of appropriate value:

$$B_n = \left(\frac{2}{T}\right)(2)\sum_{i=0}^{(k-1)}\int_0^{T/2} t_p E[\delta(t_i)][\sin n\omega_0 t]) \, dt \qquad (8.19)$$

$$B_n = \left(\frac{4}{T}\right)(t_p E)\left[\sum_{i=0}^{(k-1)} \sin n\omega_0 t_i\right]. \qquad (8.20)$$

In the case of $k = 5$,

$$B_n = 0.4mE\left(\sin\frac{n\pi}{10} + \sin\frac{3n\pi}{10} + \sin\frac{n\pi}{2} + \sin\frac{7n\pi}{10} + \sin\frac{9n\pi}{10}\right). \qquad (8.21)$$

For various values of n and for $m = 0.2$, the results are given in Table 8.1.

TABLE 8.1	
Coefficient	Value
B_1	$0.2589E$
B_3	$0.0989E$
B_5	$0.0800E$
B_7	$0.0989E$
B_9	$0.2589E$
B_{11}	$-0.2589E$

The preceding equations show that varying m can reduce the fundamental amplitude as required, but the harmonic content relative to the fundamental remains relatively large. Furthermore, the proportion of harmonic to fundamental stays relatively unchanged as the pulse width is varied. This technique is suitable only as a means to reduce voltage amplitude and thus is not used widely.

If the preceding PWM method is modified to permit a varying pulse width during the cycle, then an improved voltage waveform results. The number of pulses per half-cycle remains an integer quantity as before, but now the width of each pulse is varied or modulated according to its position within the half-cycle. The variation of pulse width is proportional to the sine of the angular position and is shown in Figure 8.9. The actual width of each pulse, of course, also is proportional to the desired output voltage amplitude.

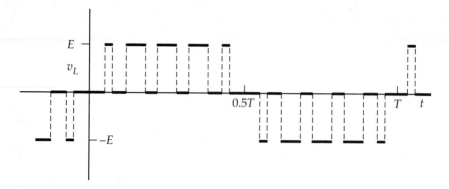

FIGURE 8.9

An approximate analysis for the coefficients of the Fourier series can be done as follows (the discrete pulse widths are given by the symbol t_{pi}):

$$t_{pi} = m(\sin \omega_0 t_i)\left(\frac{T}{2k}\right),\qquad(8.22)$$

where k is once again the number of pulses per half-cycle and

$$t_i = \left[\left(\frac{T}{2k}\right)(i + 0.5)\right],\qquad i = 0, 1, 2, \ldots, (k-1).\qquad(8.23)$$

The coefficients of the Fourier series are found by evaluating Equation 8.24:

$$B_n = \left(\frac{4}{T}\right)\int_0^{T/2} E t_{pi}[\delta(t_i)](\sin n\omega_0 t)\, dt.\qquad(8.24)$$

On substituting Equation 8.22, we obtain the result of Equation 8.25:

$$B_n = \left(\frac{2mE}{k}\right)\left[\sum_{i=0}^{k-1} (\sin \omega_0 t_i)(\sin n\omega_0 t_i)\right].\qquad(8.25)$$

For the case in which $k = 5$,

$$B_n = (0.4mE)\begin{bmatrix}\left(\sin\dfrac{\pi}{10}\right)\left(\sin\dfrac{n\pi}{10}\right) + \left(\sin\dfrac{3\pi}{10}\right)\left(\sin\dfrac{3n\pi}{10}\right) \\[2mm] + \left(\sin\dfrac{\pi}{2}\right)\left(\sin\dfrac{n\pi}{2}\right) + \left(\sin\dfrac{7\pi}{10}\right)\left(\sin\dfrac{7n\pi}{10}\right) \\[2mm] + \left(\sin\dfrac{9\pi}{10}\right)\left(\sin\dfrac{9n\pi}{10}\right)\end{bmatrix}\qquad(8.26)$$

Upon evaluation of this equation, the results in Table 8.2 are obtained.

—— **TABLE 8.2** ——

Coefficient	Value
B_1	mE
B_3	0
B_5	0
B_7	0
B_9	mE
B_{11}	$-mE$
B_{13}	0
B_{15}	0
B_{17}	0
B_{19}	$-mE$
B_{21}	$-mE$

Ideally, the result is a complete suppression of the low-order harmonics and a fundamental component directly proportional to the relative pulse width. If additional harmonics are evaluated, nonzero values occur for harmonic orders as given by Equation 8.27. These higher-order terms are of the same relative size as the fundamental, but because they are high-order harmonics they are suppressed more easily by filtering elements. In Equation 8.27, r is any positive integer:

$$n = 2kr \pm 1. \tag{8.27}$$

In the actual implementation, the pulses cannot be truly represented by impulse functions, because the pulse has a finite width. Furthermore, the usual implementation, as shown later, causes a slight shift in the position of the center of the pulse as compared to its ideal position. As a result, the preceding analysis is only approximately correct.

An exact Fourier series of the preceding illustration for a value of $k = 5$ and for $m = 0.2$ yields the results in Tables 8.3 and 8.4. These results differ only very slightly from the values in Table 8.2, which were calculated by using the impulse representation.

———— **TABLE 8.3** ————

	Pulse	
Number	Centered At	Width
1	$18°$	$2.22°$
2	$54°$	$5.82°$
3	$90°$	$7.20°$
4	$126°$	$5.82°$
5	$162°$	$2.22°$

The results tabulated in Table 8.4 differ only slightly from the results in Table 8.2 using a value of $m = 0.2$. The difference that can occur using realistic waveforms with finite rise time probably is of the same order as the differences between the ideal results in Table 8.2 and the deviation shown in Table 8.4.

_____ TABLE 8.4 _____

Coefficient	Value
B_1	$0.1999E$
B_3	$0.0003E$
B_5	$0.0000E$
B_7	$0.0016E$
B_9	$0.1921E$
B_{11}	$-0.1883E$
B_{13}	$-0.0053E$
B_{15}	$-0.0002E$

It is evident that there are very substantial 9th and 11th harmonics, which are comparable to the fundamental amplitude. If these can be successfully filtered, then the solution using five pulses per half-cycle is satisfactory. If this filtering is not possible, then we require a larger number of pulses per half-cycle. In this manner, the harmonics from the switching operations can be of higher frequency and more easily removed by filtering.

EXAMPLE 8.4

Using the preceding PWM method, will a value of $k = 9$ limit the ripple current RMS value to 5% of the fundamental in the following inverter?

$$E = 200 \text{ V} \qquad R = 10 \ \Omega$$

$$f = 100 \text{ Hz} \qquad L = 0.02 \text{ H}.$$

The fundamental voltage is to be 100-V peak value.

Solution

$$m = \frac{100}{200} = 0.5$$

From Equation 8.25:

$$B_1 = \left[\frac{(2)(E)(0.5)}{9} \right] \begin{bmatrix} (\sin 10°)(\sin 10°) + (\sin 30°)(\sin 30°) \\ + (\sin 50°)(\sin 50°) + (\sin 70°)(\sin 70°) \\ + (\sin 90°)(\sin 90°) + (\sin 110°)(\sin 110°) \\ + (\sin 130°)(\sin 130°) + (\sin 150°)(\sin 150°) \\ + (\sin 170°)(\sin 170°) \end{bmatrix}$$

$$= 0.5E.$$

$$B_3 = \left[\frac{(2)(E)(0.5)}{9}\right] \begin{bmatrix} (\sin 10°)(\sin 30°) + (\sin 30°)(\sin 90°) \\ + (\sin 50°)(\sin 150°) + (\sin 70°)(\sin 210°) \\ + (\sin 90°)(\sin 270°) + (\sin 110°)(\sin 330°) \\ + (\sin 130°)(\sin 390°) + (\sin 150°)(\sin 450°) \\ + (\sin 170°)(\sin 510°) \end{bmatrix}$$

$$= 0.$$

The first nonzero harmonic is evaluated from Equation 8.27 with $r = 1$:

$$n = [(2)(9)(1)] + 1 = 19 \qquad \text{or} \qquad n = [(2)(9)(1)] - 1 = 17$$

$$B_{17} = 0.5E = 100 \text{ V}$$

$$B_{19} = 0.5E = 100 \text{ V.}$$

The 21st and higher harmonics are zero up to the 33rd-order harmonic. If these higher harmonics are neglected, the harmonic current can be calculated.

$$|I_1| = \left|\frac{B_1}{Z_1}\right| = \left|\frac{100}{10 + j12.56}\right|$$

$$= 6.23\text{-A peak} = 4.40\text{-A RMS}$$

$$|I_{17}| = \left|\frac{B_{17}}{Z_{17}}\right| = \left|\frac{100}{10 + j(17)(12.56)}\right|$$

$$= 0.47\text{-A peak}$$

$$|I_{19}| = \left|\frac{B_{19}}{Z_{19}}\right| = \left|\frac{100}{10 + j(19)(12.56)}\right|$$

$$= 0.42\text{-A peak}$$

$$\text{Harmonic RMS value} = \left[\frac{(0.47)^2 + (0.42)^2}{2}\right]^{1/2}$$

$$= 0.444 \text{ A.}$$

Thus, the harmonic component of load current, including additional harmonics, exceeds 10% of the fundamental current. The value of k can be increased to provide a solution. ∎

Both analog and digital methods can be used to generate the switch turn-on signals required to implement this PWM method. One analog process that has been used to generate a triangular waveform with a frequency $2k$ times that of the inverter output as well as generate a signal-level absolute value sinusoid of the desired frequency and of the desired amplitude, which is shown in Figure 8.10.

A pulse is initiated at the intersection of the sinusoid with a negative slope part of the triangular waveform. The pulse is terminated when the sinusoid intersects with a positive slope part of the triangular waveform. The figure shows

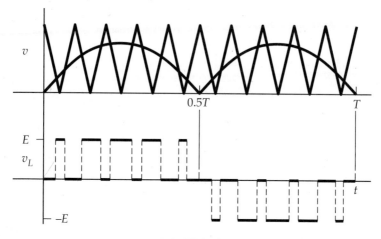

FIGURE 8.10

that each pulse has a duration that varies approximately sinusoidally throughout each cycle. Furthermore, each pulse length is related to the amplitude of the sinusoid shown in Figure 8.10. The logic must be such that the polarity of the output is reversed for each half-cycle.

In the example of Figure 8.10, for $k = 5$, the first pulse should be centered at approximately $18°$ from the origin. For the case of $m = 0.2$, intersections of the sinusoid with the triangular waveform occur at $16.95°$ and $19.18°$, with the pulse centered at $18.07°$ instead of $18°$. This small difference has a negligible but nonzero effect on the resulting harmonics that are present. The pulse width is $2.23°$, which essentially is the value used in calculating the values in Tables 8.3 and 8.4.

For the case of $m = 0.2$ and $k = 5$ as shown in Figure 8.10, the Fourier series coefficients are determined as listed in Table 8.5. Again, only negligible differences exist between the values in the table and those previously obtained.

TABLE 8.5

Coefficient	Value
B_1	$0.2000E$
B_3	$0.0000E$
B_5	$0.0000E$
B_7	$0.0032E$
B_9	$0.1903E$
B_{11}	$-0.1903E$
B_{13}	$-0.0032E$
B_{15}	$-0.0003E$

Implementing this method of pulse-width modulation requires a means of directing proper signals to each of the switches to generate the PWM pattern in Figure 8.10. Each element making up the four ideal switches of the bridge inverter must be furnished the proper control signal at each switching instant. The circuit in Figure 8.11 shows a bridge inverter with the four switches implemented by four BJTs and four diode elements. The graph in Figure 8.12 shows a PWM switching pattern with five pulses per half-cycle. For the purpose of the graph, the load current is approximated by a sinusoidal waveform even though the actual current has higher-order harmonics. Figure 8.12 also shows transistor collector currents, diode currents, and required transistor base currents. Because the load current direction at any instant is unknown, the transistor base currents must be generated in certain intervals even though a diode in parallel actually provides the conduction path.

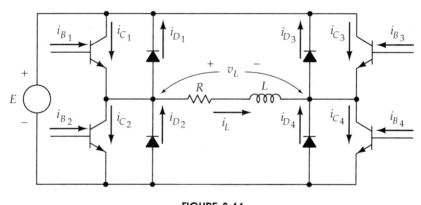

FIGURE 8.11

For the sake of simplicity, two details are not shown in Figures 8.11 and 8.12. Snubber circuits across each transistor should be provided to control the collector-to-emitter voltage during transistor turnoff. In addition, to prevent a possible short circuit on the source voltage, the newly conducting transistor is inhibited from turn on for a short period after the turnoff of the previously conducting transistor in the same pole. This is necessary to allow the first transistor to be completely off before the second transistor turns on. For example, in Figure 8.12 the pulses for the base current of Q_1 occur immediately after the completion of the pulses of base current for Q_2. This is the time at which a short delay of a few microseconds for the base current of Q_1 is required.

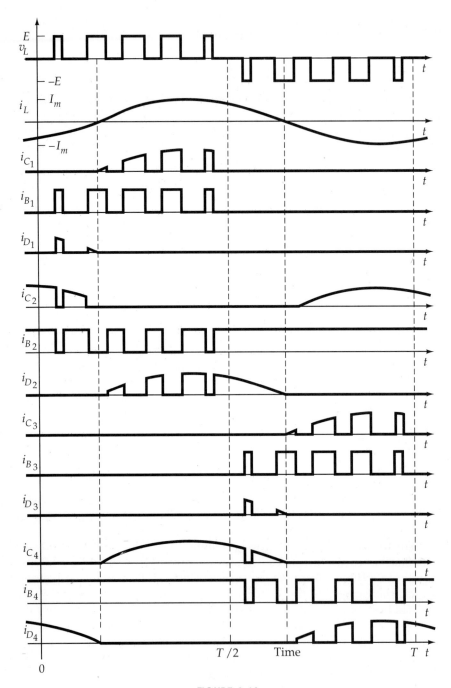

FIGURE 8.12

8.4

POLYPHASE INVERTERS

The various techniques in the preceding sections can be used to construct a polyphase inverter. This almost certainly will be the polyphase version of the bridge inverter and, as a practical matter, it will be a three-phase inverter. A bridge inverter permits the use of one DC source as input to the system. The circuit arrangement in Figure 8.13 is the obvious extension of the single-phase case.

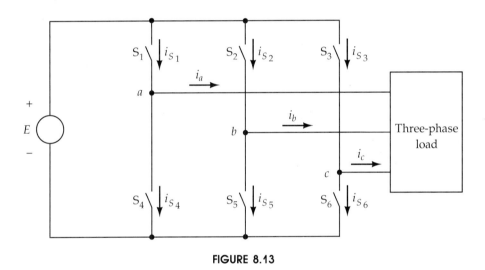

FIGURE 8.13

The inverter's six switches are opened and closed periodically to produce the desired output waveform. The pattern of switching determines the inverter output frequency and the manner in which the voltage and harmonics are controlled. The arrangement in Figure 8.13 can be described as a voltage source inverter. A reasonable approximation to an ideal voltage source is used for a power source. A filter capacitor at the output of a rectifier is a frequently used practical implementation for this voltage source. The DC source currents change as required to satisfy the circuit equations.

Another possibility is a current source inverter. The voltage source in Figure 8.13 is replaced by a current source. This usually is implemented by a phase-controlled rectifier in series with a relatively large value inductor. This inductor maintains constant current throughout the time of any one cycle of operation. The actual value of this constant current is variable, depending on the load requirements. This mode of operation will not be discussed further in this text.

Six-Step Inverter

The simplest control closes each switch for 180° of the output cycle and opens the switch for the remaining 180°. The six switches are closed in a cyclic pattern to produce a three-phase output: S_2 is closed 120° after S_1, and S_3 is closed 120° after S_2; S_4 is closed 180° after S_1, with S_5 and S_6 closed 180° after S_2 and S_3, respectively. The result of this switching operation is that a switch closes (and one also opens) each 60° The output is described as a six-step waveform. The switches that are closed are shown in Table 8.6.

_____ **TABLE 8.6** _____

Interval (°)	Switches Closed
0– 60	1–3–5
60–120	1–5–6
120–180	1–2–6
180–240	2–4–6
240–300	2–3–4
300–360	3–4–5

To determine the various waveforms of the load voltage, let the load be a balanced, wye-connected, resistive load of $R\,\Omega$ per phase. The circuit analysis can be done by considering in turn each of the six intervals. During the interval 0°–60°, the circuit is as shown in Figure 8.14(a). The closure of switches S_1 and S_3 puts Phases a and c in parallel, with Phase b connected to the source by way of S_5. As a result of this connection, the voltages are as given in Table 8.7. During the interval from 60° to 120°, the circuit is as shown in Figure 8.14(b). The values for all six intervals of one cycle also are given in Table 8.7, and are used to plot the graphs in Figure 8.15.

The graph for any one of the line-neutral voltages has six discontinuities per cycle that correspond to the six switching points per cycle. This, of course, is the origin of the "six-step" term that describes this inverter.

As long as the load is resistive, the line current to the load is the same waveform as the line-neutral voltage. Most inverter applications are at least partly inductive, so the line-current waveform is different from that of the line-neutral voltage. Many such six-step inverters are used to drive an induction motor; the current waveform in Figure 8.16 illustrates such a motor load for one phase.

During the 0°–60° interval, the value of i_a is first negative but then changes with time to a positive value. S_1 is closed during this interval; this switch and the other five switches thus must possess a bidirectional current capability. Most generally, a PN-junction diode is placed in parallel with another element such as a BJT. The BJT carries the positive portion of the current, and the inverse-connected diode carries the negative part of the current. (During the interval

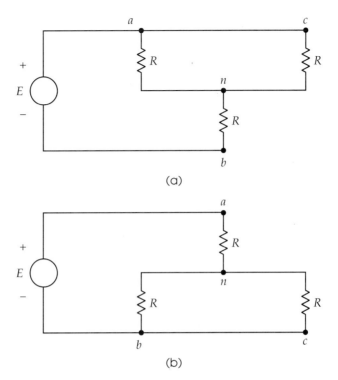

(a)

(b)

FIGURE 8.14

TABLE 8.7

Voltage	Interval (°)					
	0–60	60–120	120–180	180–240	240–300	300–360
v_{an}	$E/3$	$2E/3$	$E/3$	$-E/3$	$-2E/3$	$-E/3$
v_{bn}	$-2E/3$	$-E/3$	$E/3$	$2E/3$	$E/3$	$-E/3$
v_{cn}	$E/3$	$-E/3$	$-2E/3$	$-E/3$	$E/3$	$2E/3$
v_{ab}	E	E	0	$-E$	$-E$	0
v_{bc}	$-E$	0	E	E	0	$-E$
v_{ca}	0	$-E$	$-E$	0	E	E

$180°$—$360°$, switch S_4 is closed, with the result that the BJT carries the negative part of i_a and the PN-junction diode carries the positive part of i_a.)

To evaluate the stress on the switching device, a detailed examination at one switching point is in order. In Figure 8.16, the region near $t = 0$ is examined in detail. This region is shown with the time scale expanded in Figure 8.17. For the very expanded time scale, i_a may be considered to be constant, at least for

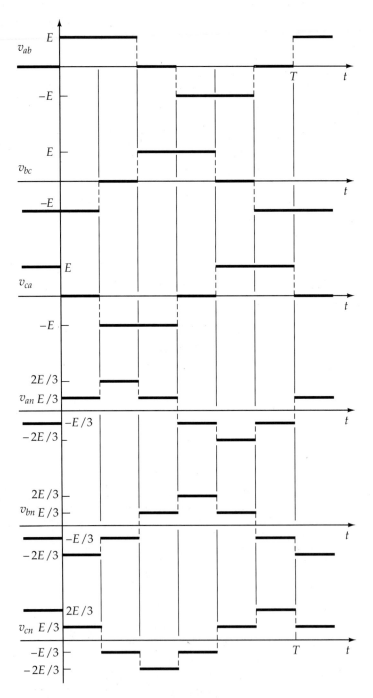

FIGURE 8.15

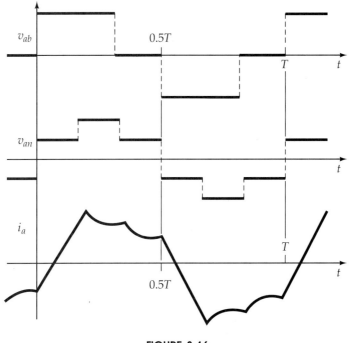

FIGURE 8.16

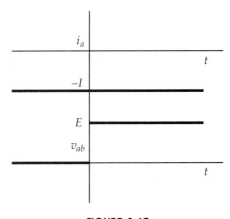

FIGURE 8.17

the two or three microseconds of the switching action. In Figure 8.17, the voltage plotted is v_{ag}, which is the voltage across S_4. Figure 8.18 shows the pertinent circuit elements, with S_4 implemented with a BJT in parallel with a PN-junction diode.

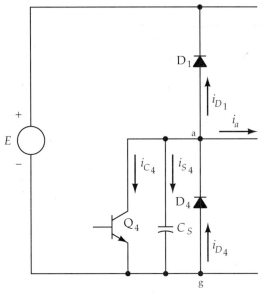

FIGURE 8.18

Just before the switching point, Q_4 has been conducting i_a as its collector current (i_a is negative). At the switching point, Q_4 begins to turnoff; as it does so, its collector current is reduced to less than the magnitude of i_a. The current i_a must be maintained because the load is inductive. The only way the current equation can be satisfied at Node a is for diode D_1 to conduct. As this occurs, D_1 is no longer reverse-biased, the voltage across D_1 goes to zero, and the voltage v_{ag} becomes equal to E. This means that transistor Q_4 must support a collector-to-emitter voltage of E at the same time that it has appreciable collector current. Thus, a potential RBSOA problem exists. If the inverter designer has underutilized the transistor capability, there may be no problem; but if the designer is using the transistor near its operating limit, a problem is possible. A snubber is required to shape the transistor load line so as to move it into the safe part of the RBSOA graph. Generally, snubber components cost less than the use of an unduly large transistor.

With a snubber present, the transistor's collector-to-emitter voltage cannot rise rapidly, with the result that the snubber carries part of the load current until the transistor is fully turned off. Only after the collector current is zero, or nearly so, does the collector-to-emitter voltage reach full value and only then does the diode of the other switch begin to conduct. This behavior, similar to that considered in Chapter 4, is shown in Figure 8.19.

As previously mentioned, the six-step inverter is used frequently to drive a three-phase induction motor. In those cases, the inverter output voltage and frequency must be changed together to prevent undesirable changes in the

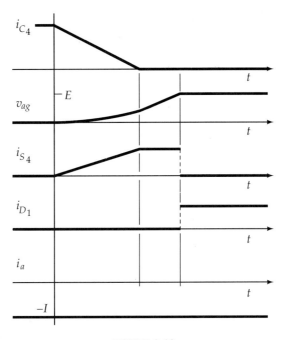

FIGURE 8.19

motor's maximum flux density. The motor is designed so that magnetic saturation does not occur at normal operating voltage and frequency.

The area under a half-cycle at rated line-neutral voltage at rated frequency
determines the motor's maximum flux density under normal conditions. The
relations in Equations 8.28 and 8.29 express this requirement for a sinusoidal
applied voltage. These equations make use of the fact that maximum flux density
depends on average voltage:

$$KB_{max} = \text{area} = \left(\frac{2}{\pi}\right)\left[1.414\left(\frac{V_1}{1.732}\right)\right]\left(\frac{T_1}{2}\right) \tag{8.28}$$

$$= 0.260 V_1 T_1. \tag{8.29}$$

In these equations, V_1 is the rated RMS L–L voltage of the motor, T_1 is the
rated period, and K is a constant that incorporates motor dimensions and number
of turns.

The area under a half-cycle of a six-step waveform applied to the motor
is related to maximum flux density in a similar manner for the variable frequency
case in Equation 8.30:

$$KB_{max} = \text{area} = \left[\left(\frac{E}{3}\right) + \left(\frac{2E}{3}\right) + \left(\frac{E}{3}\right)\right]\left(\frac{T}{6}\right). \tag{8.30}$$

If the maximum flux density in Equation 8.30 is specified at the same value as for normal sinusoidal motor voltage, Equations 8.29 and 8.30 may be combined to produce Equation 8.31:

$$E = (1.170V_1 T_1)f, \qquad\qquad (8.31)$$

where f is the variable output frequency of the six-step inverter.

The DC bus voltage required for constant maximum flux density must vary in proportion to output frequency. Such inverters usually are operated in a mode, which satisfies Equation 8.31. Generally, this is described as a "constant volts/hertz" mode of operation.

If the motor is required to operate above its normal rated frequency, the inverter frequently is designed so that constant volts/hertz may not be obtained in this frequency range. The maximum value of DC bus voltage generally is required for operation at or near rated frequency. Above rated frequency, a larger value of bus voltage thus is not available. The motor therefore operates at less than rated maximum flux density and is unable to produce the same maximum torque as is available at lower frequency operation. This mode tends to limit the maximum output power and frequently is described as a "constant horsepower" mode of operation.

E X A M P L E   8 . 5

A six-step variable frequency inverter supplies a 230-V, three-phase, 60-Hz induction motor from a 230-V, 60-Hz single-phase source. The arrangement of the rectifier limits the variable DC bus voltage to 300 V. Find:

(a) the DC bus voltage for 10-Hz operation

(b) the highest frequency for which normal motor flux density can be maintained

(c) the fraction of maximum motor torque that can be developed at 100-Hz inverter output.

Solution

(a) Using Equation 8.31:

$$E = (1.17)(230)\left(\frac{1}{60}\right)(10) = 44.9 \text{ V}.$$

(b) Again using Equation 8.31:

$$300 = (1.17)(230)\left(\frac{1}{60}\right)(f)$$

$$f = 66.9 \text{ Hz}.$$

(c) For $f = 100$ Hz, the maximum flux in the motor is reduced because E is limited to 300 V. The value of E should be

$$E = (1.17)(230)\left(\frac{1}{60}\right)(100) = 448.5 \text{ V}.$$

The fraction of normal flux density is given by the ratio of actual to desired voltage:

$$\% \text{ Flux density} = \frac{300}{448.5} = 66.9\%.$$

Maximum torque therefore is reduced to this value rather than the normal available maximum torque at rated conditions.   ∎

PWM: Polyphase Inverter

The six-step inverter discussed in the preceding section requires a relatively simple inverter control, but this is accomplished at the expense of providing a required variable DC source voltage. If the inverter is of the PWM type, then a variable DC source voltage no longer is required. The PWM process can control the inverter output voltage magnitude, as well as control the output's harmonic content.

The PWM method in the polyphase inverter is more restricted in the sense that the method must provide a balanced set of voltages and must be arranged so that no even harmonics are introduced. One such restriction is that the number of pulses per half-cycle be divisible by three. A further restriction is that the number of pulses be odd. The process can be implemented in more than one way, so the method described is only a representative one. It may not be an optimal method, but it has the property of being relatively simple to understand and similar to the single-phase process.

In Figure 8.20, a triangular modulating wave is shown along with two sinusoids that are displaced by 120°. The sinusoids that have the desired output amplitude are centered around the middle of the triangular waveform. The process is applied to the basic three-phase bridge inverter shown in Figure 8.13. The a pole of the inverter, which consists of switches S_1 and S_4, is controlled in the following manner. If the a sinusoid is greater than the triangular waveform, then switch S_1 is closed with S_4 being open. Alternately, if the sinusoid is less than the triangular waveform, S_4 is closed with S_1 being open. The resulting voltage of Point a with respect to the DC negative bus, Point g, is shown in Figure 8.21. In a similar manner, Phase b pole is controlled using the B sinusoid, with the result also shown in the figure. The pattern is the same as for Phase A except that it is shifted to the right by 120°. Although not shown, Phase C is controlled in a similar manner.

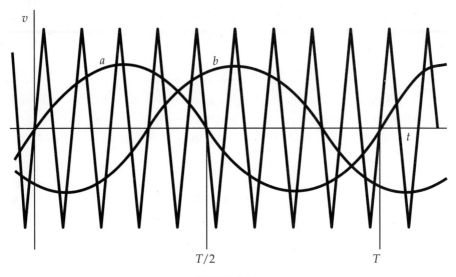

FIGURE 8.20

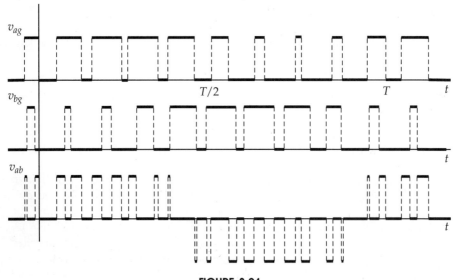

FIGURE 8.21

One of the line-to-line voltages applied to the inverter load (usually a three-phase motor) also is shown in Figure 8.21. This voltage is found by subtracting the B pole voltage from that for the A pole. It should be noted that the voltages such as from A to the negative bus are not the same as the line-to-neutral voltages of the motor.

PWM Analysis

With the triangular timing wave shown in Figure 8.21, let there be k periods of the triangular waveform for each full period of the sinusoid. This is in contrast to the definition of k in the single-phase case. The value of m as applied in this case is the fraction that the peak of the sinusoid bears to one-half of the triangular peak-to-peak amplitude.

If the resulting pole voltage in Figure 8.21 has the DC part, which is $E/2$, removed, then the resulting waveform is an odd function with half-period symmetry. As a result, only odd-order sine terms are in the Fourier series for the remaining part. After the DC part is removed, there are k pulses per half-period. These pulses are of alternating sign. The pulses shown in Figure 8.21 can be represented approximately by pulses whose width and position are given in the following equations.

The pulse width t_{pi} is given by Equation 8.32:

$$t_{pi} = \left(\frac{T}{2k}\right)[1 + (-1)^i(m)(\sin \omega_0 t_i)] \qquad i = 1, 2, \ldots, k. \qquad \textbf{(8.32)}$$

In Equation 8.32, the pulse locations for a half-period are given by Equation 8.33:

$$t_i = \left(\frac{T}{2k}\right)(i - 0.5) \qquad i = 1, 2, \ldots, k. \qquad \textbf{(8.33)}$$

If Equations 8.32 and 8.33 are used to calculate pulse widths and locations, the results for $k = 9$ and $m = 0.2$ are given in Table 8.8(a). If the modulating method shown in Figures 8.20 and 8.21 is used to determine the pulse widths and locations, the numbers in Table 8.8(b) result.

TABLE 8.8

	(a) Pulse			(b) Pulse	
Number	Location	Width	Number	Location	Width
1	10°	19.31°	1	9.67°	19.34°
2	30°	22.00°	2	30.33°	21.98°
3	50°	16.94°	3	49.81°	16.98°
4	70°	23.76°	4	70.14°	23.68°
5	90°	16.00°	5	90.00°	16.04°
6	110°	23.76°	6	109.86°	23.68°
7	130°	16.94°	7	130.19°	16.98°
8	150°	22.00°	8	149.67°	21.98°
9	170°	19.31°	9	170.33°	19.34°

The intersections of the triangular waveform and sinusoidal waveform were determined by a simultaneous numerical solution of appropriate equations. A comparison of the two tables shows little difference between the ideal pulse width and locations as compared to what might be implemented in practice.

The pulses in Table 8.8 are negative for odd pulse numbers and positive for even pulse numbers.

The Fourier series coefficients for the pulses in Equations 8.32 and 8.33 can be expressed by integrating over a half-period. Each pulse again is replaced by an equivalent impulse function:

$$B_n = 2\left(\frac{2}{T}\right) \int_0^{T/2} \left(\frac{E}{2}\right) t_{pi}[(-1)^i \delta(t_i)] \sin n\omega_0 t \, dt. \tag{8.34}$$

Using properties of an impulse function, the above result can be expressed by Equation 8.35:

$$B_n = \left(\frac{E}{k}\right)\left[\sum_{i=1}^{k}(-1)^i \sin n\omega_0 t_i + \sum_{i=1}^{k} m(\sin \omega_0 t_i)(\sin n\omega_0 t_i)\right]. \tag{8.35}$$

The first summation is identically zero for all n, so the result can be simplified to Equation 8.36:

$$B_n = \left(\frac{mE}{k}\right) \sum_{i=1}^{k} (\sin \omega_0 t_i)(\sin n\omega_0 t_i). \tag{8.36}$$

This result is for the harmonics in the pole voltage. The line-to-line motor voltage is found by using the difference between two of the pole voltages, as shown in Equation 8.37. There is no DC part of the line-to-line voltages because of this difference:

$$v_{ab} = v_{ag} - v_{bg}. \tag{8.37}$$

The line-to-line voltage contains the same harmonics as the pole voltage, except for harmonics that are multiples of three—these cannot exist. This results because the three pole voltages differ by $120°$, and such harmonics that are multiples of three have pole voltages that differ by $360°$. When the above difference of pole voltages is formulated, such harmonics do not then appear in the line-to-line voltage.

EXAMPLE 8.6

In the graphs in Figures 8.20 and 8.21, let $k = 9$ and $m = 0.5$. Find the harmonic amplitudes for the output line-to-line voltages.

Solution   Evaluating the harmonics for the pole voltage by Equations 8.33 and 8.36 gives the following results:

$$B_1 = 0.25E \qquad B_{11} = 0$$
$$B_3 = 0 \qquad B_{13} = 0$$

$$B_5 = 0 \qquad\qquad B_{15} = 0$$
$$B_7 = 0 \qquad\qquad B_{17} = 0.25E$$
$$B_9 = 0 \qquad\qquad B_{19} = 0.25E.$$

In addition to the values shown, B_{35}, B_{37}, and some higher-order harmonics also are nonzero.

The magnitudes of the harmonics of the line-to-line voltages are given by Equation 8.37:

$$\left|B_1\right| = (1.732)(0.25)E = 0.433E$$
$$\left|B_{17}\right| = 0.433E$$
$$\left|B_{19}\right| = 0.433E. \qquad\qquad\qquad ■$$

In the preceding example, the maximum fundamental line-to-line voltage would have been $0.866E$ if $m = 1.0$ had been used. This is the largest value possible with the modulating method shown. For the same DC bus voltage using the six-step method, the corresponding value is $1.10E$. One method to increase the fundamental voltage is by increasing the amplitude of the comparison sinusoid so that it exceeds the triangular waveform; this removes pulses from the $90°$ and $270°$ portion of the pole voltage. The harmonic content will change, but the result is acceptable; this is done only at high output voltage and therefore at high output frequency. Some of the harmonics, although low in order (perhaps 11th and 13th), have a large absolute frequency, and their effects are reduced to an acceptable level by the filtering action of the load impedance.

Number of Pulses per Cycle

In the operation of a PWM inverter over the usual range of output frequency, if the benefits of the PWM are to be realized, then it is important to limit the amplitude of the harmonic currents to a small value. As the inverter output frequency is reduced toward zero, even a relatively high harmonic term such as the 17th may have a frequency that is small as an absolute number. As an example, the current that results from this term could be large. To solve this problem, it is usual to increase the number of pulses per cycle as the frequency is reduced. This means that additional harmonic terms can be reduced in the output.

Because there are constraints on the number of pulses per cycle such as being an integer and being divisible by three, the usual practice is to increase the number by discrete steps at several points in the range of output frequency. At the lowest frequency, the number of pulses per cycle typically would be greater than 100. For motor operation at the frequency where this change is to occur, there can be a back-and-forth switching in the number of pulses per cycle for small frequency changes. To eliminate this problem, it is usual to introduce a small amount of hysteresis so that switching the pulse number occurs at a different frequency for increasing output frequency than it does for decreasing output frequency.

8.5
PROBLEMS

8.1   An inverter like that in Figure 8.3 supplies a load of 25 Ω in series with an inductance of 0.05 H; $E = 250$ V and $T = 8$ ms. Find:

(a) peak switch current   (b) BJT conduction time

(c) diode conduction time   (d) average diode current.

8.2   In an inverter like that in Figure 8.3 the following data are known: $E = 150$ V, $R = 20$ Ω, and $T = 10$ ms.

(a) Find a value of load inductance such that the peak load current does not exceed 5 A.

(b) Find the average diode current.

8.3   A bridge inverter like that in Figure 8.5 has the following data: $E = 200$ V, $R = 30$ Ω, $L = 0.16$ H, $T = 12.5$ ms. The switches are implemented using PN-junction diodes and BJTs. Find:

(a) peak switch current

(b) BJT conduction time each half-cycle

(c) diode conduction time each half-cycle

(d) the average source current

(e) the average load power.

8.4   In a bridge inverter using the technique of Figure 8.6, the value of α_1 is 25°; $E = 100$ V. Find the fundamental and third harmonic components of the output voltage.

8.5   In Problem 8.4, the value of B_1 is required to be 110 V.

(a) Find a value of α_1 to accomplish this.

(b) Find the corresponding value of B_3.

8.6   Using the switching method in Figure 8.7, an inverter is required to eliminate the fifth and seventh harmonic components. Find:

(a) values of α_1 and α_2

(b) the fundamental output voltage if $E = 100$ V.

8.7   An inverter uses the PWM method shown in Figure 8.8; $E = 80$ V, $k = 7$, $m = 0.5$, and $T = 12.5$ ms. Find:

(a) the width of each pulse   (b) the value of B_1, B_3, and B_5.

8.8   An inverter uses the sinusoidal PWM method shown in Figure 8.9; $T = 10$ ms, $E = 100$ V, $R = 20\ \Omega$, $L = 0.06$ H, $m = 0.6$, and $k = 7$. Find:

(a) the fundamental component of load current

(b) the order of the first nonzero harmonic component

(c) the RMS value of load current, including all nonzero harmonics through the 29th.

8.9   A load consisting of $R = 25\ \Omega$ in series with $L = 0.1$ H is supplied with a fundamental voltage component of 100 V from a 200-V DC source. The modulation method is PWM like that in Figure 8.9. The total harmonic current must not exceed 8% of the fundamental RMS current value. Select a k value that meets this objective, if $f = 100$ Hz.

8.10   Using the graphs in Figure 8.10 and with $k = 5$, evaluate B_{13} for $m = 0.4$. Also determine the actual switching points.

8.11   A six-step inverter is supplied from a variable DC voltage. The load is a standard three-phase, 460-V induction motor. The DC voltage has an upper limit of 550 V.

(a) Find the appropriate DC bus voltage for an output frequency of 40 Hz.

(b) What fraction of normal motor flux density can be maintained with an output frequency of 90 Hz?

8.12   A three-phase PWM inverter with $E = 325$ V supplies a three-phase load; $k = 15$ and $m = 0.6$.

(a) Find the amplitude of the first four nonzero harmonics other than the fundamental.

(b) Using a load impedance of $(10 + jn10)\ \Omega$/phase, Y-connected, find the RMS value of the harmonic load current compared to the fundamental.

8.13   A PWM, three-phase inverter drives a 460-V, three-phase, 60-Hz induction motor using $k = 15$. The DC bus voltage is 650 V.

(a) What is the largest value of output frequency for which the full fundamental voltage can be maintained using this modulation method?

(b) What fraction of rated maximum fundamental torque can be developed at a frequency of 80 Hz?

CHAPTER · 9

Design Considerations

To realize a successful design, the semiconductor switches must survive in their environment. Two areas of the environment that we will consider in this chapter are device-junction temperature and the control of excessive values of switch current or voltage. If too little attention is given to these areas, the equipment, in which the switches are installed, may be subject to frequent failure.

9.1
SEMICONDUCTOR JUNCTION TEMPERATURE

The junction temperature of a semiconductor device is critical in determining the device's survival and lifetime in any application. Calculation of junction temperature therefore is a necessary part of the design process.

The actual heat-flow process is three-dimensional, but experience has shown that one-dimensional analysis is satisfactory for most purposes. With this simplification, a thermal resistance between the device junction and other portions of the heat-transfer path can be used to model the junction heating process for time-invariant cases. For time-varying cases, thermal resistance is replaced by transient thermal impedance.

Steady-State Junction Temperature

In the steady-state, junction-temperature calculations are modeled by a thermal resistance that has several components and is expressed in $^\circ C/W$. For a power semiconductor mounted on a heat sink, three components are generally considered. The first is the thermal resistance between the device junction and the device case denoted as R_{JC}; the second is the thermal resistance, R_{CS}, which models the imperfect interface between the semiconductor device case and the heat sink; and finally there is the thermal resistance, R_{SA}, which models the effect of heat rejection to the surrounding ambient environment.

The electrical circuit analog for the thermal circuit is shown in Figure 9.1. An equation for the solution of this steady-state process is that of Equation 9.1, where P is the average power generated in the junction region of the semiconductor device, T_A is the surrounding ambient temperature, and T_J is the junction temperature:

$$T_J = T_A + P(R_{JC} + R_{CS} + R_{SA}).\qquad(9.1)$$

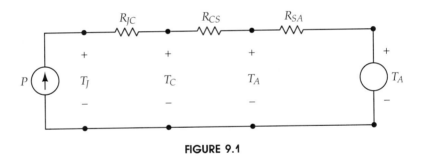

FIGURE 9.1

The value of R_{JC} is determined by the internal device construction and is fixed by semiconductor die size, internal-mounting considerations, and the particular semiconductor package. The manufacturer specifies the value as a maximum on the device datasheet.

The interface between the semiconductor and the heat sink can be quite variable depending upon manufacturing procedures and assembly methods. The microscopic surfaces of the device and heat sink are not perfectly flat, parallel surfaces. Contact at the mating surface is imperfect, and a temperature differential exists between the two surfaces. In addition to this imperfect contact, it may be necessary to isolate electrically the semiconductor package from the heat sink. This causes a further increase in the thermal resistance of the interface.

Materials that are otherwise suitable for this electrical isolation also should be good thermal conductors. This requirement is almost contradictory. Materials that are used for this purpose with reasonable success include mica sheets, plastic films such as Kapton©, aluminum washers with electrically insulating anodized surfaces, and beryllium oxide wafers.

The interface between the device case and the heat sink frequently is improved by including a thermal grease to fill the air gap between the two surfaces. The thermal conduction property of the grease is much better than the air that is displaced. The interface region shown in Figure 9.2 is a greatly exaggerated view of the region between the semiconductor device and the heat sink. Better contact can be achieved by forcing the two surfaces closer together by the mounting used as well as by using a thermal grease.

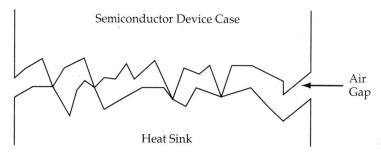

FIGURE 9.2

The numerical effect of using a thermal grease is evident from the following. A TO-204 case device has a value of approximately $0.5°$ C/W for R_{CS} when mounted without a thermal grease. Using a film of thermal grease in the gap decreases the thermal resistance to approximately $0.15°$ C/W. If an insulator such as a hard anodized aluminum washer is used, these numbers are approximately $1.2°$ C/W and $0.3°$ C/W, respectively. These numbers demonstrate the need to use a thermal grease to lower semiconductor junction temperature and thereby improve reliability. In addition, the added thermal resistance resulting from electrical isolation of the semiconductor package is evident.

The transfer of heat from heat sink to ambient environment occurs primarily by air moving over the heat sink's surface from either natural convection or forced air motion. The heat sink usually is provided with multiple fins or other means to increase the surface area for a given overall volume. Heat transfer by radiation usually is a very small part of the process. Most applications use commercial heat sinks that have heat-transfer characteristics well documented by their suppliers. The thermal characteristic of the interface between the device and the heat sink also is provided.

EXAMPLE 9.1

A MOSFET of type MTM8N60 operates in a steady-state thermal condition and dissipates 10 W. It is mounted on a heat sink with $R_{SA} = 2.5°$ C/W. The surrounding ambient air is at $70°$ C. Find:

(a) the device junction temperature if mounted directly on the heat sink using a thermal grease ($R_{CS} = 0.15°$ C/W)

(b) the device junction temperature if mounted on the heat sink using an anodized aluminum insulating washer without any thermal grease ($R_{CS} = 1.2°$ C/W).

Solution

(a) From Appendix B, the datasheet for this device gives $R_{JC} = 0.83°$ C/W. From Equation 9.1:

$$T_J = 70 + 10(0.83 + 0.15 + 2.5) = 104.8° \text{ C}.$$

(b) Using a new value for R_{CS} in Equation 9.1:

$$T_J = 70 + 10(0.83 + 1.2 + 2.5) = 115.3° \text{ C}. \qquad \blacksquare$$

EXAMPLE 9.2

A BJT with power dissipation of 12 W is mounted on a heat sink in an ambient air temperature of $85°$ C. The semiconductor device is in a TO-204 package; its R_{CS} value can be reduced to $0.2°$ C/W by using a thermal grease. The value of R_{JC} is $0.83°$ C/W. The junction temperature cannot exceed $175°$ C. Complete the design by finding a suitable heat-sink thermal resistance.

Solution   Using Equation 9.1:

$$175 = 85 + 12(0.83 + 0.2 + R_{SA})$$
$$R_{SA} = 6.47° \text{ C/W}.$$

For reasons of reliability it is not desirable to operate the device at the limiting junction temperature. Good design requires a heat sink that is more capable than the value just calculated. $\blacksquare$

Single-Pulse Operation

Many power-electronics circuits operate in an on–off mode with time-varying power dissipation in the switching devices. The corresponding junction temperature is a function of time and the peak junction temperature must be limited to a safe value.

The concept of *transient thermal impedance* is useful in such calculations. The graph in Figure 9.3 shows the variation of junction temperature with time following the application of a certain junction power dissipation. Later, at time t_1, the power becomes zero and the junction temperature begins to decrease. The time interval in such situations usually is short enough that the semiconductor case temperature, T_C, does not change during the interval. The value of T_C thus may be considered constant for such temperature calculations. The constant nature of the case temperature is a result of the very large thermal storage capacity of the semiconductor case as compared to the thermal storage capacity of the semiconductor junction. Because the junction temperature is a function of time, it is possible to express junction temperature as in Equation 9.2:

$$T_J = T_C + r(t)R_{JC}P. \tag{9.2}$$

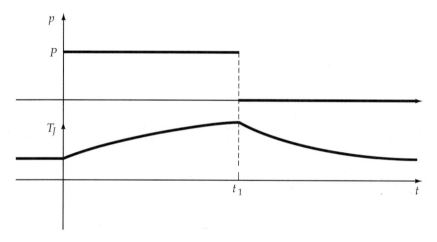

FIGURE 9.3

In Equation 9.2, $r(t)$ is a normalized thermal resistance expressed as a function of the time duration of the power pulse, thereby enabling a relation between temperature and time to be written. For large values of t_1, the value of $r(t)$ approaches unity and the value of R_{JC} determines the junction temperature rise above the case temperature. The graph in Figure 9.4 shows a typical variation of $r(t)$ as a function of time for a single-pulse situation.

EXAMPLE 9.3

A MOSFET of type MTM8N60 is used in a single-pulse mode to conduct 10 A with a drain-source voltage of 20 V for 10 ms. The device case temperature is 75° C. Find the junction temperature at the end of the pulse duration.

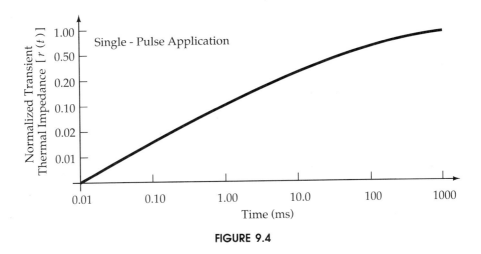

FIGURE 9.4

Solution   From the graph in Appendix B for single-pulse operation, $r(t) = 0.31$ for $t = 10$ ms. Also from the datasheet, $R_{JC} = 0.83°$ C/W. Using Equation 9.2:

$$T_J = 75 + (200)(0.31)(0.83) = 126.5° \text{ C}.$$

Upon removal of junction power dissipation at $t = 10$ ms, the junction temperature begins to decrease.   ∎

EXAMPLE 9.4

A MOSFET of type MTM8N60 is used in a single-pulse mode to conduct 20 A with a drain-source voltage of 12 V. With an initial case temperature of 50° C, find the pulse duration permitted by a maximum junction temperature of 120° C. From Example 9.3, the value of $R_{JC} = 0.83°$ C/W.

Solution   Using Equation 9.2:

$$120 = 50 + [r(t)](0.83)(20)(12)$$
$$r(t) = 0.602.$$

From the datasheet, the value of $r(t)$ corresponds to 65 ms.   ∎

Periodic Pulses

With periodic pulses of power to the semiconductor junction, the temperature also is periodic. The junction's thermal capacity limits the junction temperature excursion to less than the ultimate temperature that would be attained if the peak pulse power were to continue. Semiconductor datasheets frequently contain normalized transient thermal impedance curves for this case as well as for the single-pulse case. The graph in Figure 9.5 defines several of the terms to be

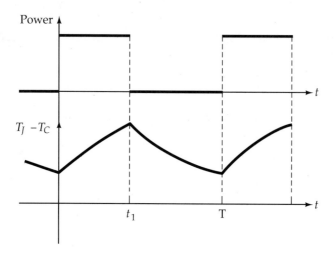

FIGURE 9.5

used. In such an operating mode, the interval T generally is short enough that the case temperature may be considered constant.

The relation between junction temperature and time still is expressed by Equation 9.2. In this case, however, $r(t)$ depends on the value of the duty cycle expressed by Equation 9.3 as well as the value of t_1:

$$D = \frac{t_1}{T}. \qquad (9.3)$$

The graph in Figure 9.6 shows typical values of $r(t)$ as a function of t_1 and D.

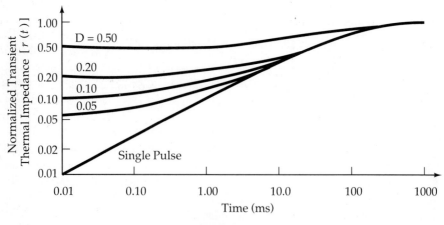

FIGURE 9.6

In this situation, Equation 9.2 remains valid. The values obtained from a graph like that in Figure 9.6 can be used in Equation 9.2 to obtain peak junction temperature at the end of each pulse interval. Example 9.5 illustrates such a calculation.

EXAMPLE 9.5

A BJT operates in a periodic manner at a frequency of 2 kHz. For 100 μs of each period, the device has a power dissipation of 100 W with zero dissipation during the remainder of each period. Use the data presented in Figure 9.6; $T_A = 65°$ C, $R_{CS} = 0.4°$ C/W, $R_{JC} = 1.2°$ C/W, and $T_J = 130°$ C maximum. Find:

(a) the maximum permitted value of T_C

(b) the required value of R_{SA}.

Solution

(a) From the graph in Figure 9.6 for $D = 0.2$ and $t = 100$ μs, the value of $r(t) = 0.21$. Using Equation 9.2:

$$130 = T_C + (0.21)(1.2)(100)$$
$$T_C = 104.8° \text{ C.}$$

(b) From Equation 9.1 and using an average value of dissipation of 20 W,

$$T_C = T_A + P(R_{CS} + R_{SA})$$
$$104.8 = 65 + 20(0.4 + R_{SA})$$
$$R_{SA} = 1.59° \text{ C/W.} \qquad \blacksquare$$

Some device datasheets do not supply data of the form shown in Figure 9.6, but do supply data such as those in Figure 9.4. In these cases, the peak junction temperature can be calculated by using superposition. To ensure that the peak calculated junction temperature represents a steady-state value, the calculation method must account for the time needed to reach an equilibrium state. The graph in Figure 9.7 shows the variation of junction temperature in relation to junction power. Peak junction temperature at the end of a power pulse is what is given when calculations are done using a graph like that in Figure 9.6.

If superposition is to be used for peak junction-temperature calculation, the graph in Figure 9.8 can be used to replace the pulse pattern in Figure 9.7. For the time before time equals zero, the junction power is the average power that corresponds to peak power and duty cycle. For $t > 0$, the actual periodic pulse power is used.

In Figure 9.8, the condition of average power existing before $t = 0$ produces a case and heat-sink temperature that corresponds to the average power

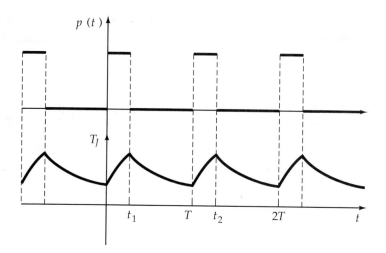

FIGURE 9.7

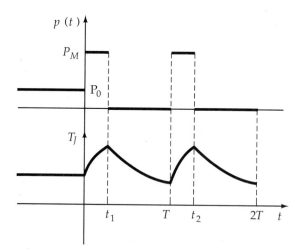

FIGURE 9.8

conditions. The period of power pulses is assumed to be so short that case temperature does not vary for time greater than zero. Within the accuracy of such calculations, the junction temperature thermal time constant generally is short enough that peak junction temperature calculated at $t = t_2$ is essentially at the steady-state value of peak junction temperature.

For the first pulse in Figure 9.8, the value of junction temperature at t_1 is higher than for succeeding pulses. This occurs because junction temperature at

$t = 0$ is higher than at the start of later pulses. At the time of the second pulse, conditions are nearly those of the periodic steady-state operation. The calculation process uses the superposition of several power components as shown in Figure 9.9. When combined, the components shown in this figure represent the actual waveform in Figure 9.8. Additional components could be used to represent conditions at the end of the third pulse in order for the junction temperature to be closer to the periodic equilibrium state. This refinement generally is not necessary for reasonable accuracy.

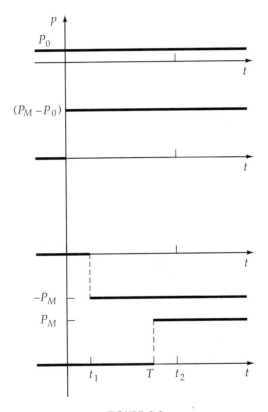

FIGURE 9.9

The junction temperature at $t = t_2$ can be calculated by summing the effects of each power component. The transient thermal impedance is calculated by using the interval that each power component has existed at $t = t_2$. The resulting peak junction temperature is calculated by using Equation 9.4:

$$T_J = T_C + (R_{JC})\{P_0 + (P_m - P_0)[r(t_2)] - [P_m r(T)] + [P_m r(t_1)]\}. \qquad (9.4)$$

In Equation 9.4, P_0 is given by Equation 9.5:

$$P_0 = P_m\left(\frac{t_1}{T}\right). \qquad (9.5)$$

EXAMPLE 9.6

A BJT, with the single-pulse $r(t)$ characteristic in Figure 9.4, has a peak power dissipation of 60 W occurring in a periodic manner for 2 ms of each period of 5 ms; $T_A = 60°$ C, $R_{JC} = 1.0°$ C/W, $R_{CS} = 0.3°$ C/W, and $R_{SA} = 1.5°$ C/W. Find the peak junction temperature.

Solution   Using Equation 9.5, the average power dissipation can be found so that the case temperature can be calculated:

$$P_0 = (60)\left(\frac{2}{5}\right) = 24 \text{ W}$$

$$T_C = T_A + P_0(R_{CS} + R_{SA})$$
$$= 70 + 24(0.3 + 1.5) = 113.2° \text{ C.}$$

From Figure 9.4, values of $r(t)$ are determined at 2 ms, 5 ms, and 7 ms. Using Equation 9.4:

$$T_J = 113.2 + 1.0[24 + (36)(0.27) - 60(0.24) + (60)(0.15)]$$
$$= 141.5° \text{ C.} \qquad \blacksquare$$

Some periodic situations produce power dissipation that is not constant during the conduction interval. The graph in Figure 9.10 represents the type of

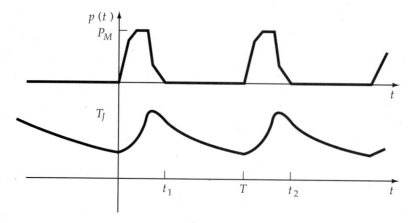

FIGURE 9.10

irregular power dissipation versus time that can occur in selected cases. Calculation of exact peak junction temperature for this case is difficult. The pulse shown in Figure 9.10 can be replaced by a periodic pulse of constant power of a different duration.

The graph in Figure 9.11 shows periodic power versus time, with constant power during the ON time and with the same energy loss per pulse as the actual pulse in Figure 9.10. The constant power in Figure 9.11 has a value equal to the peak value in Figure 9.10. The value of t_1' in Figure 9.11 therefore is necessarily smaller than t_1 in Figure 9.10.

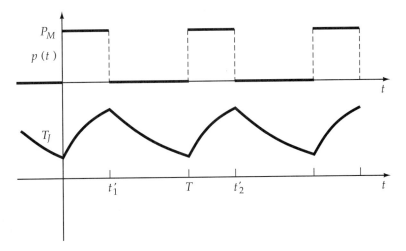

FIGURE 9.11

Peak junction temperature in Figure 9.11 is at least as large as the peak temperature in Figure 9.10 because the total energy dissipation is provided in a shorter interval. Calculations based on the modeling in Figure 9.11 are conservative; therefore, a design for which the junction temperature is satisfactory using Figure 9.11 is acceptable in regard to junction temperature.

Design procedure involves determining the peak pulse power and the area under each pulse in Figure 9.10. An equivalent pulse with the same period and constant power P_M is determined. For Figure 9.11, the pulse duration is calculated by Equation 9.6:

$$t_1' = \frac{\text{actual energy loss per pulse}}{P_M}. \tag{9.6}$$

Peak junction temperature for this equivalent pulse train is calculated by using the methods in the preceding sections.

EXAMPLE 9.7

A BJT is operated in a periodic manner with the losses as shown in Figure 9.12. The values of $r(t)$ may be determined from Figure 9.4; $R_{JC} = 0.9°\,C/W$, $R_{CS} = 0.4°\,C/W$, and $T_A = 70°\,C$. Find:

(a) the peak value of $(T_J - T_C)$

(b) the value of R_{SA} that limits the peak value of T_J to $140°\,C$.

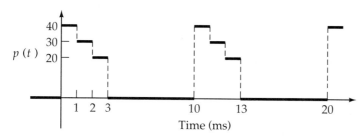

FIGURE 9.12

Solution

(a) The energy per pulse can be determined from the graph in Figure 9.12:

$$\text{Energy} = (40)(0.001) + (30)(0.001) + 20(0.001) = 0.090\;\text{J}.$$

Using Equation 9.6 with a value of 40 W for P_M, the equivalent time, t'_1, can be calculated:

$$t'_1 = \frac{0.090}{40} = 0.00225\;\text{s}.$$

From Figure 9.4, the values of $r(t)$ are determined at times of 2.25 ms, 10 ms, and 12.25 ms. These values are 0.16, 0.31, and 0.34, respectively.

From Equation 9.5, P_0 can be calculated:

$$P_0 = \left(\frac{2.25}{10}\right)(40) = 9\;\text{W}.$$

Using Equation 9.4, the value of $T_J - T_C$ can be calculated:

$$T_J - T_C = 0.9[9 + (31)(0.34) - 40(0.31) + (40)(0.16)]$$
$$= 12.2°\,C.$$

(b)
$$T_C = 140 - 12.2 = 127.8°\,C$$

From Equation 9.1:

$$T_C = T_A + P_0(R_{CS} + R_{SA})$$
$$127.8 = 70 + 9(0.4 + R_{SA})$$
$$R_{SA} = 6.0°\,C/W.$$

∎

9.2
PROTECTION

Power-electronics equipment requires protection against internal faults, external faults, and external disturbances. For example, an internal fault such as the failure of an SCR to turnoff should not cause damage to other components. An external short circuit of the load should not cause damage to an internal component. Finally, an electrical transient on the incoming power line should not cause semiconductor damage. Each of these generally can be prevented by suitable design. If possible, the protective feature should allow the system to resume normal operation when the problem has been removed.

Overcurrent Protection

One example of overcurrent protection is illustrated by the case of a buck converter whose load resistance is decreased by an overload or by a short circuit on the output terminals. The filter inductor current therefore increases above some preset limit. Protection is provided by decreasing the duty cycle D until the output current is within an acceptable range. The circuit diagram in Figure 9.13 shows a widely used means of protection.

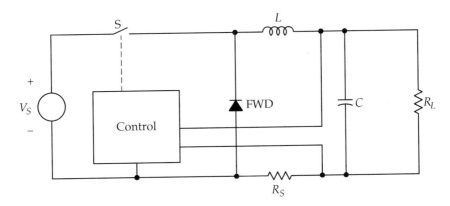

FIGURE 9.13

The value of the voltage across R_S is sensed and compared to a preset limit. If this voltage exceeds the limit, the control terminates the closure of switch S. The limitation of output current can be on a cycle-by-cycle basis of reduction in the duty cycle D. When the cause of excessive load current is removed, normal operation resumes.

During the process of current limiting, of course, normal output voltage is not maintained. The actual value of output voltage depends upon the severity of overload. The output voltage goes to zero for a complete load short circuit.

Other circuit arrangements, such as the one represented in Figure 9.14, may require a different protective method. In this figure, a short circuit occurs across the load at Point X. Some parasitic circuit inductance remains and is represented by the inductor of value L_p. The collector current increases rapidly and after a short time reaches a value for which the base current is unable to maintain the transistor in saturation. If something is not done, the transistor is quickly destroyed as both the values of v_{CE} and the transistor power increase. The collector current does not increase beyond that determined by base current and transistor current gain. The graph in Figure 9.15 shows the relations for a short interval after the fault occurs.

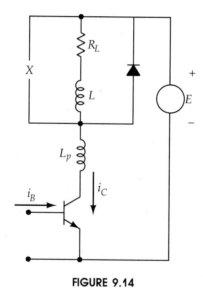

FIGURE 9.14

As soon as the collector current becomes large enough for the transistor to move into the linear mode, the value of v_{CE} increases. The circuit in Figure 9.16 can be used to detect this increase and to remove the transistor base drive. In normal operation with the transistor in saturation, v_X is small, but as the transistor comes out of saturation, v_X increases to a value of 12 V. At Q_1 turn on,

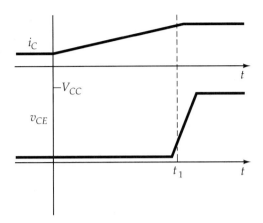

FIGURE 9.15

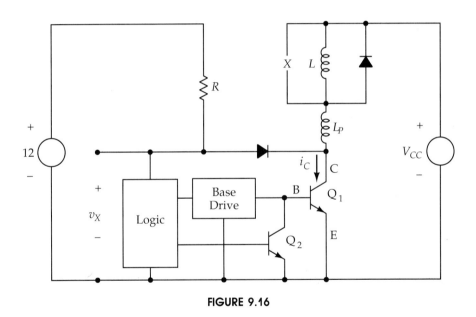

FIGURE 9.16

the operation of v_X must be disabled for a short time until Q_1 can be driven into saturation. One simple means of removing the base drive is to provide transistor Q_2 in Figure 9.16. Upon sensing excessive v_{CE} of Q_1, the base current of Q_1 is diverted to ground by conduction of Q_2.

The transistor is capable of surviving this mode of operation provided both that its rated $V_{CEO(SUS)}$ is large enough for the source voltage and that the base current is removed rapidly enough. In this condition, the transistor already is out of the saturation region so there is no storage delay for collector current turnoff.

Overvoltage Protection

An example for the need for overvoltage protection is seen with a buck chopper that has its output voltage increase above the desired level because of an internal failure. Two means of protection can be used to handle such a situation.

Consider the case in which the logic circuit fails in some manner, the duty cycle increases beyond a desired value, and loads served by the output are threatened. A protection circuit can be used to override the logic and remove the drive from the main switch. If this fails to protect the load, however, a second line of defense uses a "crowbar" circuit. A fast-acting SCR is used to short circuit the load terminals as is seen in Figure 9.17. The short circuit reduces the output voltage, thereby protecting the load from overvoltage damage. The crowbar's operational level and initiation speed should be designed in a way that best protects the load.

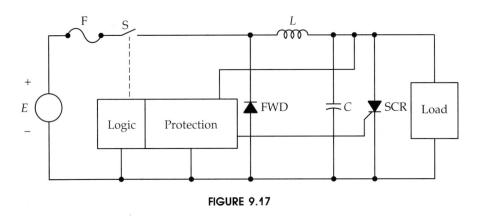

FIGURE 9.17

In Figure 9.17, the intent of the protection circuit is twofold. SCR turnon rapidly reduces the load voltage. In addition, if the problem is that switch S is shorted, then large current occurs in the fuse and it opens to remove power from the output. Suitable coordination of all circuit elements can ensure that overvoltage will not damage the load.

If the problem is a faulty logic drive to switch S that cannot be overcome by disabling the logic, then the fuse should be a fast-acting type. Various manufacturers have designed fuses for the purpose of protecting semiconductor switches such as S.

Temperature Protection

To provide a reliable design, all components must operate within their rated design temperature. Various measures can be taken to protect apparatus against excessive temperature. For example, an internal temperature-controlled switch can be used. If the internal ambient temperature increases above some preset limit, the switch closes and changes something in the output to reduce the thermal stress. The increased temperature could result from an abnormally high external ambient temperature or from a temporary external overload.

An overload condition can be tolerated for a short time. This is seen with an adjustable frequency inverter that supplies an induction motor. If the motor is overloaded temporarily, the inverter output current increases above the normal value. Although the inverter may have been designed to handle increased current for a short time without overheating, it cannot handle an overload of indefinite duration.

After some period of inverter-temperature increase, a protective circuit will detect the increase and initiate some change to protect the inverter. In particular, the inverter current could be reduced by decreasing the inverter's output frequency to something less than the desired value.

Because the inverter's internal temperature responds slowly to changes in inverter load and the semiconductor junction temperatures respond much more rapidly, another variable might be better than temperature as an indicator of overload. One successful means is that of inverter current. If we evaluate the time integral of load current in excess of a rated value, we can use it as an indicator of excessive temperature and of the need for corrective action. The circuit in Figure 9.18 shows one means of accomplishing this objective. The transistor current varies in an on–off manner. The peak value has an upper limit in steady-state operation. If this value is exceeded, the duration must be limited. In the figure, amplifier A_1 with capacitor C_1 serves as a sample-and-hold circuit for the peak value of transistor current. Amplifier A_2 together with R_4 serves to

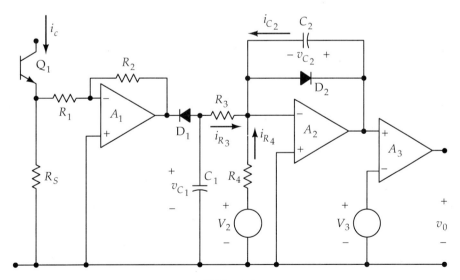

FIGURE 9.18

set the current threshold that actuates the associated integrating circuit. The output of A_2 is the time integral of the excess current. Finally, the output of A_2 is compared to the value of V_3 in amplifier A_3.

If the output of amplifier A_2 exceeds the value of V_3, the output voltage of amplifier A_3 changes sign. The change in V_O can be used as a signal to change something in the equipment to reduce the collector current of Q_1. The action taken might be to reduce inverter frequency, which would reduce motor torque and thus indirectly reduce the current in the transistor Q_1. Or the change in V_O might be used as a signal to shut down the equipment.

EXAMPLE 9.8

The circuit in Figure 9.18 is used to protect a transistor from excessive current. The emitter current is periodic and unidirectional with peak values occurring at 10-ms intervals. Peak values of 20 A are the largest values that do not cause excessive temperature occurring on a steady-state basis. Peak values of 30 A are acceptable for a maximum interval of 10 s. The amplifiers shown may be assumed to be ideal. The peak voltage across R_S may not normally exceed 0.4 V. Voltages V_2 and V_3 of 10 V are available. Find:

(a) values of R_1, R_2, and R_S to produce a normal value of $v_{C_1} = -4$ V for 20-A peak current

(b) values of R_3 and C_1 such that the voltage v_{C_1} does not decay more than 1% between successive peaks of transistor current

(c) values of R_4 and C_2 that cause V_O to change sign at 10 s if the transistor current is 30 A during the 10-s interval.

Solution

(a) With an upper limit for the voltage across R_S, we can determine the value of R_S:

$$R_S = \frac{0.4}{20} = 0.02 \ \Omega.$$

The gain provided by A_1 has a magnitude of 10 as determined by the given information. This gain determines the ratio of R_2 to R_1. The selection of actual values is relatively arbitrary:

$$\frac{R_2}{R_1} = 10.$$

Values of $R_2 = 50$ K and $R_1 = 5$ K are satisfactory. In this calculation, the voltage across D_1 has been neglected.

(b) The inverting terminal of A_2 is a virtual ground, so R_3 serves to discharge C_1 between peaks of transistor current. To meet the requirement of 1%

discharge during a 10-ms interval, a 1-s time constant for R_3C_1 is required:

$$R_3C_1 = 1.$$

A selection of $C_1 = 1\ \mu F$ and $R_3 = 1\ M\Omega$ meets the time-constant requirement. The small current in R_3 during operation may require special care in selecting A_2 with regard to its input bias current.

(c) The input from V_2 and R_4 must cancel the current in R_3 for a peak transistor current of 20 A in order that v_{C_2} not change in value for this level of current. For the condition that transistor current is 20 A:

$$v_{C_1} = -4\ V$$

$$i_{R_3} = -4\ \mu A$$

$$i_{R_4} = +4\ \mu A.$$

With $V_2 = 10\ V$, the current in R_4 requires a value of 2.5 MΩ for R_4. For the condition of 30-A peak transistor current,

$$v_{C_1} = -6\ V$$

$$i_{R_3} = -6\ \mu A$$

$$i_{C_2} = 2\ \mu A.$$

The value of v_{C_2} must change by 10 V during a 10-s interval. This condition determines C_2:

$$(10)(C_2) = (i_{C_2})(10)$$
$$C_2 = 2 \times 10^{-6}\ F. \qquad \blacksquare$$

External Transients

Another area of the protection process is that of external transients. Equipment must be protected from any damage that results from excessive input voltage. It also must be made as immune as possible to the effect of external disturbances, which may not cause damage but which may affect correct operation of the equipment. A more complete consideration of this latter area of susceptibility to electromagnetic interference is beyond the scope of this textbook.

A typical requirement is that a circuit's input be protected from excessive voltage transients. A general model that represents such a system with a protective element is shown in Figure 9.19. The protection element is a nonlinear element which conducts a large current for voltage in excess of some threshold value. This threshold is selected so that normal operating voltage causes very little current in the shunt protective element. For voltage above this threshold,

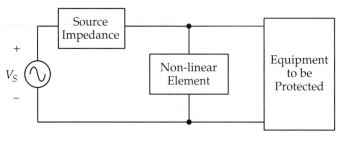

FIGURE 9.19

the current increases rapidly. The graph in Figure 9.20 is typical of the characteristic required. Generally, such elements are bidirectional with similar characteristics in the first and third quadrants.

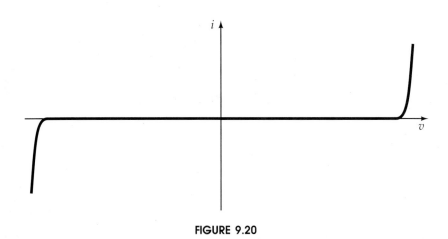

FIGURE 9.20

Commercial devices that have the characteristics shown in Figure 9.20 include metal-oxide varistors and back-to-back zener diodes. In using these components, proper design must ensure operation within a device's power rating. The source impedance must be large enough to restrict protective device current and power to an acceptable level. An approximate piecewise linear analysis can be performed to obtain the circuit in Figure 9.21, which models the circuit arrangement in Figure 9.19 and the element in Figure 9.20 for large positive currents. The source impedance is represented by an inductor of value L_S.

The transient voltage source in Figure 9.21 is a pulse source of value E. The circuit model represents circuit operation only for positive values of E. Negative E values require either reversal of elements or additional elements

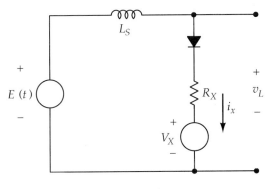

FIGURE 9.21

in the model. The current when the pulse begins is given by Equations 9.7 and 9.8. These equations neglect any preexisting currents supplied to the actual load by the normal source:

$$\frac{di_X}{dt} = \left(\frac{1}{L_S}\right)(E - V_X - Ri_X) \tag{9.7}$$

$$i_X = \left(\frac{E - V_X}{R_X}\right)(1 - e^{-t/\tau}), \tag{9.8}$$

where

$$\tau = \frac{L_S}{R_X}.$$

The voltage v_L supplied to the load is given by Equation 9.9:

$$v_L = V_X + R_X i_X = V_X + (E - V_X)(1 - e^{-t/\tau}). \tag{9.9}$$

The value of v_L starts at the value of V_X and increases with time. If the pulse lasted long enough, then v_L would equal E, but for an effective design, R_X should be small. The time constant should be long compared to the expected pulse duration. The results from Example 9.9 illustrate the relations involved.

EXAMPLE 9.9

A disturbance of 5000 V lasting 5 μs is impressed upon a circuit that can be modeled by Figure 9.21. The value of v_L is to be limited to a peak value of 300 V. The protective element can be modeled by 1.5 Ω in series with 280 V. The normal peak source voltage is less than 280 V. Find:

(a) the minimum value of L_S

(b) the energy delivered to the protective element.

Solution

(a) At the end of the 5-μs pulse, the value of v_L may not exceed 300 V. Using Equation 9.9, the value of τ may be determined:

$$300 = 280 + (5000 - 280)(1 - e^{-5/\tau})$$

$$\tau = 1180 \ \mu\text{s}.$$

Therefore,

$$L_S = R_X \tau = 1770 \ \mu\text{H}.$$

(b) i_X during the pulse interval is found by Equation 9.8:

$$i_X = \left(\frac{5000 - 280}{1.5}\right)(1 - e^{-t/\tau})$$

$$= 3147(1 - e^{-t/\tau}).$$

At the end of 5 μs, the value of i_X is 13.34 A. During this interval, the current has varied in an essentially linear manner because the interval is so short compared to the time constant. The value of v_X therefore also varies in a nearly linear manner. These linear relations are as shown:

$$i_X = \left(\frac{13.34}{5 \times 10^{-6}}\right)t = 2.668 \times 10^6 t$$

$$v_X = 280 + 1.5i_X.$$

The energy is the result of integrating the product of v_X and i_X over the 5-μs interval:

$$\text{Energy} = \int_0^{5 \times 10^{-6}} (280 + 1.5i_X)(i_X) \, dt$$

$$= 9.78 \times 10^{-3} \ \text{J}.$$

The energy absorption capability of the protective element must be in excess of 10 mJ so that it is not damaged by the transient voltage disturbance. ∎

9.3
PROBLEMS

9.1   A BJT in a TO-204 package generates 15 W of losses; $R_{JC} = 0.8°$ C/W, $R_{SA} = 4°$ C/W, and $T_A = 65°$ C.

(a) Find the values of T_J and T_C if the device is mounted directly to the heat sink without thermal grease; $R_{CS} = 0.6°$ C/W.

(b) Repeat part (a) if an insulator is used between the case and the heat sink without thermal grease; $R_{CS} = 1.5°\,C/W$.

9.2 Repeat Problem 9.1 with thermal grease used in each part. For part (a), $R_{CS} = 0.2°\,C/W$; and for part (b), $R_{CS} = 0.7°\,C/W$.

9.3 A MOSFET generates 25 W of losses. Design the heat sink to limit junction temperature to $125°\,C$; $R_{JC} = 0.83°\,C/W$, $R_{CS} = 0.2°\,C/W$, and $T_A = 50°\,C$.

9.4 A MOSFET is to be used in a circuit to conduct 20 A. $R_{DS(ON)} = 0.08\,\Omega$ at $T_J = 120°\,C$; $R_{JC} = 0.9°\,C/W$, $R_{CS} = 0.15°\,C/W$, and $T_A = 40°\,C$. Find the required maximum value of R_{SA}.

9.5 A MOSFET of type MTM8N60 is used to conduct in a single-pulse mode for a duration of 1 ms. The power dissipation is 100 W. At the beginning of the pulse, $T_C = 100°\,C$. Using the data from Appendix B, find the junction temperature at the end of the pulse.

9.6 A MOSFET of type MTM8N60 conducts current in a single-pulse mode for a duration of 10 ms. At the beginning, $T_C = 85°\,C$. Find the current that can be permitted if the ending junction temperature is limited to $100°\,C$. Use data from Appendix B and assume that the worst case $R_{DS(ON)}$ is 50% greater than the typical value.

9.7 A 1N3880 rectifier diode is used in a circuit to conduct 30 A in a single-pulse mode. If the initial case temperature is $100°\,C$, find the maximum duration of the pulse using datasheet values from Appendix B. The value of T_J is limited to $150°\,C$.

9.8 A MOSFET of type MTM8N60 operates in a periodic conduction mode of 5 ms on and 20 ms off. The power dissipation during conduction is 80 W; $R_{CS} = 0.2°\,C/W$, $R_{SA} = 2°\,C/W$, and $T_A = 55°\,C$. Find:

(a) the case temperature

(b) the peak junction temperature.

9.9 A BJT of type MJ10006 operates in a periodic conduction mode of 6 ms on and 24 ms off with a power dissipation of 40 W when conducting; $R_{CS} = 0.5°\,C/W$ and $T_A = 60°\,C$. Find the maximum value of R_{SA} if the maximum value of T_J is to be limited to $140°\,C$.

9.10 A 1N3880 rectifier diode is used in a circuit to conduct 35 A for 100 μs in a periodic manner. The total period is 1 ms; $T_A = 60°\,C$, $R_{SA} = 4.2°\,C/W$, and $R_{CS} = 0.8°\,C/W$. Find:

(a) the value of T_C **(b)** the peak value of T_J.

9.11 A 1N3880 rectifier diode is used to conduct a current that varies linearly from 30 A to 20 A during a conduction period of 200 μs. The diode does not conduct during an 800-μs interval. The pattern is repeated in a periodic manner; $T_A = 70°$ C, $R_{SA} = 5°$ C/W, and $R_{CS} = 0.8°$ C/W. Find:

(a) an equivalent power loss versus time that can be used for calculation

(b) the peak junction temperature using this equivalent loss.

9.12   A MOSFET of type MTM8N60 is used in a periodic mode with power dissipation as follows:

Interval (μs)	Power (W)
$0 < t < 100$	100
$100 < t < 200$	0
$200 < t < 300$	100
$300 < t < 1000$	0

The pattern is repeated at a frequency of 1000 Hz; $R_{CS} = 0.4°$ C/W, $T_A = 60°$ C, and $T_J = 130°$ C. Find:

(a) an equivalent periodic power dissipation

(b) the required value of R_{SA}.

9.13   A transient pulse of 4000 V amplitude lasting for 2 μs is impressed on a protective element as in Figure 9.21. When conducting, the protective element can be modeled by 200 V in series with 1.0 Ω; $L_S = 1$ mH. Find:

(a) the peak voltage

(b) the energy delivered to the protective element.

9.14   A protective circuit like that in Figure 9.21 is to be designed. The transient voltage can be modeled by 5000 V lasting for 4 μs. The existing system source impedance can be modeled by 500 μH. The available protective element can be modeled by a voltage source of 250 V in series with 1.5 Ω. The protective element can absorb 20 mJ on any one pulse. Find the additional inductance that may need to be added to the source inductance.

APPENDIX·A

Piecewise
Linear Circuit
Analysis

Piecewise linear circuit analysis techniques are useful in solving certain arrangements in power-electronics circuits. In these circuits, the resistance elements frequently are negligible because one objective is to minimize losses in controlling the transfer of energy from input to output. Furthermore, for the relatively short time of interest in many cases, the decay resulting from resistance is quite negligible.

A.1

SINGLE ENERGY STORAGE ELEMENT

The circuit arrangement in Figure A.1 is quite simple but frequently occurring. The switch is closed at $t = 0$, with some initial inductor current. The differential equation for the circuit is that in Equation A.1. The diode current is zero because the diode is reverse-biased. The piecewise linear model for the diode thus is an open circuit:

$$\frac{di}{dt} = \frac{v}{L} = \frac{E}{L} \tag{A.1}$$

$$i(t) = \left(\frac{E}{L}\right)t + I(0). \tag{A.2}$$

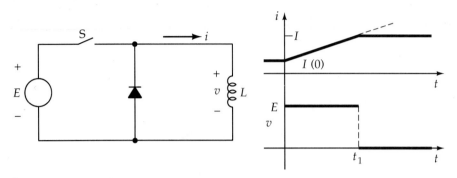

FIGURE A.1

Inductor current has a positive derivative versus time and continues to increase without limit. This can be only an approximation because the inductor must have some resistance and thus the current has some limit. In Figure A.1, if the dotted curve continued it would show the exponential nature of the current versus time. The ultimate current would be quite large and require a long time to attain this limit. For the very short interval at the beginning of the transient, the resistance thus may be neglected with little error.

After an interval t_1, the switch in Figure A.1 is opened. The inductor current must be a continuous function of time, and it continues to exist in the diode element. If an ideal diode element is assumed, then v is zero and from Equation A.1 the rate of change of i becomes zero as shown in Figure A.1.

Actually, for $t > t_1$, the current must slowly decay because the circuit losses cannot be exactly zero. The diode voltage during conduction may be small but it is nonzero. But for a short interval beyond t_1, the current may be considered constant with little error.

A circuit dual of the voltage source and inductor is shown in Figure A.2 for a current source and capacitor. Equation A.3 is the corresponding differential

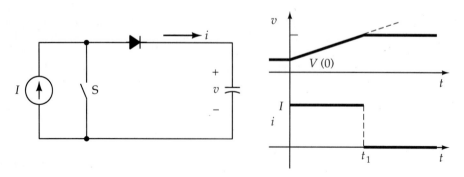

FIGURE A.2

equation for this circuit:

$$\frac{dv}{dt} = \frac{i}{C} = \frac{I}{C} \tag{A.3}$$

$$v(t) = \left(\frac{I}{C}\right)t + V(0). \tag{A.4}$$

At $t = 0$, the switch is opened and the current source charges the capacitor at a constant rate. In this case, the capacitor's leakage resistance (in parallel) is neglected. In most cases this is a better approximation than that involved in neglecting the series resistance of an inductor. In any case, the linear graph in Figure A.2 is but the very beginning of an exponential curve with a very large final value.

At $t = t_1$, the switch is closed and the source current is diverted from the capacitor. The capacitor voltage remains constant because the diode now is reverse-biased and no discharge of the capacitor occurs. Actually, some reverse current is present, but it is small and the capacitor voltage decays very slowly. Any leakage conductance of the capacitor dielectric also contributes to the capacitor voltage decay, although this is generally quite small.

EXAMPLE A.1

An inductor of 200 μH is connected as shown in Figure A.1 to a 5-V source. There is an initial current of 3 A. The switch is closed for 100 μs and then opened. Find:

(a) the inductor current after 100 μs assuming an ideal inductor

(b) the current at $t = 100$ μs, if there is an inductor resistance of 0.01 Ω

(c) the inductor current for part (b) after the switch has been open 100 μs.

Solution

(a) From Equation A.1:

$$\frac{di}{dt} = \frac{5}{200 \times 10^{-6}} = 25{,}000 \text{ A/s}.$$

After 100 μs, the inductor current remains constant.
For $t > 100$ μs:

$$i = (100 \times 10^{-6})(25{,}000) + 3.0 = 5.5 \text{ A}.$$

(b) For such an RL circuit,

$$i = \left(\frac{E}{R}\right)(1 - e^{-t/\tau}) + I(0)\, e^{-t/\tau},$$

where

$$\tau = \frac{200 \times 10^{-6}}{0.01} = 0.02 \text{ s.}$$

Substituting numbers for $t = 100 \ \mu s$,

$$i = \left(\frac{5}{0.01}\right)(1 - e^{-0.0001/0.02}) + 3\,e^{-0.0001/0.02}$$

$$= 2.494 + 2.985 = 5.479 \text{ A.}$$

(c) Starting with a new time origin for decay of the RL circuit,

$$i = 5.479\,e^{-t/\tau} = 5.479\,e^{-0.0001/0.02}$$

$$= 5.451 \text{ A.}$$

The results of parts (b) and (c) are very close to the value found in part (a).

∎

EXAMPLE A.2

The current source in Figure A.2 charges the capacitor for 20 ms and then the switch is closed. The diode has a leakage current of 1 μA for a reverse voltage of the value calculated in part (a); $v(0) = 50$ V, $C = 16 \ \mu F$, and $I = 0.1$ A. Find:

(a) the capacitor voltage at the end of the charging interval

(b) the capacitor voltage 5 seconds after the switch is closed.

Solution

(a)
$$v(t) = \left(\frac{0.1}{16 \times 10^{-6}}\right)t + 50 = 6250t + 50.$$

At $t = 20$ ms,

$$v = (6250)(0.02) + 50 = 175 \text{ V.}$$

(b) After the switch is closed, the capacitor current $i = -1 \times 10^{-6}$ A;

$$\frac{dv}{dt} = (-1 \times 10^{-6})(16 \times 10^{-6}) = -0.0625 \text{ V/s.}$$

After 5 seconds, the capacitor voltage will have changed by the following amount:

$$\Delta v = (-0.0625)(5) = -0.313 \text{ V}$$
$$v = 175 - 0.313 = 174.7 \text{ V.}$$

∎

A.2
LOSSLESS *LC* CIRCUITS

The *LC* circuit shown in Figure A.3 is a basic lossless second-order system. Equations describing circuit behavior are given in Equations A.5 and A.6 for the period after the switch is closed:

$$E = L\left(\frac{di_L}{dt}\right) + v_C \qquad (A.5)$$

$$i_L = C\left(\frac{dv_C}{dt}\right). \qquad (A.6)$$

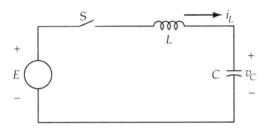

FIGURE A.3

The two circuit equations are subject to initial conditions on i_L and v_C. The solution of these equations is obtained by the usual methods for differential equations:

$$i_L = E\left(\frac{C}{L}\right)^{0.5} \sin \omega_0 t + I_L(0) \cos \omega_0 t - V_C(0)\left(\frac{C}{L}\right)^{0.5} \sin \omega_0 t \qquad (A.7)$$

$$v_C = E(1 - \cos \omega_0 t) + I_L(0)\left(\frac{L}{C}\right)^{0.5} \sin \omega_0 t + V_C(0) \cos \omega_0 t \qquad (A.8)$$

$$\omega_0 = \left(\frac{1}{LC}\right)^{0.5}. \qquad (A.9)$$

These equations show an oscillatory solution that is the superposition of three terms. The first term in the current response results from the source voltage. The second term results from the initial inductor current from some previous circuit state. Finally, the third term results from the initial capacitor voltage. Similar statements can be made about the equation for capacitor voltage. These equations can be used to find the solution at a future time starting with any given initial system state.

The graphs in Figure A.4 show the relation between the response for i_L and v_C that results from the source voltage E. In a similar manner, Figure A.5 shows the relations for an initial inductor current, and Figure A.6 shows the relations for an initial capacitor voltage. In each figure, the resulting response has only one source.

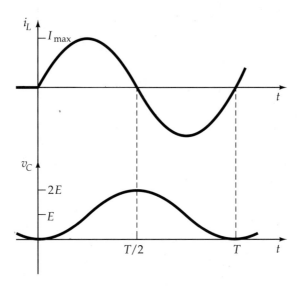

FIGURE A.4

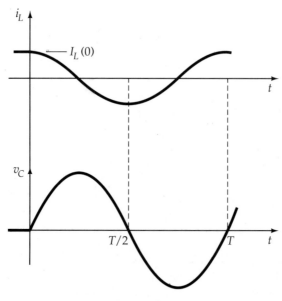

FIGURE A.5

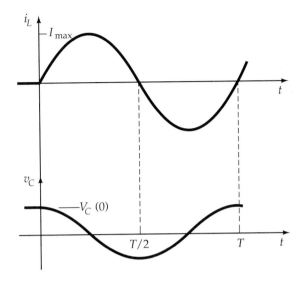

FIGURE A.6

E X A M P L E A . 3

In Figure A.3, the following information is given: $E = 100$ V, $I_L(0) = 5$ A, $V_C(0) = 25$ V, $L = 100\ \mu$H, and $C = 10\ \mu$F. Find the value of i_L and v_C at $t = 40\ \mu$s.

Solution Substituting in Equations A.7, A.8, and A.9:

$$\omega_0 = \left[\frac{1}{(100 \times 10^{-6})(10 \times 10^{-6})}\right]^{0.5} = 31{,}623 \text{ rad/s}$$

$$\left(\frac{C}{L}\right)^{0.5} = 0.316 \text{ mho}$$

and

$$\left(\frac{L}{C}\right)^{0.5} = 3.16\ \Omega$$

$$i_L = (100)(0.316)\sin\omega_0 t + 5\cos\omega_0 t - (25)(0.316)\sin\omega_0 t$$
$$= 23.7\sin\omega_0 t + 5\cos\omega_0 t$$

$$v_C = 100(1 - \cos\omega_0 t) + (5)(3.16)\sin\omega_0 t + 25\cos\omega_0 t$$
$$= 100 - 75\cos\omega_0 t + 15.8\sin\omega_0 t.$$

At $t = 40\ \mu$s, $i_L = 24.1$ A and $v_C = 92.5$ V.   ∎

With the addition of a nonlinear element to the second-order system, piece-wise linear analysis again is useful in the solution. The circuit in Figure A.7(a)

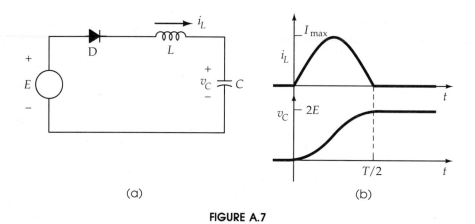

(a)   (b)

FIGURE A.7

contains an ideal diode in series with the remainder of the circuit. There is no initial energy storage. The graphs in Figure A.7(b) for the interval $0 < t < T/2$ are identical to those in Figure A.4 for the same time interval. For $t > T/2$, the current is negative in Figure A.4, but it may not be negative in Figure A.7(b) as a result of the diode element. The capacitor voltage remains at the value $2E$ because discharge is not possible. The transient therefore is complete following the half-period interval. The circuit remains in this state unless some switching action occurs to change the circuit arrangement.

Another useful initial state to consider is that of Figure A.8. The capacitor initially is charged with a negative voltage value and at $t = 0$ the SCR (ideal) is

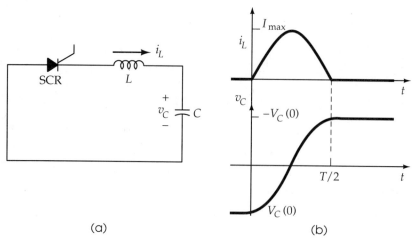

(a)   (b)

FIGURE A.8

turned on. There is no initial inductor current. The current completes one half-period of oscillation with the result of capacitor voltage reversal at the end of the transient. Negative current is not possible, so the oscillation terminates after the first half-cycle. This arrangement frequently is used to reverse a capacitor voltage in SCR commutation circuits.

If a small series resistance is added to the circuit in Figure A.3, the solution changes to a damped oscillatory one. Equation A.3 changes to Equation A.10 and the solution changes to the results in Equations A.11 through A.16:

$$E = L\left(\frac{di_L}{dt}\right) + Ri_L + v_C \tag{A.10}$$

$$i_L = \left(\frac{\omega_0}{\omega_d}\right)(e^{-\alpha t})\left\{[E - V_C(0)]\left(\frac{C}{L}\right)^{0.5} \sin \omega_d t + I_L(0) \cos (\omega_d t + \theta)\right\} \tag{A.11}$$

$$v_C = E + \left(\frac{\omega_0}{\omega_d}\right)(e^{-\alpha t})\left\{[V_C(0) - E] \cos (\omega_d t - \theta) + I_L(0)\left(\frac{L}{C}\right)^{0.5} \sin \omega_d t\right\}, \tag{A.12}$$

where

$$\omega_0 = (LC)^{-0.5} \tag{A.13}$$

$$\alpha = \frac{R}{2L} \tag{A.14}$$

$$\omega_d = (\omega_0^2 - \alpha^2)^{0.5} \tag{A.15}$$

$$\theta = \tan^{-1}\left(\frac{\alpha}{\omega_d}\right). \tag{A.16}$$

For a small value of R, all of the results in Equations A.11 through A.16 differ very little from the lossless case. The next example illustrates the very small effect.

EXAMPLE A.4

In the circuit in Figure A.8, the following values are given: $L = 100\ \mu H$, $C = 1.0\ \mu F$, $V_C(0) = -100$ V, and $I_L(0) = 0$. The capacitor voltage is reversed by turning on the SCR. Find:

(a) the capacitor voltage after an ideal reversal

(b) the peak inductor current

(c) the capacitor voltage after reversal if there is a circuit resistance of 0.1 Ω

(d) the capacitor voltage after reversal if the SCR is represented by a 0.8-V source during conduction (for this part, there is no resistance in the circuit).

Solution

(a) After an ideal reversal of capacitor voltage, the value is found by using Equation A.8. The voltage is the same magnitude but of opposite sign:

$$v_C\left(\frac{T}{2}\right) = V_C(0)\cos \pi = +100 \text{ V.}$$

(b) From Equation A.7:

$$I_{peak} = -(-100)\left(\frac{1}{100}\right)^{0.5} = 10 \text{ A.}$$

(c) Using Equations A.11 through A.16, the following results are obtained:

$$\alpha = \frac{0.1}{(2)(100 \times 10^{-6})} = 500$$

$$\omega_0 = [(100 \times 10^{-6})(1 \times 10^{-6})]^{-0.5} = 100{,}000 \text{ rad/s}$$

$$\omega_d = [(100{,}000)^2 - (500)^2]^{0.5} = 99{,}998.7 \text{ rad/s}$$

$$v_C = 100\left(\frac{100{,}000}{99{,}998.7}\right)e^{-500t}\cos(99{,}998.7t - \theta)$$

$$\theta = \tan^{-1}\left(\frac{500}{99{,}998.7}\right) = 0.0050 \text{ rad.}$$

The capacitor voltage is required at the instant that $i_L = 0$. This occurs at $t = T/2$ using ω_d:

$$\frac{T}{2} = \frac{\pi}{\omega_d} = 31.416 \times 10^{-6} \text{ s.}$$

Evaluation of v_C at this time gives

$$v_C = -100.001\,e^{-0.0157}\cos(3.1416 - 0.0050) = 98.44 \text{ V.}$$

(d) The model representing the circuit now includes an 0.8 V source as well as an ideal SCR so that conduction can be initiated at $t = 0$ and reverse current does not occur. Figure A.9 is a piecewise linear model for the circuit.
    Using Equation A.8, the value of v_C can be found:

$$v_C = -0.8(1 - \cos \omega_0 t) - 100 \cos \omega_0 t.$$

At $t = T/2$, the above expression is evaluated to yield a value of v_C:

$$v_C = +98.4 \text{ V.}$$

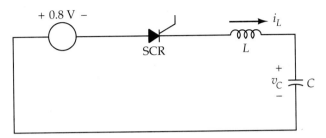

FIGURE A.9

The results show that relatively little error is introduced if the idealized solution is used.   ∎

EXAMPLE A.5

The circuit in Figure A.10 is part of an SCR commutation circuit. The SCR and diode can be considered ideal. The SCR begins conduction at $t = 0$; $E = 200$ V, $L = 100~\mu H$, $C = 2~\mu F$, $I = 20$ A, $v_C(0) = -200$ V, and $i_L(0) = 0$. The current source is ideal. Find:

(a) the time required for i_L to reach a value of 20 A
(b) the value of v_D as a function of time
(c) the time required for v_D to become positive and the diode thus to begin conduction
(d) the variation of i_L versus time after the diode begins conduction
(e) the time at which i_L becomes zero
(f) the final capacitor voltage.

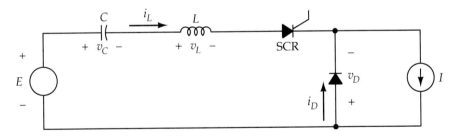

FIGURE A.10

Solution

(a) For this interval, the diode conducts and the circuit is replaced by that in Figure A.11(a). This circuit operates the same as that in Figure A.3, and

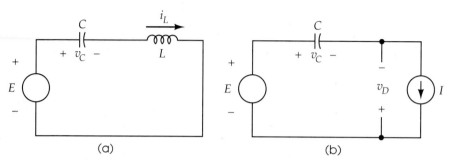

FIGURE A.11

Equations A.7, A.8, and A.9 apply:

$$\omega_0 = \left[\frac{1}{(100 \times 10^{-6})(2 \times 10^{-6})}\right]^{0.5} = 70{,}710 \text{ rad/s}$$

$$i_L = [200 - (-200)]\left(\frac{2}{100}\right)^{0.5} \sin 70{,}710t = 20 \text{ A}$$

$$t = 5.11 \times 10^{-6} \text{ s.}$$

At this time, the solution of Equation A.8 gives a value for v_C:

$$v_C = -174.2 \text{ V.}$$

(b) During this first 5.11-μs interval, $i_L < 20$ A and thus $i_D > 0$. The diode conducts, and the value of $v_D = 0$. After the time when $i_L = 20$ A, $i_D = 0$ and v_D no longer is constrained to be zero and may be negative. For $t > 5.11$ μs, i_L is constant at 20 A and $v_L = 0$. The new model for this interval is shown in Figure A.11(b). The value of v_C, using a new time origin, changes linearly with time:

$$v_C = -174.2 + \left(\frac{20}{C}\right)t.$$

The value of v_D is obtained from the KVL:

$$v_D = -E + v_C = -374.2 + (10 \times 10^6)t.$$

(c) From part (b), $v_D = 0$ at $t = 37.42 \times 10^{-6}$ s. Thereafter, if the same model were maintained, v_D would become positive. A new model is required to reflect the fact that conduction of the diode requires that v_D remain zero.

(d) At the time the diode begins conduction, a new piecewise linear model is required. This also is shown in Figure A.11(a). In this model, $v_C(0) = 200$ V and $i_L(0) = 20$ A from the previous solution in part (b) using a new time origin. This is a basic *LC* circuit with initial conditions in which E and $v_C(0)$ happen to be equal. The resulting current is solely a result of the initial current value obtained by using Equation A.7. With a new time origin, the expression for i_L is determined:

$$i_L = 20 \cos \omega_0 t.$$

(e) The inductor current becomes zero at $\omega_0 t = \pi/2$. This occurs at $t = 22.21$ μs. The entire process for the three intervals is shown in Figure A.12. The total time for the three parts of the process is 64.74 μs.

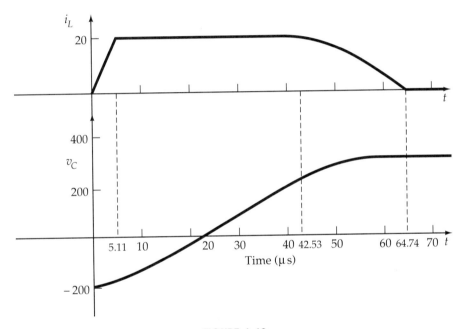

FIGURE A.12

(f) During the third interval, $v_C(t)$ is found using Equation A.8 with E and $V_C(0)$ equal to each other:

$$v_C(t) = 200 + 20 \left(\frac{100}{2} \right)^{0.5} \sin \omega_0 t$$

$$= 200 + 141.4 \sin \omega_0 t.$$

At $\omega_0 t = \pi/2$, $v_C(t)$ becomes a maximum value of 341.4 V and remains at this value thereafter.   ∎

A.3

LC CIRCUIT DUALS

The LC circuits in the preceding section have had their LC elements in series. A dual of these circuits with the LC elements in parallel is useful in certain power-electronics circuits. The approach is quite similar to that of the previous section.

The circuit in Figure A.13 is the dual of the circuit of Figure A.3. Equations A.7, A.8, and A.9 can be rewritten for this case by interchanging current and voltage variables. These results are given in Equations A.17, A.18, and A.19 for the interval that the switch is open. Note also the exchange of position of the L and C variables in these equations:

$$v_C = I\left(\frac{L}{C}\right)^{0.5} \sin \omega_0 t + V_C(0) \cos \omega_0 t - I_L(0)\left(\frac{L}{C}\right)^{0.5} \sin \omega_0 t \qquad \textbf{(A.17)}$$

$$i_L = I(1 - \cos \omega_0 t) + V_C(0)\left(\frac{C}{L}\right)^{0.5} \sin \omega_0 t + I_L(0) \cos \omega_0 t \qquad \textbf{(A.18)}$$

$$\omega_0 = \left(\frac{1}{LC}\right)^{0.5}. \qquad \textbf{(A.19)}$$

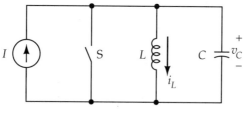

FIGURE A.13

The graphs of current and voltage are shown in Figure A.14 for the case of no initial energy storage. These are the same as the graphs in Figure A.4 except for an interchange of current and voltage variables.

The circuit in Figure A.13 is modified by the addition of an ideal diode as shown in Figure A.15. The switch S is opened at $t = 0$ with no initial energy storage existing in L or C. Upon opening switch S, the piecewise linear model in Figure A.15 is that for Figure A.13, and the response is the same as shown in Figure A.14 for the first half-period. Following this half-period, the value of v_C is zero and would become negative thereafter except for the presence of the diode, which conducts and maintains v_C at zero. A new circuit model is required, one that forces v_C to remain at zero.

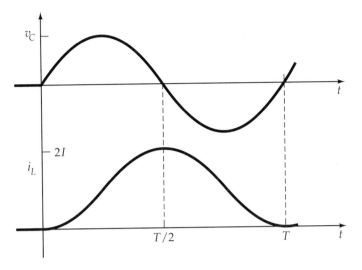

FIGURE A.14

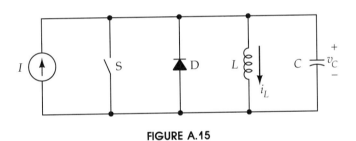

FIGURE A.15

The zero value of v_C for $t > T/2$ requires that i_L be constant for $t > T/2$. The graph in Figure A.16 shows these relations for a case of no initial energy storage.

E X A M P L E   A . 6

In the circuit in Figure A.15, S opens at $t = 0$. The following values are known: $I = 10$ A, $I_L(0) = -5$ A, $V_C(0) = 0$, $L = 10$ μH, and $C = 0.1$ μF. Find:

(a) the oscillation frequency

(b) the peak value of v_C

(c) the value of the inductor current when the diode begins conduction

(d) the length of time for the inductor current to change from an initial negative to a positive value.

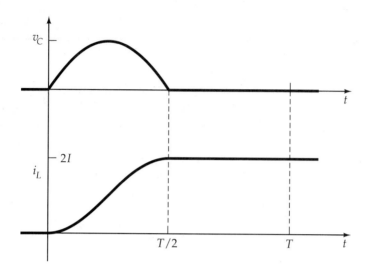

FIGURE A.16

Solution

(a)
$$\omega_0 = \left[\frac{1}{(10 \times 10^{-6})(0.1 \times 10^{-6})} \right]^{0.5} = 1 \times 10^6 \text{ rad/s}$$

$$f = \frac{\omega_0}{2\pi} = \frac{1 \times 10^6}{2\pi} = 159{,}150 \text{ Hz.}$$

(b) Because $V_C(0) = 0$, the value of $v_C(t)$ as expressed by Equation A.17 is a sine function with peak occurring at $t = T/4$:

$$v_C\left(\frac{T}{4}\right) = 10\left(\frac{10}{0.1}\right)^{0.5} - (-5)\left(\frac{10}{0.1}\right)^{0.5}$$

$$= 150 \text{ V.}$$

(c) The diode begins conduction at $t = T/2$ when v_C becomes zero. The inductor current is found from Equation A.18:

$$i_L = 10(1 - \cos \omega_0 t) - 5 \cos \omega_0 t = 10 - 15 \cos \omega_0 t$$

$$i_L\left(\frac{T}{2}\right) = 10 - 15(-1) = 25 \text{ A.}$$

(d) Using the relation from part (c) and setting $i_L = 0$ gives the following result:

$$0 = 10 - 15 \cos \omega_0 t$$

$$\omega_0 t = 0.841 \text{ rad}$$

$$t = 0.84 \times 10^{-6} \text{ s.}$$

■

A.4

PROBLEMS

A.1   In the circuit in Figure A.1, the switch is closed at $t = 0$ and opened at 100 μs; $E = 100$ V, $L = 500$ μs, and $i(0) = 0$. Find the inductor current at $t = 200$ μs.

A.2   In Problem A.1, the inductor has a nonzero resistance. Find the maximum value of this resistance so that the current at $t = 400$ μs is not reduced from the ideal value by more than 1%.

A.3   In the circuit in Figure A.2, the switch is opened at $t = 0$; $I = 0.1$ A, $C = 2$ μF, and $v(0) = 8$ V. How much time is required for v to attain a value of 25 V?

A.4   In Problem A.3, the capacitor is modeled with a resistor of 500 kΩ in parallel. Find the effect of this resistor in changing the time required to attain $v = 25$ V.

A.5   In Figure A.3, circuit values are specified as well as initial values resulting from a previous arrangement. Switch S is closed at $t = 0$; $E = 200$ V, $V_C(0) = -50$ V, $I_L(0) = -20$ A, $L = 250$ μH, and $C = 5$ μF. Find the value of t for the first occurrence of $i_L = 0$.

A.6   A small series resistance is added to the circuit in Figure A.3; $E = 300$ V, $V_C(0) = -100$ V, $I_L(0) = 0$, $L = 500$ μH, and $C = 1$ μF. Find the largest permissible value of this resistance, if the first positive peak of capacitor voltage is not to be reduced by more than 1% from its ideal value.

A.7   In Figure A.7, the capacitor is required to be charged to 400 V within 500 μs of energizing the circuit. There is no initial energy storage. The peak current may not exceed 15 A. Specify values for L and C assuming a lossless circuit.

A.8   In the circuit in Figure A.8, the capacitor voltage is to be reversed in 100 μs from an initial value of 150 V. Peak SCR current is limited to 20 A. Design values for L and C.

A.9   In Figure A.17, the switch is opened at $t = 0$. From previous operation of the circuit, there is initial energy storage for both the inductor and the capacitor; $I = 10$ A, $I_L(0) = -4$ A, $V_C(0) = 50$ V, $L = 100$ μH, $C = 1$ μF, and D is ideal. Find:

(a) the peak value of i_L

(b) the final value of v_C

(c) the time required for the circuit to reach the condition of part (b).

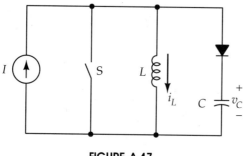

FIGURE A.17

A.10 In Problem A.9, the inductor has a nonzero resistance value. What is the largest value this resistance can be, if the maximum value of v_C is not to be reduced by more than 2% from the ideal value?

A.11 From previous operation, the circuit in Figure A.18 has initial energy storage. The switch is opened at $t = 0$; $E = 100$, $L = 500\ \mu H$, $V_C(0) = 0$, $I = 20$ A, $C = 10\ \mu F$, and $I_L(0) = 15$ A. Find:

(a) the initial piecewise linear circuit

(b) the time at which the diode must change state

(c) the piecewise linear circuit that applies for time greater than the value found in part (b)

(d) the circuit behavior during this second circuit configuration.

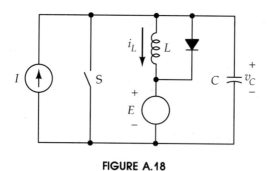

FIGURE A.18

Semiconductor Data

B.1 1N5400

MOTOROLA
■ **SEMICONDUCTOR** ■
TECHNICAL DATA

**1N5400
thru
1N5406**   ■

LEAD MOUNTED
STANDARD RECOVERY RECTIFIERS

. . . designed for use in power supplies and other applications having
need of a device with the following features:

- High Current to Small Size
- High Surge Current Capability
- Low Forward Voltage Drop
- Economical Plastic Package
- Available in Volume Quantities

**STANDARD
RECOVERY RECTIFIERS**

**50–600 VOLTS
3 AMPERE**

MAXIMUM RATINGS

Rating	Symbol	1N5400	1N5401	1N5402	1N5404	1N5406	Unit
Peak Repetitive Reverse Voltage Working Peak Reverse Voltage DC Blocking Voltage	V$_{RRM}$ V$_{RWM}$ V$_R$	50	100	200	400	600	Volts
Nonrepetitive Peak Reverse Voltage	V$_{RSM}$	100	200	300	525	800	Volts
Average Rectified Forward Current (Single Phase Resistive Load, (1/2" Leads, T$_L$ = 105°C)	I$_O$	←		3.0		→	Amp
Nonrepetitive Peak Surge Current (Surge Applied at Rated Load Conditions)	I$_{FSM}$	←		200 (one cycle)		→	Amp
Operating and Storage Junction Temperature Range	T$_J$, T$_{stg}$	←		− 65 to + 175		→	°C

THERMAL CHARACTERISTICS

Characteristic	Symbol	Typ	Unit
Thermal Resistance, Junction to Ambient (PC Board Mount, 1/2" Leads)	R$_{\theta JA}$	53	°C/W

*ELECTRICAL CHARACTERISTICS

Characteristic	Symbol	Min	Typ	Max	Unit
Instantaneous Forward Voltage (1) (i$_F$ = 9.4 Amp)	v$_F$	—	—	1.2	Volts
Average Reverse Current (1) DC Reverse Current (Rated dc Voltage, T$_L$ = 150°C)	I$_{R(AV)}$ I$_R$	— —	— —	500 500	μA

*JEDEC Registered Data.

(1) Measured in a single-phase half-wave circuit such as shown in Figure 6.25 of EIA RS-282,
November 1963. Operated at rated load conditions T$_L$=105°C, I$_O$=3.0 A, V$_r$=V$_{RWM}$.

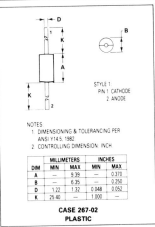

NOTES:
1. DIMENSIONING & TOLERANCING PER ANSI Y14.5, 1982.
2. CONTROLLING DIMENSION: INCH

DIM	MILLIMETERS		INCHES	
	MIN	MAX	MIN	MAX
A	—	9.39	—	0.370
B	—	6.35	—	0.250
D	1.22	1.32	0.048	0.052
K	25.40	—	1.000	—

STYLE 1:
PIN 1. CATHODE
2. ANODE

**CASE 267-02
PLASTIC**

MECHANICAL CHARACTERISTICS

Case: Transfer Molded Plastic
Finish: External Leads are Plated.
Leads are readily Solderable
Polarity: Indicated by Cathode Band
Weight: 1.1 Grams (Approximately)
Maximum Lead Temperature for
Soldering Purposes:
240°C, ⅛" from case for 10 s
at 5.0 lb. tension

B.1 1N5400 *cont'd*

FIGURE 1 — FORWARD VOLTAGE

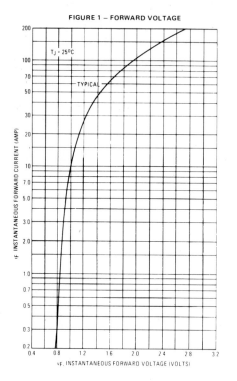

FIGURE 2 — MAXIMUM NONREPETITIVE SURGE CURRENT

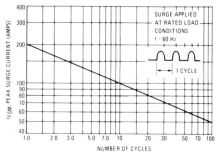

FIGURE 3 — CURRENT DERATING VARIOUS LEAD LENGTHS

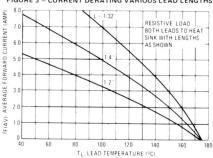

NOTE 1 — AMBIENT MOUNTING DATA

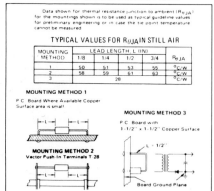

FIGURE 4 — CURRENT DERATING PC BOARD MOUNTING

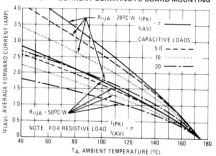

B.2 1N3879

MOTOROLA
■ **SEMICONDUCTOR** ■
TECHNICAL DATA

Designers Data Sheet

STUD MOUNTED
FAST RECOVERY POWER RECTIFIERS

. . . designed for special applications such as dc power supplies, inverters, converters, ultrasonic systems, choppers, low RF interference, sonar power supplies and free wheeling diodes. A complete line of fast recovery rectifiers having typical recovery time of 150 nanoseconds providing high efficiency at frequencies to 250 kHz.

FAST RECOVERY
POWER RECTIFIERS
50-600 VOLTS
6 AMPERES

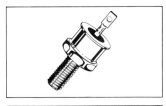

Designer's Data for "Worst Case" Conditions

The Designers Data sheets permit the design of most circuits entirely from the information presented. Limit curves — representing boundaries on device characteristics — are given to facilitate "worst case" design.

*MAXIMUM RATINGS

Rating	Symbol	1N3879	1N3880	1N3881	1N3882	1N3883	MR1366	Unit
Peak Repetitive Reverse Voltage Working Peak Reverse Voltage DC Blocking Voltage	V_{RRM} V_{RWM} V_R	50	100	200	300	400	600	Volts
Non-Repetitive Peak Reverse Voltage	V_{RSM}	75	150	250	350	450	650	Volts
RMS Reverse Voltage	$V_{R(RMS)}$	35	70	140	210	280	420	Volts
Average Rectified Forward Current (Single phase, resistive load, $T_C = 100°C$)	I_O	6.0						Amps
Non-Repetitive Peak Surge Current (surge applied at rated load continuous)	I_{FSM}	150 (one cycle)						Amps
Operating Junction Temperature Range	T_J	-65 to +150						°C
Storage Temperature Range	T_{stg}	-65 to +175						°C

THERMAL CHARACTERISTICS

Characteristic	Symbol	Max	Unit
Thermal Resistance, Junction to Case	$R_{\theta JC}$	3.0	°C/W

Motorola guarantees the listed value, although parts having higher values of thermal resistance will meet the current rating.
Thermal resistance is not required by the JEDEC registration.

*ELECTRICAL CHARACTERISTICS

Characteristic	Symbol	Min	Typ	Max	Unit
Instantaneous Forward Voltage ($I_F = 19$ Amp, $T_J = 150°C$)	v_F	—	1.2	1.5	Volts
Forward Voltage ($I_F = 6.0$ Amp, $T_C = 25°C$)	V_F	—	1.0	1.4	Volts
Reverse Current (rated dc voltage) $T_C = 25°C$ $T_C = 100°C$	I_R	—	10 0.5	15 1.0	μA mA

REVERSE RECOVERY CHARACTERISTICS

Characteristic	Symbol	Min	Typ	Max	Unit
Reverse Recovery Time *($I_{FM} = 1.0$ Amp to $V_R = 30$ Vdc, Figure 16) ($I_{FM} = 36$ Amp, di/dt = 25 A/μs, Figure 17)	t_{rr}	— —	150 200	200 400	ns
Reverse Recovery Current *($I_F = 1.0$ Amp to $V_R = 30$ Vdc, Figure 16)	$I_{RM(REC)}$	—	—	2.0	Amp

*Indicates JEDEC Registered Data for 1N3879 Series.

STYLE 1:
PIN 1. CATHODE
2. ANODE
STYLE 2:
PIN 1. ANODE
2. CATHODE

10-32UNF-2A

NOTES:
1. DIMENSIONING AND TOLERANCING PER ANSI Y14.5M, 1982.
2. CONTROLLING DIMENSION: INCH.

DIM	MILLIMETERS		INCHES	
	MIN	MAX	MIN	MAX
A	10.75	11.12	0.423	0.438
C	—	10.28	—	0.405
D	4.07	4.69	0.160	0.185
E	1.91	4.44	0.075	0.175
F	2.29	2.41	0.090	0.095
J	10.72	11.50	0.422	0.453
K	18.80	20.32	0.740	0.800

CASE 245A-02
DO-203AA
METAL

MECHANICAL CHARACTERISTICS

CASE: Welded, hermetically sealed

FINISH: All external surfaces corrosion resistant and readily solderable

POLARITY: Cathode to Case

WEIGHT: 5.6 Grams (approximately)

MOUNTING TORQUE: 15 in-lbs max.

B.2 1N3879 *cont'd*

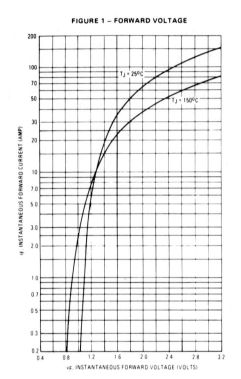

FIGURE 1 – FORWARD VOLTAGE

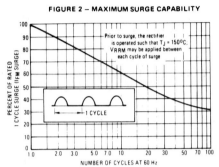

FIGURE 2 – MAXIMUM SURGE CAPABILITY

NOTE 1

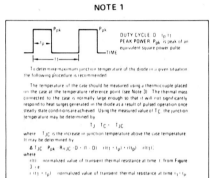

FIGURE 3 – THERMAL RESPONSE

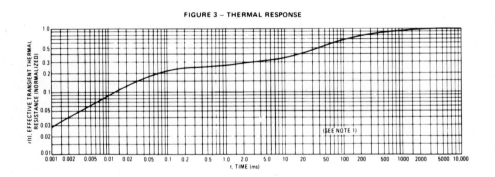

B.2 1N3879 *cont'd*

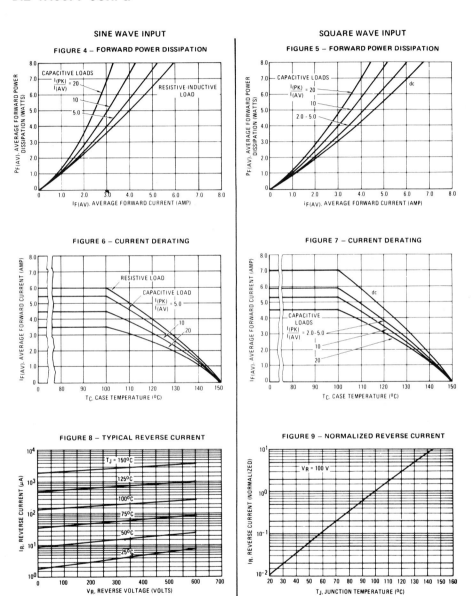

SINE WAVE INPUT
FIGURE 4 – FORWARD POWER DISSIPATION

SQUARE WAVE INPUT
FIGURE 5 – FORWARD POWER DISSIPATION

FIGURE 6 – CURRENT DERATING

FIGURE 7 – CURRENT DERATING

FIGURE 8 – TYPICAL REVERSE CURRENT

FIGURE 9 – NORMALIZED REVERSE CURRENT

B.2 1N3879 *cont'd*

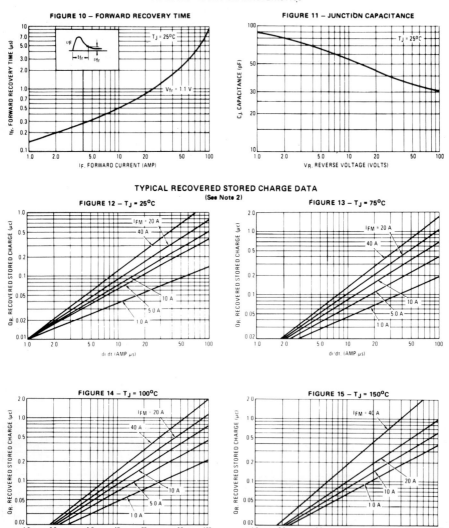

TYPICAL DYNAMIC CHARACTERISTICS

FIGURE 10 — FORWARD RECOVERY TIME

FIGURE 11 — JUNCTION CAPACITANCE

TYPICAL RECOVERED STORED CHARGE DATA
(See Note 2)

FIGURE 12 — T_J = 25°C

FIGURE 13 — T_J = 75°C

FIGURE 14 — T_J = 100°C

FIGURE 15 — T_J = 150°C

B.2 1N3879 *cont'd*

FIGURE 16 — JEDEC REVERSE RECOVERY CIRCUIT

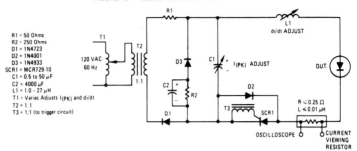

R1 = 50 Ohms
R2 = 250 Ohms
D1 = 1N4723
D2 = 1N4001
D3 = 1N4933
SCR1 = MCR729-10
C1 ≈ 0.5 to 50 μF
C2 ≈ 4000 μF
L1 = 1.0 - 27 μH
T1 = Variac Adjusts I(PK) and di/dt
T2 = 1:1
T3 = 1:1 (to trigger circuit)

120 VAC
60 Hz

NOTE 2

Reverse recovery time is the period which elapses from the time that the current, thru a previously forward biased rectifier diode, passes thru zero going negatively until the reverse current recovers to a point which is less than 10% peak reverse current.

Reverse recovery time is a direct function of the forward current prior to the application of reverse voltage.

For any given rectifier, recovery time is very circuit dependent. Typical and maximum recovery time of all Motorola fast recovery power rectifiers are rated under a fixed set of conditions using I_F = 1.0 A, V_R = 30 V. In order to cover all circuit conditions, curves are given for typical recovered stored charge versus commutation di/dt for various levels of forward current and for junction temperatures of 25°C, 75°C, 100°C, and 150°C.

To use these curves, it is necessary to know the forward current level just before commutation, the circuit commutation di/dt, and the operating junction temperature. The reverse recovery test current waveform for all Motorola fast recovery rectifiers is shown.

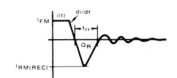

From stored charge curves versus di/dt, recovery time (t_{rr}) and peak reverse recovery current ($I_{RM(REC)}$) can be closely approximated using the following formulas:

$$t_{rr} = 1.41 \times \left[\frac{Q_R}{di/dt} \right]^{1/2}$$

$$I_{RM(REC)} = 1.41 \times \left[Q_R \times di/dt \right]^{1/2}$$

B.3 1N5826

MOTOROLA
■ SEMICONDUCTOR ■
TECHNICAL DATA

1N5826
1N5827
1N5828

Designers Data Sheet

HOT CARRIER POWER RECTIFIER

. . . employing the Schottky Barrier principle in a large area metal-to-silicon power diode. State of the art geometry features epitaxial construction with oxide passivation and metal overlap contact. Ideally suited for use as rectifiers in low-voltage, high-frequency inverters, free wheeling diodes, and polarity protection diodes.

- Extremely Low vF
- Low Stored Charge, Majority Carrier Conduction
- Low Power Loss/High Efficiency
- High Surge Capacity

Designer's Data for "Worst Case" Conditions

The Designers Data sheets permit the design of most circuits entirely from the information presented. Limit curves — representing boundaries on device characteristics — are given to facilitate "worst case" design.

SCHOTTKY
BARRIER
RECTIFIERS

15 AMPERE
20,30,40 VOLTS

*MAXIMUM RATINGS

Rating	Symbol	1N5826	1N5827	1N5828	Unit
Peak Repetitive Reverse Voltage Working Peak Reverse Voltage DC Blocking Voltage	V$_{RRM}$ V$_{RWM}$ V$_R$	20	30	40	Volts
Non-Repetitive Peak Reverse Voltage	V$_{RSM}$	24	36	48	Volts
Average Rectified Forward Current V$_{R(equiv)}$ ≤ 0.2 V$_{R(dc)}$, T$_C$ = 85°C	I$_O$	◄———— 15 ————►			Amp
Ambient Temperature Rated V$_{R(dc)}$, P$_{F(AV)}$ = 0, R$_{\theta JA}$ = 5.0°C/W	T$_A$	95	90	85	°C
Non-Repetitive Peak Surge Current (surge applied at rated load conditions, halfwave, single phase, 60 Hz)	I$_{FSM}$	◄— 500 (for 1 cycle) —►			Amp
Operating and Storage Junction Temperature Range (Reverse voltage applied)	T$_J$, T$_{stg}$	◄— -65 to +125 —►			°C
Peak Operating Junction Temperature (Forward Current Applied)	T$_{J(pk)}$	◄———— 150 ————►			°C

*THERMAL CHARACTERISTICS

Characteristic	Symbol	Max	Unit
Thermal Resistance, Junction to Case	R$_{\theta JC}$	2.5	°C/W

*ELECTRICAL CHARACTERISTICS (T$_C$ = 25°C unless otherwise noted.)

Characteristic	Symbol	1N5826	1N5827	1N5828	Unit
Maximum Instantaneous Forward Voltage (1) (i$_F$ = 8.0 Amp) (i$_F$ = 15 Amp) (i$_F$ = 47.1 Amp)	v$_F$	 0.380 0.440 0.670	 0.400 0.470 0.770	 0.420 0.500 0.870	Volts
Maximum Instantaneous Reverse Current @ rated dc Voltage (1) T$_C$ = 100°C	i$_R$	 10 75	 10 75	 10 75	mA

*Indicates JEDEC Registered Data.

(1) Pulse Test: Pulse Width = 300 µs, Duty Cycle = 2.0%.

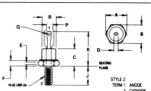

NOTES:
1. ALL RULES AND NOTES ASSOCIATED WITH REFERENCED DO-4 OUTLINE SHALL APPLY.
2. DIMENSIONING AND TOLERANCING PER ANSI Y14.5M, 1982.
3. CONTROLLING DIMENSION: INCH.

STYLE 2:
TERM 1. ANODE
2. CATHODE

DIM	MILLIMETERS MIN	MILLIMETERS MAX	INCHES MIN	INCHES MAX
A	—	12.82	—	0.505
B	10.77	11.09	0.424	0.437
C	—	10.28	—	0.405
D	—	6.35	—	0.250
E	1.53	—	0.060	—
F	1.91	4.44	0.075	0.175
J	10.72	11.50	0.422	0.453
K	15.24	20.32	0.600	0.800
P	4.14	4.80	0.163	0.189
Q	1.53	2.41	0.060	0.095
R	6.74	10.76	0.265	0.424

CASE 56-03
DO-203AA
METAL

MECHANICAL CHARACTERISTICS
CASE: Welded, hermetically sealed
FINISH: All external surfaces corrosion resistant and terminal leads are readily solderable
POLARITY: Cathode to Case
MOUNTING POSITION: Any
MOUNTING TORQUE: 15 in-lb max

B.3 1N5826 *cont'd*

NOTE 1: DETERMINING MAXIMUM RATINGS

Reverse power dissipation and the possibility of thermal runaway must be considered when operating this rectifier at reverse voltages above 0.2 V_{RWM}. Proper derating may be accomplished by use of equation (1):

$$T_{A(max)} = T_{J(max)} - R_{\theta JA} P_{F(AV)} - R_{\theta JA} P_{R(AV)} \qquad (1)$$

where

$T_{A(max)}$ = Maximum allowable ambient temperature

$T_{J(max)}$ = Maximum allowable junction temperature (125°C or the temperature at which thermal runaway occurs, whichever is lowest).

$P_{F(AV)}$ = Average forward power dissipation

$P_{R(AV)}$ = Average reverse power dissipation

$R_{\theta JA}$ = Junction-to-ambient thermal resistance

Figures 1, 2 and 3 permit easier use of equation (1) by taking reverse power dissipation and thermal runaway into consideration. The figures solve for a reference temperature as determined by equation (2):

$$T_R = T_{J(max)} - R_{\theta JA} P_{R(AV)} \qquad (2)$$

Substituting equation (2) into equation (1) yields:

$$T_{A(max)} = T_R - R_{\theta JA} P_{F(AV)} \qquad (3)$$

Inspection of equations (2) and (3) reveals that T_R is the ambient temperature at which thermal runaway occurs or where $T_J = 125°C$, when forward power is zero. The transition from one boundary condition to the other is evident on the curves of Figures 1, 2 and

3 as a difference in the rate of change of the slope in the vicinity of 115°C. The data of Figures 1, 2 and 3 is based upon dc conditions. For use in common rectifier circuits, Table I indicates suggested factors for an equivalent dc voltage to use for conservative design; i.e.:

$$V_{R(equiv)} = V_{in(PK)} \times F \qquad (4)$$

The Factor F is derived by considering the properties of the various rectifier circuits and the reverse characteristics of Schottky diodes.

Example: Find $T_{A(max)}$ for 1N5828 operated in a 12-Volt dc supply using a bridge circuit with capacitive filter such that $I_{DC} = 10$ A ($I_{F(AV)} = 5$ A), $I_{(PK)}/I_{(AV)} = 20$, Input Voltage = 10 V(rms), $R_{\theta JA} = 5°C/W$.

Step 1:   Find $V_{R(equiv)}$. Read F = 0.65 from Table I ∴
$V_{R(equiv)} = (1.41)(10)(0.65) = 9.18$ V

Step 2:   Find T_R from Figure 3. Read $T_R = 121°C$ @ $V_R = 9.18$ & $R_{\theta JA} = 5°C/W$

Step 3:   Find $P_{F(AV)}$ from Figure 4.** Read $P_{F(AV)} = 10$ W @ $\frac{I_{(PK)}}{I_{(AV)}} = 20$ & $I_{F(AV)} = 5$ A

Step 4:   Find $T_{A(max)}$ from equation (3). $T_{A(max)} = 121-(5)(10) = 71°C$

** Value given are for the 1N5828. Power is slightly lower for the other units because of their lower forward voltage.

TABLE I – VALUES FOR FACTOR F

Circuit	Half Wave		Full Wave, Bridge		Full Wave, Center Tapped * †	
Load	Resistive	Capacitive *	Resistive	Capacitive	Resistive	Capacitive
Sine Wave	0.5	1.3	0.5	0.65	1.0	1.3
Square Wave	0.75	1.5	0.75	0.75	1.5	1.5

*Note that $V_{R(PK)} \approx 2\, V_{in(PK)}$.

* †Use line to center tap voltage for V_{in}.

FIGURE 1 — MAXIMUM REFERENCE TEMPERATURE – 1N5826

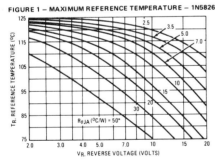

FIGURE 2 — MAXIMUM REFERENCE TEMPERATURE – 1N5827

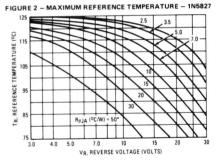

FIGURE 3 — MAXIMUM REFERENCE TEMPERATURE – 1N5828

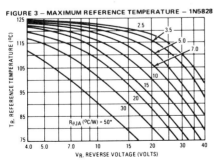

FIGURE 4 — FORWARD POWER DISSIPATION

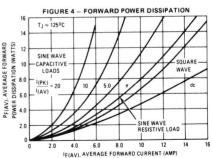

*No external heat sink.

B.3 1N5826 *cont'd*

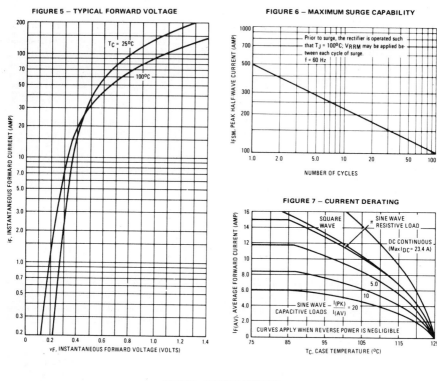

FIGURE 5 – TYPICAL FORWARD VOLTAGE

i_F, INSTANTANEOUS FORWARD CURRENT (AMP) vs v_F, INSTANTANEOUS FORWARD VOLTAGE (VOLTS)

$T_C = 25°C$

$100°C$

FIGURE 6 – MAXIMUM SURGE CAPABILITY

I_{FSM}, PEAK HALF-WAVE CURRENT (AMP) vs NUMBER OF CYCLES

Prior to surge, the rectifier is operated such that $T_J = 100°C$; V_{RRM} may be applied between each cycle of surge.
$f = 60$ Hz

FIGURE 7 – CURRENT DERATING

$I_{F(AV)}$, AVERAGE FORWARD CURRENT (AMP) vs T_C, CASE TEMPERATURE (°C)

SQUARE WAVE

SINE WAVE π RESISTIVE LOAD

DC CONTINUOUS (Max I_{DC} = 23.4 A)

5.0

10

SINE WAVE $\frac{I(PK)}{I(AV)} = 20$ CAPACITIVE LOADS

CURVES APPLY WHEN REVERSE POWER IS NEGLIGIBLE

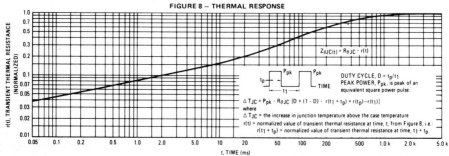

FIGURE 8 – THERMAL RESPONSE

$r(t)$, TRANSIENT THERMAL RESISTANCE (NORMALIZED) vs t, TIME (ms)

$Z_{\theta JC(t)} = R_{\theta JC} \cdot r(t)$

t_p P_{pk} P_{pk}

t_1 TIME

DUTY CYCLE, $D = t_p/t_1$
PEAK POWER, P_{pk}, is peak of an equivalent square power pulse.

$\Delta T_{JC} = P_{pk} \cdot R_{\theta JC} [D + (1 - D) \cdot r(t_1 + t_p) + r(t_p) - r(t_1)]$
where
ΔT_{JC} = the increase in junction temperature above the case temperature
$r(t)$ = normalized value of transient thermal resistance at time, t, from Figure 8, i.e.:
$r(t_1 + t_p)$ = normalized value of transient thermal resistance at time, $t_1 + t_p$.

B.3 1N5826 *cont'd*

FIGURE 9 – NORMALIZED REVERSE CURRENT

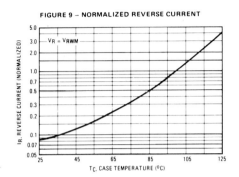

FIGURE 10 – TYPICAL REVERSE CURRENT

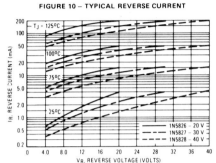

FIGURE 11 – CAPACITANCE

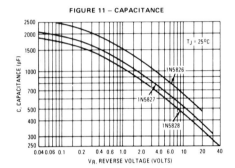

NOTE 2 – HIGH FREQUENCY OPERATION

Since current flow in a Schottky rectifier is the result of majority carrier conduction, it is not subject to junction diode forward and reverse recovery transients due to minority carrier injection and stored charge. Satisfactory circuit analysis work may be performed by using a model consisting of an ideal diode in parallel with a variable capacitance. (See Figure 11).

Rectification efficiency measurements show that operation will be satisfactory up to several megahertz. For example, relative waveform rectification efficiency is approximately 70 per cent at 2.0 MHz, e.g., the ratio of dc power to RMS power in the load is 0.28 at this frequency, whereas perfect rectification would yield 0.406 for sine wave inputs. However, in contrast to ordinary junction diodes, the loss in waveform efficiency is not indicative of power loss; it is simply a result of reverse current flow through the diode capacitance, which lowers the dc output voltage.

Copyright of Motorola, Inc. Used by permission.

B.4 2N4167

Silicon Controlled Rectifiers
Reverse Blocking Triode Thyristor

. . . multi-purpose PNPN silicon controlled rectifiers suited for industrial, consumer, and military applications. Offered in a choice of space-saving, economical packages for mounting versatility.

- Uniform Low-Level Noise-Immune Gate Triggering — I_{GT} = 10 mA (Typ) @ T_C = 25°C
- Low Forward "On" Voltage — v_T = 1 V (Typ) @ 5 Amp @ 25°C
- High Surge-Current Capability — I_{TSM} = 100 Amp Peak
- Shorted Emitter Construction

**2N4167
thru
2N4174
2N4183
thru
2N4190**

**SCRs
8 AMPERES RMS
25 thru 600 VOLTS**

**CASE 86-01
2N4167 thru 2N4174**

**CASE 87L-01
2N4183 thru 2N4190**

MAXIMUM RATINGS (Apply over operating temperature range and for all case types unless otherwise noted.)

Rating	Symbol	Value	Unit
*Peak Repetitive Forward and Reverse Blocking Voltage (1) 2N4167, 83, 2N4168, 84, 2N4169, 85, 2N4170, 86, 2N4171, 87, 2N4172, 88, 2N4173, 89, 2N4174, 90	V_{DRM} or V_{RRM}	25 50 100 200 300 400 500 600	Volts
Forward Current RMS	$I_{T(RMS)}$	8	Amps
*Peak Forward Surge Current (One cycle, 60 Hz, T_J = −40 to +100°C)	I_{TSM}	100	Amps
Circuit Fusing (T_J = −40 to +100°C; t ≤ 8.3 ms)	I^2t	40	A^2s
*Peak Gate Power	P_{GM}	5	Watts
*Average Gate Power	$P_{G(AV)}$	0.5	Watt
*Peak Gate Current	I_{GM}	2	Amps
Peak Gate Voltage (2)	V_{GM}	10	Volts
*Operating Temperature Range	T_J	−40 to +100	°C
*Storage Temperature Range	T_{stg}	−40 to +150	°C
Stud Torque		15	in. lb.

*Indicates JEDEC Registered Data.

(1) Ratings apply for zero or negative gate voltage. Devices should not be tested for blocking capability in a manner such that the voltage applied exceeds the rated blocking voltage.

(2) Devices should not be operated with a positive bias applied to the gate concurrently with a negative potential applied to the anode.

B.4 2N4167 *cont'd*

THERMAL CHARACTERISTICS

Characteristic	Symbol	Typ	Max	Unit
Thermal Resistance, Junction to Case	$R_{\theta JC}$	1.5	2.5*	°C/W
Thermal Resistance, Case to Ambient (See Figure 11) 2N4183–98	$R_{\theta CA}$	50	—	°C/W

*Indicates JEDEC Registered Data.

ELECTRICAL CHARACTERISTICS (T_C = 25°C unless otherwise noted.)

Characteristic	Symbol	Min	Typ	Max	Unit
*Peak Forward or Reverse Blocking Current (Rated V_{DRM} or V_{RRM}, gate open) T_J = 25°C T_J = 100°C	I_{DRM}, I_{RRM}	— —	— —	10 2	μA mA
Gate Trigger Current (Continuous dc) (1) (V_D = 7 Vdc, R_L = 100 Ω) *(V_D = 7 Vdc, R_L = 100 Ω, T_C = −40°C)	I_{GT}	— —	10 —	30 60	mA
Gate Trigger Voltage (Continuous dc) (V_D = 7 Vdc, R_L = 100 Ω) *(V_D = 7 Vdc, R_L = 100 Ω, T_C = −40°C) *(V_D = 7 Vdc, R_L = 100 Ω, T_J = 100°C)	V_{GT}	— — 0.2	0.75 — —	1.5 2.5 —	Volts
*Forward "On" Voltage (pulsed, 1 ms max, duty cycle ≤ 1%) (I_{TM} = 15.7 A)	V_{TM}	—	1.4	2	Volts
Holding Current (V_D = 7 Vdc, gate open) *(V_D = 7 Vdc, gate open, T_C = −40°C)	I_H	— —	10 —	30 60	mA
Turn-On Time ($t_d + t_r$) (I_G = 20 mAdc, I_F = 5 Adc, V_D = Rated V_{DRM})	t_{on}	—	1	—	μs
Turn-Off Time (I_F = 5 Adc, I_R = 5 Adc) (I_F = 5 Adc, I_R = 5 Adc, T_J = 100°C, V_D = Rated V_{DRM}) (dv/dt = 30 V/μs)	t_{off}	— —	15 25	— —	μs
Forward Voltage Application Rate (Exponential) (Gate open, T_J = 100°C, V_D = Rated V_{DRM})	dv/dt	—	50	—	V/μs

*Indicates JEDEC Registered Data

(1) For optimum operation, i.e. faster turn-on, lower switching losses, best di/dt capability, recommended I_{GT} = 200 mA minimum.

TYPICAL TRIGGER CHARACTERISTICS

FIGURE 1 – PULSE CURRENT TRIGGERING

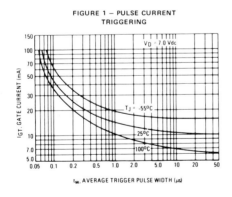

FIGURE 2 – CAPACITIVE DISCHARGE TRIGGERING

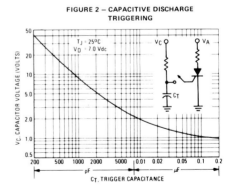

B.4 2N4167 *cont'd*

CURRENT DERATING

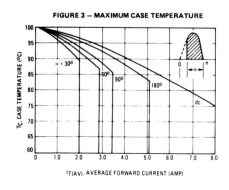

FIGURE 3 — MAXIMUM CASE TEMPERATURE

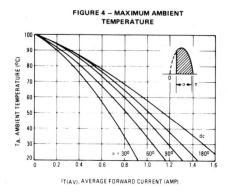

FIGURE 4 — MAXIMUM AMBIENT TEMPERATURE

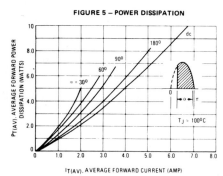

FIGURE 5 — POWER DISSIPATION

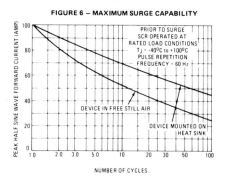

FIGURE 6 — MAXIMUM SURGE CAPABILITY

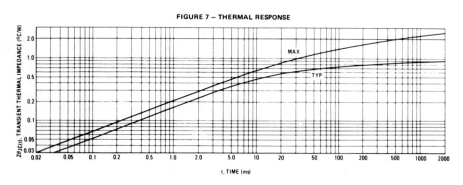

FIGURE 7 — THERMAL RESPONSE

MOTOROLA THYRISTOR DEVICE DATA

B.4 2N4167 *cont'd*

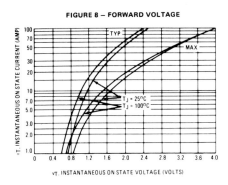

FIGURE 8 – FORWARD VOLTAGE

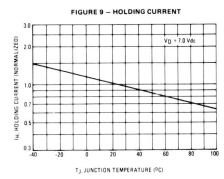

FIGURE 9 – HOLDING CURRENT

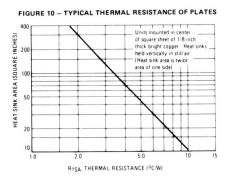

FIGURE 10 – TYPICAL THERMAL RESISTANCE OF PLATES

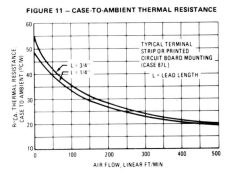

FIGURE 11 – CASE-TO-AMBIENT THERMAL RESISTANCE

MOTOROLA THYRISTOR DEVICE DATA

B.5 2N6546

MOTOROLA
■ SEMICONDUCTOR ■
TECHNICAL DATA

**2N6546
2N6547**

Designers Data Sheet

SWITCHMODE SERIES
NPN SILICON POWER TRANSISTORS

The 2N6546 and 2N6547 transistors are designed for high-voltage, high-speed, power switching in inductive circuits where fall time is critical. They are particularly suited for 115 and 220 volt line operated switch-mode applications such as:

● Switching Regulators
● PWM Inverters and Motor Controls
● Solenoid and Relay Drivers
● Deflection Circuits

Specification Features —
High Temperature Performance Specified for:
Reversed Biased SOA with Inductive Loads
Switching Times with Inductive Loads
Saturation Voltages
Leakage Currents

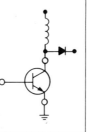

**15 AMPERE
NPN SILICON
POWER TRANSISTORS**

300 and 400 VOLTS
175 WATTS

Designer's Data for
"Worst Case" Conditions

The Designers Data Sheet permits the design of most circuits entirely from the information presented. Limit data — representing device characteristics boundaries — are given to facilitate "worst case" design.

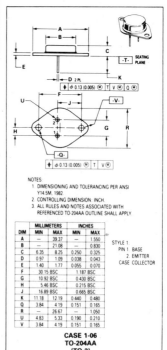

NOTES:
1. DIMENSIONING AND TOLERANCING PER ANSI Y14.5M, 1982.
2. CONTROLLING DIMENSION: INCH.
3. ALL RULES AND NOTES ASSOCIATED WITH REFERENCED TO-204AA OUTLINE SHALL APPLY

DIM	MILLIMETERS		INCHES	
	MIN	MAX	MIN	MAX
A	—	39.37	—	1.550
B	—	21.08	—	0.830
C	6.35	8.25	0.250	0.325
D	0.97	1.09	0.038	0.043
E	1.40	1.77	0.055	0.070
F	30.15 BSC		1.187 BSC	
G	10.92 BSC		0.430 BSC	
H	5.46 BSC		0.215 BSC	
J	16.89 BSC		0.665 BSC	
K	11.18	12.19	0.440	0.480
Q	3.84	4.19	0.151	0.165
R	—	26.67	—	1.050
U	4.83	5.33	0.190	0.210
V	3.84	4.19	0.151	0.165

STYLE 1:
PIN 1. BASE
2. EMITTER
CASE COLLECTOR

**CASE 1-06
TO-204AA
(TO-3)**

*MAXIMUM RATINGS

Rating	Symbol	2N6546	2N6547	Unit
Collector-Emitter Voltage	$V_{CEO(sus)}$	300	400	Vdc
Collector-Emitter Voltage	$V_{CEX(sus)}$	350	450	Vdc
Collector-Emitter Voltage	V_{CEV}	650	850	Vdc
Emitter Base Voltage	V_{EB}	9.0		Vdc
Collector Current — Continuous — Peak (1)	I_C I_{CM}	15 30		Adc
Base Current — Continuous — Peak (1)	I_B I_{BM}	10 20		Adc
Emitter Current — Continuous — Peak (1)	I_E I_{EM}	25 50		Adc
Total Power Dissipation @ T_C = 25°C @ T_C = 100°C Derate above 25°C	P_D	175 100 1.0		Watts W/°C
Operating and Storage Junction Temperature Range	T_J, T_{stg}	-65 to +200		°C

THERMAL CHARACTERISTICS

Characteristic	Symbol	Max	Unit
Thermal Resistance, Junction to Case	$R_{\theta JC}$	1.0	°C/W
Maximum Lead Temperature for Soldering Purposes: 1/8'' from Case for 5 Seconds	T_L	275	°C

*Indicates JEDEC Registered Data
(1) Pulse Test: Pulse Width = 5.0 ms, Duty Cycle ⩽ 10%.

B.5 2N6546 *cont'd*

*ELECTRICAL CHARACTERISTICS ($T_C = 25^oC$ unless otherwise noted.)

Characteristic	Symbol	Min	Max	Unit
OFF CHARACTERISTICS (1)				
Collector-Emitter Sustaining Voltage	$V_{CEO(sus)}$			Vdc
(I_C = 100 mA, I_B = 0) 2N6546		300	–	
2N6547		400	–	
Collector-Emitter Sustaining Voltage	$V_{CEX(sus)}$			Vdc
(I_C = 8.0 A, V_{clamp} = Rated V_{CEX}, T_C = 100°C) 2N6546		350	–	
2N6547		450	–	
(I_C = 15 A, V_{clamp} = Rated V_{CEO} – 100 V, 2N6546		200	–	
T_C = 100°C) 2N6547		300	–	
Collector Cutoff Current	I_{CEV}			mAdc
(V_{CEV} = Rated Value, $V_{BE(off)}$ = 1.5 Vdc)		–	1.0	
(V_{CEV} = Rated Value, $V_{BE(off)}$ = 1.5 Vdc, T_C = 100°C)		–	4.0	
Collector Cutoff Current	I_{CER}			mAdc
(V_{CE} = Rated V_{CEV}, R_{BE} = 50 Ω, T_C = 100°C)		–	5.0	
Emitter Cutoff Current	I_{EBO}	–	1.0	mAdc
(V_{EB} = 9.0 Vdc, I_C = 0)				
SECOND BREAKDOWN				
Second Breakdown Collector Current with base forward biased	$I_{S/b}$	0.2	–	Adc
t = 1.0 s (non-repetitive) (V_{CE} = 100 Vdc)				
ON CHARACTERISTICS (1)				
DC Current Gain	h_{FE}			–
(I_C = 5.0 Adc, V_{CE} = 2.0 Vdc)		12	60	
(I_C = 10 Adc, V_{CE} = 2.0 Vdc)		6.0	30	
Collector-Emitter Saturation Voltage	$V_{CE(sat)}$			Vdc
(I_C = 10 Adc, I_B = 2.0 Adc)		–	1.5	
(I_C = 15 Adc, I_B = 3.0 Adc)		–	5.0	
(I_C = 10 Adc, I_B = 2.0 Adc, T_C = 100°C)		–	2.5	
Base-Emitter Saturation Voltage	$V_{BE(sat)}$			Vdc
(I_C = 10 Adc, I_B = 2.0 Adc)		–	1.6	
(I_C = 10 Adc, I_B = 2.0 Adc, T_C = 100°C		–	1.6	
DYNAMIC CHARACTERISTICS				
Current-Gain – Bandwidth Product	f_T	6.0	28	MHz
(I_C = 500 mAdc, V_{CE} = 10 Vdc, f_{test} = 1.0 MHz)				
Output Capacitance	C_{ob}	125	500	pF
(V_{CB} = 10 Vdc, I_E = 0, f_{test} = 1.0 MHz)				
SWITCHING CHARACTERISTICS				
Resistive Load				
Delay Time	t_d	–	0.05	μs
Rise Time	t_r	–	1.0	μs
Storage Time	t_s	–	4.0	μs
Fall Time	t_f	–	0.7	μs
Inductive Load, Clamped				
Storage Time	t_s	–	5.0	μs
Fall Time	t_f	–	1.5	μs
			Typical	
Storage Time	t_s		2.0	μs
Fall Time	t_f		0.09	μs

Note for Resistive Load Delay/Rise/Storage/Fall: (V_{CC} = 250 V, I_C = 10 A, I_{B1} = I_{B2} = 2.0 A, t_p = 100 μs, Duty Cycle ≤ 2.0%)

Note for Inductive Load Clamped (first): (I_C = 10 A(pk), V_{clamp} = Rated V_{CEX}, I_{B1} = 2.0 A, $V_{BE(off)}$ = 5.0 Vdc, T_C = 100°C)

Note for Inductive Load Clamped (Typical): (I_C = 10 A(pk), V_{clamp} = Rated V_{CEX}, I_{B1} = 2.0 A, $V_{BE(off)}$ = 5.0 Vdc, T_C = 25°C)

*Indicates JEDEC Registered Data.
(1) Puse Test: Pulse Width = 300 μs, Duty Cycle = 2%.

B.5 2N6546 *cont'd*

TYPICAL ELECTRICAL CHARACTERISTICS

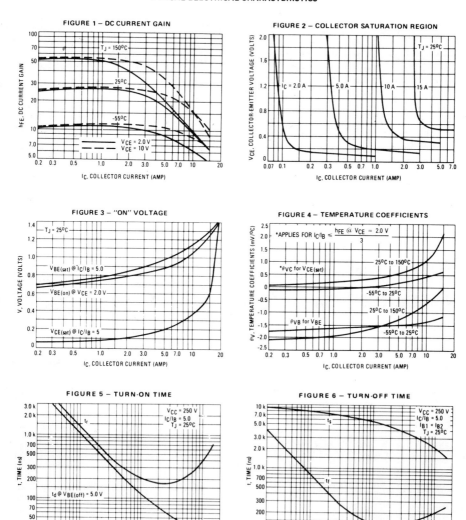

FIGURE 1 – DC CURRENT GAIN

FIGURE 2 – COLLECTOR SATURATION REGION

FIGURE 3 – "ON" VOLTAGE

FIGURE 4 – TEMPERATURE COEFFICIENTS

FIGURE 5 – TURN-ON TIME

FIGURE 6 – TURN-OFF TIME

B.5 2N6546 *cont'd*

MAXIMUM RATED SAFE OPERATING AREAS

FIGURE 7 – FORWARD BIAS SAFE OPERATING AREA

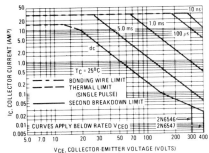

FIGURE 8 – REVERSE BIAS SAFE OPERATING AREA

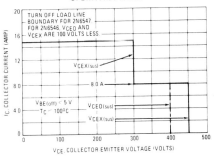

FIGURE 9 – POWER DERATING

There are two limitations on the power handling ability of a transistor: average junction temperature and second breakdown. Safe operating area curves indicate $I_C - V_{CE}$ limits of the transistor that must be observed for reliable operation; i.e., the transistor must not be subjected to greater dissipation than the curves indicate.

The data of Figure 7 is based on $T_C = 25^\circ C$; $T_{J(pk)}$ is variable depending on power level. Second breakdown pulse limits are valid for duty cycles to 10% but must be derated when $T_C \geq 25^\circ C$. Second breakdown limitations do not derate the same as thermal limitations. Allowable current at the voltages shown on Figure 7 may be found at any case temperature by using the appropriate curve on Figure 9.

$T_{J(pk)}$ may be calculated from the data in Figure 10. At high case temperatures, thermal limitations will reduce the power that can be handled to values less than the limitations imposed by second breakdown.

FIGURE 10 – THERMAL RESPONSE

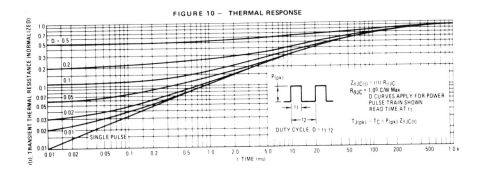

B.6 MTH8N55

MOTOROLA
■ **SEMICONDUCTOR** ■
TECHNICAL DATA

Designer's Data Sheet
Power Field Effect Transistor
N-Channel Enhancement-Mode
Silicon Gate TMOS

These TMOS Power FETs are designed for high voltage, high speed power switching applications such as switching regulators, converters, solenoid and relay drivers.

- Silicon Gate for Fast Switching Speeds — Switching Times Specified at 100°C
- Designer's Data — I_{DSS}, $V_{DS(on)}$, $V_{GS(th)}$ and SOA Specified at Elevated Temperature
- Rugged — SOA is Power Dissipation Limited
- Source-to-Drain Diode Characterized for Use With Inductive Loads

MTH8N55
MTH8N60
MTM8N60

TMOS POWER FETs
8 AMPERES
$r_{DS(on)}$ = 0.5 OHM
550 and 600 VOLTS

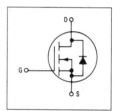

MAXIMUM RATINGS

Rating	Symbol	MTH8N55	MTH8N60 MTM8N60	Unit
Drain-Source Voltage	V_{DSS}	550	600	Vdc
Drain-Gate Voltage (R_{GS} = 1 MΩ)	V_{DGR}	550	600	Vdc
Gate-Source Voltage Continuous Non-repetitive (t_p ≤ 50 μs)	V_{GS} V_{GSM}	± 20 ± 40		Vdc Vpk
Drain Current — Continuous — Pulsed	I_D I_{DM}	8 41		Adc
Total Power Dissipation @ T_C = 25°C Derate above 25°C	P_D	150 1.2		Watts W/°C
Operating and Storage Temperature Range	T_J, T_{stg}	− 65 to 150		°C

THERMAL CHARACTERISTICS

Thermal Resistance — Junction to Case — Junction to Ambient	$R_{θJC}$ $R_{θJA}$	0.83 30		°C/W
Maximum Lead Temperature for Soldering Purposes, 1/8" from case for 5 seconds	T_L	275		°C

ELECTRICAL CHARACTERISTICS (T_C = 25°C unless otherwise noted)

Characteristic	Symbol	Min	Max	Unit
OFF CHARACTERISTICS				

Drain-Source Breakdown Voltage
(V_{GS} = 0, I_D = 0.25 mA)
    MTH8N55
    MTH8N60, MTM8N60
	$V_{(BR)DSS}$	
		
		550
		600
			
			—
			—
				Vdc

Zero Gate Voltage Drain Current (V_{DS} = Rated V_{DSS}, V_{GS} = 0) (V_{DS} = 0.8 Rated V_{DSS}, V_{GS} = 0, T_J = 125°C)	I_{DSS}	 — —	 0.2 1	mAdc

(continued)

MTM8N60
CASE 1-06
TO-204AA

MTH8N55
MTH8N60
CASE 340-02
TO-218AC

Designer's Data for "Worst Case" Conditions — The Designer's Data Sheet permits the design of most circuits entirely from the information presented. Limit curves — representing boundaries on device characteristics — are given to facilitate "worst case" design.

MOTOROLA TMOS POWER MOSFET DATA

B.6 MTH8N55 *cont'd*

ELECTRICAL CHARACTERISTICS — continued (T_C = 25°C unless otherwise noted)

Characteristic	Symbol	Min	Max	Unit
OFF CHARACTERISTICS				
Gate-Body Leakage Current, Forward (V_{GSF} = 20 Vdc, V_{DS} = 0)	I_{GSSF}	—	100	nAdc
Gate-Body Leakage Current, Reverse (V_{GSR} = 20 Vdc, V_{DS} = 0)	I_{GSSR}	—	100	nAdc
ON CHARACTERISTICS*				
Gate Threshold Voltage (V_{DS} = V_{GS}, I_D = 1 mA) T_J = 100°C	$V_{GS(th)}$	2 1.5	4.5 4	Vdc
Static Drain-Source On-Resistance (V_{GS} = 10 Vdc, I_D = 4 Adc)	$r_{DS(on)}$	—	0.5	Ohm
Drain-Source On-Voltage (V_{GS} = 10 V) (I_D = 8 Adc) (I_D = 4 Adc, T_J = 100°C)	$V_{DS(on)}$	— —	5 4	Vdc
Forward Transconductance (V_{DS} = 10 V, I_D = 4 A)	g_{FS}	4	—	mhos
DYNAMIC CHARACTERISTICS				
Input Capacitance	C_{iss}	—	2300	pF
Output Capacitance	C_{oss}	—	425	
Reverse Transfer Capacitance	C_{rss}	—	180	
SWITCHING CHARACTERISTICS* (T_J = 100°C)				
Turn-On Delay Time	$t_{d(on)}$	—	70	ns
Rise Time	t_r	—	160	
Turn-Off Delay Time	$t_{d(off)}$	—	430	
Fall Time	t_f	—	200	
Total Gate Charge	Q_g	127 (Typ)	150	nC
Gate-Source Charge	Q_{gs}	62 (Typ)	—	
Gate-Drain Charge	Q_{gd}	65 (Typ)	—	
SOURCE DRAIN DIODE CHARACTERISTICS*				
Forward On-Voltage	V_{SD}	1.2 (Typ)	2	Vdc
Forward Turn-On Time	t_{on}	Limited by stray inductance		
Reverse Recovery Time	t_{rr}	500 (Typ)	—	ns
INTERNAL PACKAGE INDUCTANCE (TO-204)				
Internal Drain Inductance (Measured from the contact screw on the header closer to the source pin and the center of the die)	L_d	5 (Typ)	—	nH
Internal Source Inductance (Measured from the source pin, 0.25″ from the package to the source bond pad)	L_s	12.5 (Typ)	—	
INTERNAL PACKAGE INDUCTANCE (TO-218)				
Internal Drain Inductance (Measured from screw on tab to center of die) (Measured from the drain lead 0.25″ from package to center of die)	L_d	4 (Typ) 5 (Typ)	— —	nH
Internal Source Inductance (Measured from the source lead 0.25″ from package to center of die)	L_s	10 (Typ)	—	

The dynamic-characteristics conditions: (V_{DS} = 25 V, V_{GS} = 0, f = 1 MHz) See Figure 11.

The switching-characteristics conditions: (V_{DD} = 25 V, I_D = 0.5 Rated I_D R_{gen} = 50 ohms) See Figures 13 and 14.

The gate-charge conditions: (V_{DS} = 0.8 Rated V_{DSS}, I_D = Rated I_D, V_{GS} = 10 V) See Figure 12.

The source-drain-diode conditions: (I_S = Rated I_D V_{GS} = 0)

*Pulse Test: Pulse Width ≤ 300 μs, Duty Cycle ≤ 2%.

B.6 MTH8N55 *cont'd*

TYPICAL ELECTRICAL CHARACTERISTICS

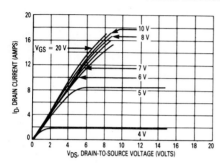

Figure 1. On-Region Characteristics

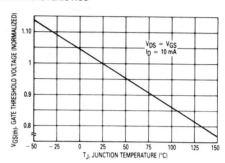

Figure 2. Gate-Threshold Voltage Variation
With Temperature

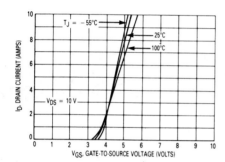

Figure 3. Transfer Characteristics

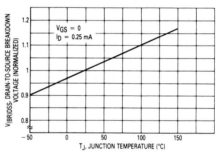

Figure 4. Breakdown Voltage Variation
With Temperature

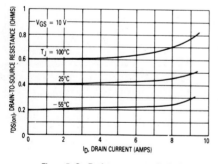

Figure 5. On-Resistance versus Drain Current

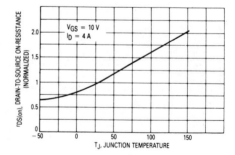

Figure 6. On-Resistance Variation
With Temperature

MOTOROLA TMOS POWER MOSFET DATA

B.6 MTH8N55 *cont'd*

SAFE OPERATING AREA INFORMATION

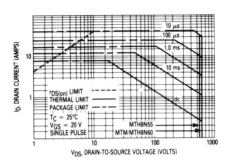

**Figure 7. Maximum Rated Forward Biased
Safe Operating Area**

FORWARD BIASED SAFE OPERATING AREA

The FBSOA curves define the maximum drain-to-source voltage and drain current that a device can safely handle when it is forward biased, or when it is on, or being turned on. Because these curves include the limitations of simultaneous high voltage and high current, up to the rating of the device, they are especially useful to designers of linear systems. The curves are based on a case temperature of 25°C and a maximum junction temperature of 150°C. Limitations for repetitive pulses at various case temperatures can be determined by using the thermal response curves. Motorola Application Note, AN569, "Transient Thermal Resistance-General Data and Its Use" provides detailed instructions.

SWITCHING SAFE OPERATING AREA

The switching safe operating area (SOA) of Figure 8 is the boundary that the load line may traverse without incurring damage to the MOSFET. The fundamental limits are the peak current, I_{DM} and the breakdown voltage, $V_{(BR)DSS}$. The switching SOA shown in Figure 8 is applicable for both turn-on and turn-off of the devices for switching times less than one microsecond.

**Figure 8. Maximum Rated Switching
Safe Operating Area**

The power averaged over a complete switching cycle must be less than:

$$\frac{T_{J(max)} - T_C}{R_{\theta JC}}$$

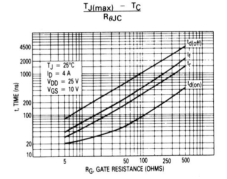

**Figure 9. Resistive Switching Time Variation
With Gate Resistance**

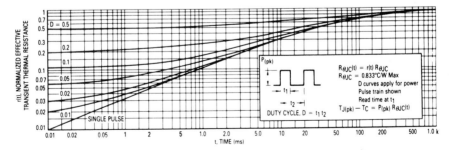

Figure 10. Thermal Response

MOTOROLA TMOS POWER MOSFET DATA

B.6 MTH8N55 *cont'd*

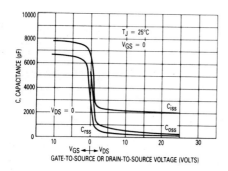

Figure 11. Capacitance Variation

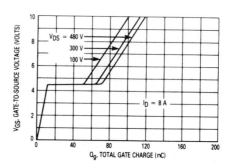

Figure 12. Gate Charge versus Gate-to-Source Voltage

RESISTIVE SWITCHING

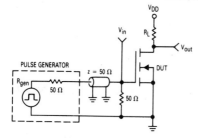

Figure 13. Switching Test Circuit

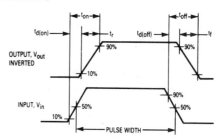

Figure 14. Switching Waveforms

OUTLINE DIMENSIONS

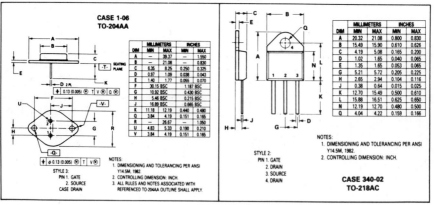

B.7 MTM15N35

MOTOROLA
■ **SEMICONDUCTOR** ■■■■■■■■■■■■■■■
TECHNICAL DATA

MTM15N35
MTM15N40

Designer's Data Sheet
Power Field Effect Transistor
N-Channel Enhancement-Mode
Silicon Gate TMOS

These TMOS Power FETs are designed for high voltage, high speed power switching applications such as switching regulators, converters, solenoid and relay drivers.

TMOS POWER FETs
15 AMPERES
$r_{DS(on)} = 0.3$ OHM
350 and 400 VOLTS

- Silicon Gate for Fast Switching Speeds — Switching Times Specified at 100°C
- Designer's Data — I_{DSS}, $V_{DS(on)}$, $V_{GS(th)}$ and SOA Specified at Elevated Temperature
- Rugged — SOA is Power Dissipation Limited
- Source-to-Drain Diode Characterized for Use With Inductive Loads

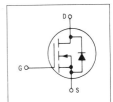

MAXIMUM RATINGS

Rating	Symbol	MTM 15N35	MTM 15N40	Unit
Drain-Source Voltage	V_{DSS}	350	400	Vdc
Drain-Gate Voltage ($R_{GS} = 1$ MΩ)	V_{DGR}	350	400	Vdc
Gate-Source Voltage — Continuous — Non-repetitive ($t_p \leq 50$ μs)	V_{GS} V_{GSM}	±20 ±40		Vdc Vpk
Drain Current — Continuous — Pulsed	I_D I_{DM}	15 70		Adc
Total Power Dissipation @ $T_C = 25$°C Derate above 25°C	P_D	250 2		Watts W/°C
Operating and Storage Temperature Range	T_J, T_{stg}	−65 to 150		°C

THERMAL CHARACTERISTICS

Thermal Resistance — Junction to Case — Junction to Ambient	$R_{\theta JC}$ $R_{\theta JA}$	0.5 30		°C/W
Maximum Lead Temperature for Soldering Purposes, 1/8" from case for 5 seconds	T_L	275		°C

CASE 197A-02
TO-204AE

Designer's Data for "Worst Case" Conditions — The Designer's Data Sheet permits the design of most circuits entirely from the information presented. SOA Limit curves — representing boundaries on device characteristics — are given to facilitate "worst case" design.

MOTOROLA TMOS POWER MOSFET DATA

B.7 MTM15N35 *cont'd*

ELECTRICAL CHARACTERISTICS (T_C = 25°C unless otherwise noted)

Characteristic		Symbol	Min	Max	Unit
OFF CHARACTERISTICS					
Drain-Source Breakdown Voltage (V_{GS} = 0, I_D = 0.25 mA) MTM15N35 MTM15N40		$V_{(BR)DSS}$	350 400	— —	Vdc
Zero Gate Voltage Drain Current (V_{DS} = Rated V_{DSS}, V_{GS} = 0) (V_{DS} = 0.8 Rated V_{DSS}, V_{GS} = 0, T_J = 125°C)		I_{DSS}	— —	0.2 1	mAdc
Gate-Body Leakage Current, Forward (V_{GSF} = 20 Vdc, V_{DS} = 0)		I_{GSSF}	—	100	nAdc
Gate-Body Leakage Current, Reverse (V_{GSR} = 20 Vdc, V_{DS} = 0)		I_{GSSR}	—	100	nAdc
ON CHARACTERISTICS*					
Gate Threshold Voltage (V_{DS} = V_{GS}, I_D = 1 mA) T_J = 100°C		$V_{GS(th)}$	2 1.5	4.5 4	Vdc
Static Drain-Source On-Resistance (V_{GS} = 10 Vdc, I_D = 7.5 Adc)		$r_{DS(on)}$	—	0.3	Ohm
Drain-Source On-Voltage (V_{GS} = 10 V) (I_D = 15 Adc) (I_D = 7.5 Adc, T_J = 100°C)		$V_{DS(on)}$	— —	— —	Vdc
Forward Transconductance (V_{DS} = 15 V, I_D = 7.5 A)		g_{FS}	6	—	mhos
DYNAMIC CHARACTERISTICS					
Input Capacitance	(V_{DS} = 25 V, V_{GS} = 0, f = 1 MHz) See Figure 11	C_{iss}	—	3000	pF
Output Capacitance		C_{oss}	—	500	
Reverse Transfer Capacitance		C_{rss}	—	200	
SWITCHING CHARACTERISTICS* (T_J = 100°C)					
Turn-On Delay Time	(V_{DD} = 25 V, I_D = 0.5 Rated I_D R_{gen} = 50 ohms) See Figures 9, 13 and 14	$t_{d(on)}$	—	60	ns
Rise Time		t_r	—	180	
Turn-Off Delay Time		$t_{d(off)}$	—	450	
Fall Time		t_f	—	180	
Total Gate Charge	(V_{DS} = 0.8 Rated V_{DSS}, I_D = Rated I_D, V_{GS} = 10 V) See Figure 12	Q_g	110 (Typ)	160	nC
Gate-Source Charge		Q_{gs}	50 (Typ)	—	
Gate-Drain Charge		Q_{gd}	60 (Typ)	—	
SOURCE DRAIN DIODE CHARACTERISTICS*					
Forward On-Voltage	(I_S = Rated I_D V_{GS} = 0)	V_{SD}	1.3 (Typ)	1.6	Vdc
Forward Turn-On Time		t_{on}	Limited by stray inductance		
Reverse Recovery Time		t_{rr}	1200 (Typ)	—	ns
INTERNAL PACKAGE INDUCTANCE					
Internal Drain Inductance (Measured from the contact screw on the header closer to the source pin and the center of the die)		L_d	5 (Typ)	—	nH
Internal Source Inductance (Measured from the source pin, 0.25" from the package to the source bond pad)		L_s	12.5 (Typ)	—	

*Pulse Test: Pulse Width ≤ 300 µs, Duty Cycle ≤ 2%.

B.7 MTM15N35 *cont'd*

TYPICAL ELECTRICAL CHARACTERISTICS

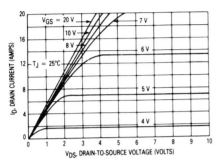

Figure 1. On-Region Characteristics

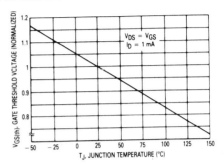

Figure 2. Gate-Threshold Voltage Variation
With Temperature

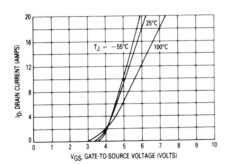

Figure 3. Transfer Characteristics

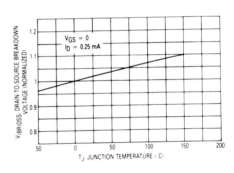

Figure 4. Breakdown Voltage Variation
With Temperature

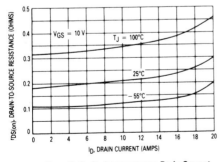

Figure 5. On-Resistance versus Drain Current

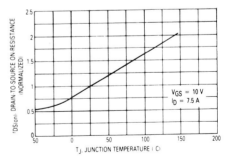

Figure 6. On-Resistance Variation
With Temperature

MOTOROLA TMOS POWER MOSFET DATA

Copyright of Motorola, Inc. Used by permission.

B.7 MTM15N35 *cont'd*

SAFE OPERATING AREA INFORMATION

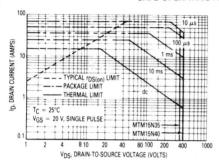

Figure 7. Maximum Rated Forward Biased Safe Operating Area

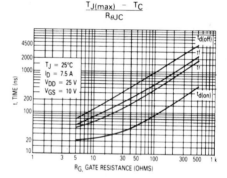

Figure 8. Maximum Rated Switching Safe Operating Area

FORWARD BIASED SAFE OPERATING AREA

The FBSOA curves define the maximum drain-to-source voltage and drain current that a device can safely handle when it is forward biased, or when it is on, or being turned on. Because these curves include the limitations of simultaneous high voltage and high current, up to the rating of the device, they are especially useful to designers of linear systems. The curves are based on a case temperature of 25°C and a maximum junction temperature of 150°C. Limitations for repetitive pulses at various case temperatures can be determined by using the thermal response curves. Motorola Application Note, AN569, "Transient Thermal Resistance-General Data and Its Use" provides detailed instructions.

SWITCHING SAFE OPERATING AREA

The switching safe operating area (SOA) of Figure 8 is the boundary that the load line may traverse without incurring damage to the MOSFET. The fundamental limits are the peak current, I_{DM} and the breakdown voltage, $V_{(BR)DSS}$. The switching SOA shown in Figure 8 is applicable for both turn-on and turn-off of the devices for switching times less than one microsecond.

The power averaged over a complete switching cycle must be less than:

$$\frac{T_{J(max)} - T_C}{R_{\theta JC}}$$

Figure 9. Resistive Switching Time Variation With Gate Resistance

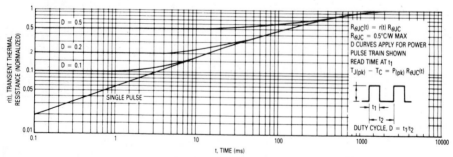

Figure 10. Thermal Response

MOTOROLA TMOS POWER MOSFET DATA

B.7 MTM15N35 *cont'd*

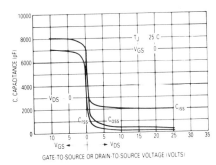

Figure 11. Capacitance Variation

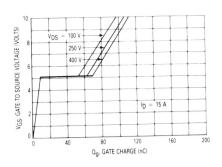

Figure 12. Gate Charge versus
Gate-to-Source Voltage

RESISTIVE SWITCHING

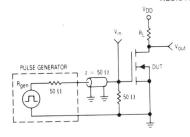

Figure 13. Switching Test Circuit

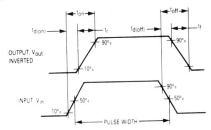

Figure 14. Switching Waveforms

OUTLINE DIMENSIONS

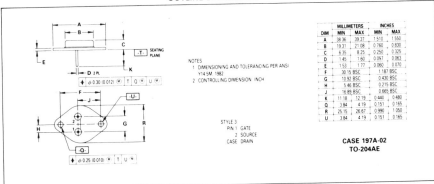

DIM	MILLIMETERS MIN	MAX	INCHES MIN	MAX
A	38.36	39.37	1.510	1.550
B	19.31	21.08	0.760	0.830
C	6.35	8.25	0.250	0.325
D	1.45	1.60	0.057	0.063
E	1.53	1.77	0.060	0.070
F	30.15 BSC		1.187 BSC	
G	10.92 BSC		0.430 BSC	
H	5.46 BSC		0.215 BSC	
J	16.89 BSC		0.665 BSC	
K	11.18	12.19	0.440	0.480
Q	3.84	4.19	0.151	0.165
R	25.15	26.67	0.990	1.050
U	3.84	4.19	0.151	0.165

NOTES
1. DIMENSIONING AND TOLERANCING PER ANSI Y14.5M, 1982
2. CONTROLLING DIMENSION: INCH

STYLE 3
PIN 1 GATE
2 SOURCE
CASE DRAIN

**CASE 197A-02
TO-204AE**

MOTOROLA TMOS POWER MOSFET DATA

Copyright of Motorola, Inc. Used by permission.

B.8 2N6027

Programmable Unijunction Transistors
Silicon Programmable Unijunction Transistors

... designed to enable the engineer to "program" unijunction characteristics such as R_{BB}, η, I_V, and I_P by merely selecting two resistor values. Application includes thyristor-trigger, oscillator, pulse and timing circuits. These devices may also be used in special thyristor applications due to the availability of an anode gate. Supplied in an inexpensive TO-92 plastic package for high-volume requirements, this package is readily adaptable for use in automatic insertion equipment.

- Programmable — R_{BB}, η, I_V and I_P.
- Low On-State Voltage — 1.5 Volts Maximum @ I_F = 50 mA
- Low Gate to Anode Leakage Current — 10 nA Maximum
- High Peak Output Voltage — 11 Volts Typical
- Low Offset Voltage — 0.35 Volt Typical (R_G = 10 k ohms)

2N6027
2N6028

PUTs
40 VOLTS
375 mW

CASE 29-02
TO-92
PLASTIC

MAXIMUM RATINGS

Rating	Symbol	Value	Unit
*Power Dissipation Derate Above 25°C	P_F $1/\theta_{JA}$	300 4	mW mW/°C
*DC Forward Anode Current Derate Above 25°C	I_T	150 2.67	mA mA/°C
*DC Gate Current	I_G	± 50	mA

Repetitive Peak Forward Current
  100 μs Pulse Width, 1% Duty Cycle
  *20 μs Pulse Width, 1% Duty Cycle
	I_{TRM}	
		1
		2
			Amps

Non-Repetitive Peak Forward Current 10 μs Pulse Width	I_{TSM}	5	Amps
*Gate to Cathode Forward Voltage	V_{GKF}	40	Volts
*Gate to Cathode Reverse Voltage	V_{GKR}	−5	Volts
*Gate to Anode Reverse Voltage	V_{GAR}	40	Volts
*Anode to Cathode Voltage (1)	V_{AK}	± 40	Volts
Operating Junction Temperature Range	T_J	−50 to +100	°C
*Storage Temperature Range	T_{stg}	−55 to +150	°C

*Indicates JEDEC Registered Data
(1) Anode positive, R_{GA} = 1000 ohms
   Anode negative, R_{GA} = open

MOTOROLA THYRISTOR DEVICE DATA

B.8 2N6027 *cont'd*

ELECTRICAL CHARACTERISTICS (T_A = 25°C unless otherwise noted.)

Characteristic		Fig. No.	Symbol	Min	Typ	Max	Unit
*Peak Current		2,9,11	I_P				µA
(V_S = 10 Vdc, R_G = 1 MΩ)	2N6027			—	1.25	2	
	2N6028			—	0.08	0.15	
(V_S = 10 Vdc, R_G = 10 k ohms)	2N6027			—	4	5	
	2N6028			—	0.70	1	
*Offset Voltage		1	V_T				Volts
(V_S = 10 Vdc, R_G = 1 MΩ)	2N6027			0.2	0.70	1.6	
	2N6028			0.2	0.50	0.6	
(V_S = 10 Vdc, R_G = 10 k ohms)	(Both Types)			0.2	0.35	0.6	
*Valley Current		1,4,5	I_V				µA
(V_S = 10 Vdc, R_G = 1 MΩ)	2N6027			—	18	50	
	2N6028			—	18	25	
(V_S = 10 Vdc, R_G = 10 k ohms)	2N6027			70	270	—	
	2N6028			25	270	—	
(V_S = 10 Vdc, R_G = 200 ohms)	2N6027			1.5	—	—	mA
	2N6028			1	—	—	
*Gate to Anode Leakage Current		—	I_{GAO}				nAdc
(V_S = 40 Vdc, T_A = 25°C, Cathode Open)				—	1	10	
(V_S = 40 Vdc, T_A = 75°C, Cathode Open)				—	3	—	
Gate to Cathode Leakage Current		—	I_{GKS}				nAdc
(V_S = 40 Vdc, Anode to Cathode Shorted)				—	5	50	
*Forward Voltage (I_F = 50 mA Peak)		1,6	V_F	—	0.8	1.5	Volts
*Peak Output Voltage		3,7	V_O	6	11	—	Volt
(V_G = 20 Vdc, C_C = 0.2 µF)							
Pulse Voltage Rise Time		3	t_r	—	40	80	ns
(V_B = 20 Vdc, C_C = 0.2 µF)							

*Indicates JEDEC Registered Data.

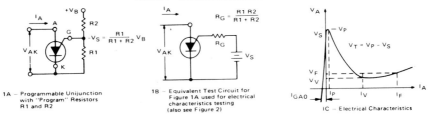

FIGURE 1 — ELECTRICAL CHARACTERIZATION

1A — Programmable Unijunction with "Program" Resistors R1 and R2

$R_G = \dfrac{R1\,R2}{R1 + R2}$

1B — Equivalent Test Circuit for Figure 1A used for electrical characteristics testing (also see Figure 2)

$V_T = V_P - V_S$

1C — Electrical Characteristics

FIGURE 2 — PEAK CURRENT (Ip) TEST CIRCUIT

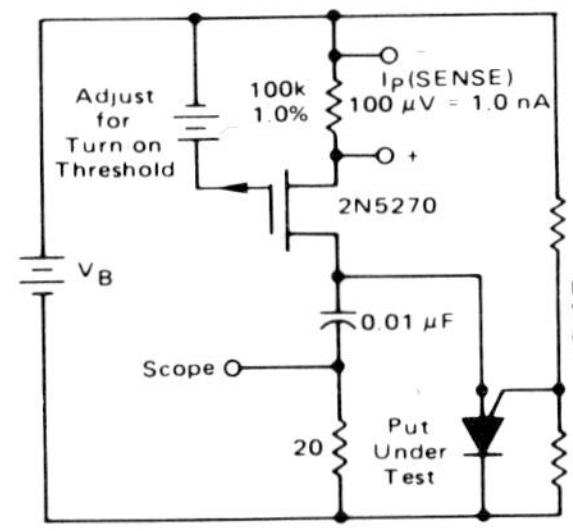

FIGURE 3 — V_O AND t_r TEST CIRCUIT

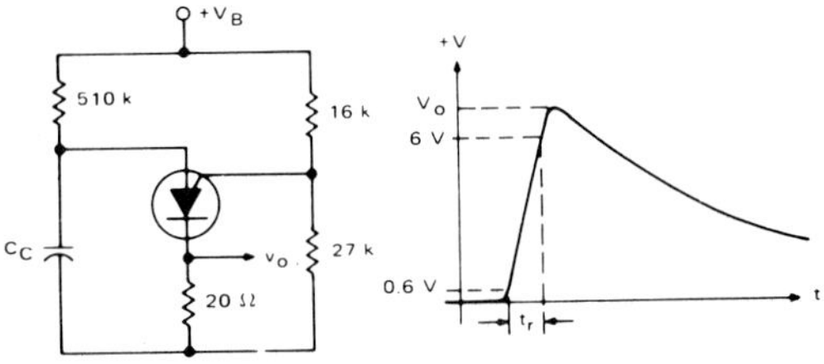

B.8 2N6027 *cont'd*

TYPICAL VALLEY CURRENT BEHAVIOR

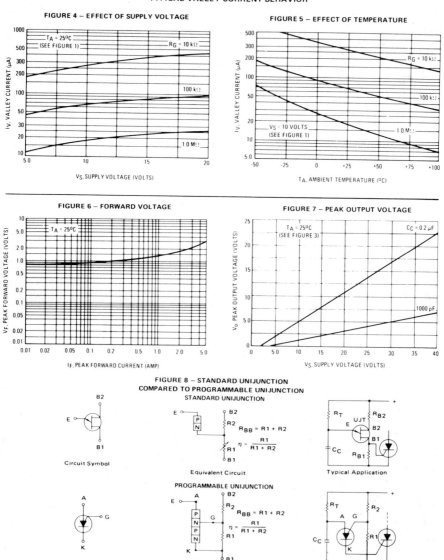

FIGURE 4 – EFFECT OF SUPPLY VOLTAGE

FIGURE 5 – EFFECT OF TEMPERATURE

FIGURE 6 – FORWARD VOLTAGE

FIGURE 7 – PEAK OUTPUT VOLTAGE

FIGURE 8 – STANDARD UNIJUNCTION COMPARED TO PROGRAMMABLE UNIJUNCTION

STANDARD UNIJUNCTION

Circuit Symbol

Equivalent Circuit

Typical Application

$R_{BB} = R1 + R2$

$\eta = \dfrac{R1}{R1 + R2}$

PROGRAMMABLE UNIJUNCTION

Circuit Symbol

Equivalent Circuit with External "Program" Resistors R1 and R2

Typical Application

$R_{BB} = R1 + R2$

$\eta = \dfrac{R1}{R1 + R2}$

MOTOROLA THYRISTOR DEVICE DATA

B.8 2N6027 *cont'd*

TYPICAL PEAK CURRENT BEHAVIOR

2N6027

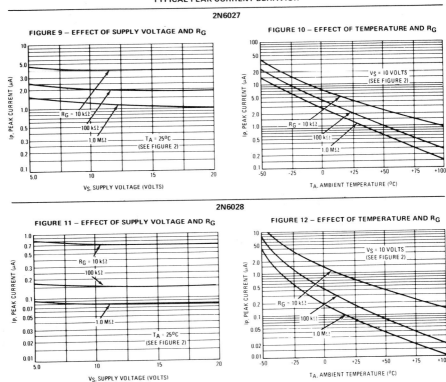

FIGURE 9 – EFFECT OF SUPPLY VOLTAGE AND R_G

FIGURE 10 – EFFECT OF TEMPERATURE AND R_G

2N6028

FIGURE 11 – EFFECT OF SUPPLY VOLTAGE AND R_G

FIGURE 12 – EFFECT OF TEMPERATURE AND R_G

INDEX